RAT HISTOPATHOLOGY

The publication of this book has been made possible by a grant from Pfizer–France.

RAT HISTOPATHOLOGY

A Glossary for Use in Toxicity and Carcinogenicity Studies

P. GREAVES

M.B., Ch.B. (Birmingham), M.R.C. Path.

Director of Pathology, Centre de Recherche, Pfizer, Amboise, France
Formerly Senior Registrar in Pathology, Westminster Hospital
(University of London), U.K.

J.M. FACCINI

Ph.D. (Cantab.), M.B., B.S., B.D.S. (Lond.), M.R.C. Path.

Director of Association Scientifique des Sociétés d'Etudes Toxicologiques,
Paris, France
Consultant Pathologist, Institut Français de Toxicologie, Lyon, France
Visiting Professor of Pathology, The Robens Institute of Industrial
Health and Safety, University of Surrey, U.K.
Formerly Reader in Pathology, University College Hospital Medical
School, London, and Honorary Consultant in Pathology, University
College Hospital, London, and
Director of Pathology, Centre de Recherche, Pfizer, Amboise, France

1984

ELSEVIER, Amsterdam – New York – Oxford

ISBN 0 444 90364 x

Library of Congress Cataloging in Publication Data

Rat histopathology.

Includes bibliographies and index.
1.Carcinogenicity testing--Dictionaries.
2. Histology, Pathological--Dictionaries. 3. Toxicology,
Experimental--Dictionaries. 4. Rats--Diseases--
Dictionaries. I. Greaves, P. II. Faccini, J.M. III. Title. [DNLM:
1. Animals, Laboratory. 2. Pathology--Terminology.
3. Rats. 4. Rodent diseases--Pathology--Terminology.
QY 15 G787]
RC268.65.G74   1984   599.32′33   84-1558
ISBN 0-444-90364-X

Published by:

Elsevier Science Publishers B.V.
P.O. Box 1126
1000 BC Amsterdam

Sole distributors for the USA and Canada:

Elsevier Science Publishing Company Inc.
52 Vanderbilt Avenue
New York, NY 10017

Printed in the Netherlands by Casparie Amsterdam

Acknowledgements

This book could not have been compiled without the help and courtesy of many friends and colleagues. We would like to mention particularly our pathologist colleagues, both past and present, who have helped us to formulate our ideas on the structure and content of this book, Drs. L.W. Ferrigan, E. Irisarri, M.-C. Michel and D. Naylor, as well as our colleagues at Pfizer, Groton (Connecticut), Drs. P. Estes, Director of Pathology, and G.L. Coleman. We would also like to thank Mr. G. Chignard for help with the haematological data and Mr. J. Martin and Mrs. M.-T. Masson for the electron microscopic work. Needless to say no microphotograph can be better than the section from which it is prepared and, in this respect, we must especially thank Mr. M. Andreu and his staff who have provided many excellent histological sections. We are also extremely grateful for the first class photographic work of Mr. M. Grandin and Miss M. Serreau of the Service d'Iconographie under Professor A. Gouaze, Faculté de Médecine, Tours. We are especially indebted to Mrs. D. Devauchelle who has tirelessly prepared numerous drafts of the manuscript and who has provided innumerable helpful suggestions to improve the final draft.

Finally, we thank Dr. A.M. Monro, Director of the Centre de Recherche, Amboise, France, Dr. I. Wrigley, Vice-President, Central Research Pfizer, Sandwich, U.K., Dr. B. Bloom, President, Central Research Pfizer, Groton, Connecticut, U.S.A. for their support and encouragement to produce this book as well as Mr. J. Soucaret, Président Directeur Général, Pfizer France for generously providing financial assistance.

Preface

In toxicology, the pathologist is called upon to prepare reports of his findings which are subsequently submitted to Regulatory Authorities. On the strength of those findings, analyses are made to assess the safety of the compound tested. Nowhere is the importance of his work more significant than in carcinogenicity studies. Although in-vitro tests show promise for the future, the carcinogen bioassay, using rodents, is currently the standard method for determining the potential carcinogenic risk to humans, it being ethically unacceptable to test chemicals directly in man (Chu et al., 1981). A large part of the assessment of carcinogenic risk to man falls squarely on the shoulders of the pathologist because the nomenclature that he uses has ultimate legal, economic and even political connotations (Editorial, *Br.Med.J., 1975;* Editorial, *Lancet,* 1976).

It is mandatory, therefore, that the pathologist uses comprehensible diagnostic terms. This is not always an easy task for a number of reasons. The terminology in use has almost always been formulated for human lesions and, whilst this is often suitable, in many cases it is not, and sometimes it is even frankly misleading. The classification of tumours, and particularly the diagnosis of malignancy, is also a continuing problem to which more systematic effort has yet to be devoted by pathologists (Golberg, 1974). Morphological criteria remain somewhat subjective and other means of investigation such as electron microscopy, biochemistry and immunology have not yet been applied to many rodent lesions (Carter, 1978). These difficulties are compounded in carcinogenicity studies by the necessity to use several hundred animals in order to obtain adequate sensitivity in the bioassay. Each animal may develop several different lesions, all of which have to be accurately recorded.

At the Pfizer Centre de Recherche, Amboise, France, these difficulties have been approached in two ways. Firstly, a computerized system of pathology based on a standard nomenclature, that of the Systematized Nomenclature of Pathology (SNOP)* of the American College of Pathologists, has been developed (Naylor, 1978; Faccini and Naylor, 1979). Secondly, a glossary of histopathological terms for use in rat pathology has been written to supplement the numerical system of codification and computerization. This book is the result of the evolution of the glossary used at Amboise.

The text, therefore, provides a detailed description of typical histopathological findings that support the use of the given diagnostic term, together with the expected circumstances that accompany the condition. In addition, literature references are provided to help explain the pathological and/or toxicological significance of the phenomenon observed. When it has been thought necessary to illustrate the description by microphotographs, these have been provided. Most microphotographs are of spontaneous lesions found in untreated control rats housed at Amboise. Where microphotographs are of lesions induced by treatment, this is indicated. Almost all illustrations have been obtained from routinely processed paraffin-embedded sections stained with haematoxylin and eosin (HE). Ultrathin sections for the few elec-

---

*Systematized Nomenclature of Pathology, SNOP (1965), College of American Pathologists, Committee on Nomenclature and Classification of Disease, Chicago, IL, currently replaced by the Systematized Nomenclature of Medicine, SNOMed (1976), College of American Pathologists, Committee on Nomenclature and Classification of Disease, Skokie, IL.

tron micrographs (E/M) were cut from tissue blocks fixed in 4% glutaraldehyde, post-fixed in osmium tetroxide and embedded in Epon. Sections were stained with uranyl acetate and lead citrate. Each term is accompanied by commonly employed synonyms. Simple general terms are not, however, defined for the glossary is not intended as a primer of pathology. The layout of the glossary essentially follows that of SNOP.

The list of diagnostic terms employed, based on SNOP, is from all diagnoses made over a period covering the last ten years at the Pfizer Centre de Recherche, Amboise. Most lesions have been observed in Sprague-Dawley (Crl:COBS.CD(SD)BR) or Long-Evans (Crl:COBS(LE)BR) rats supplied by Charles River, France. Housing conditions, diet, autopsy and histological methods have been previously described (Greaves and Faccini, 1981). However, where necessary, other sources have been used, particularly the rat colonies at the Institut Français de Toxicologie, Lyon, France (Sprague-Dawley OFA-Ico:SD(IOPS CAW) and Wistar-Ico:WI(IOPS AF/Han) supplied by Iffa-Credo, Lyon, maintained in SPF conditions).

Ample reference has also been made to human pathology. Quite apart from the insight that this can give to histopathology of the rat, it should not be forgotten that the whole basis for study of the rat is the desire to understand, and eventually treat or prevent, human disease.

No book of this type can hope to be fully comprehensive. It quite naturally reflects the authors' own interests. However, it is also a reflection of the problems in interpretation that have been faced over a number of years in the toxicological evaluation of drugs and chemicals and, therefore, it is our hope that it will be of use to workers using the rat and faced with similar problems in other toxicology laboratories.

REFERENCES

CARTER, R.L. (1978): Long-term tests for carcinogenicity. The pathologists view. In: A.D. Dayan and R.W. Brimblecombe (Eds), *Carcinogenicity Testing: Principles and Problems*, Chap. 1, pp. 1-15. MTP Press, Lancaster.

CHU, K.C., CUETO, C.Jr and WARD, J.M. (1981): Factors in the evaluation of 200 National Cancer Institute carcinogen bioassays. *J.Toxicol.Environm.Hlth, 8*, 251-280.

Editorial (1975): Insecticides and Cancer. *Br.Med.J., 1*, 170.

Editorial (1976): Seventeen principles about cancer, or something. *Lancet, 1*, 571.

FACCINI, J.M. and NAYLOR, D.C. (1979): Computer analysis and interpretation of animal pathology data. *Arch.Toxicol., Suppl. 2*, 517-520.

GOLBERG, L. (1974): Recommendations of the conference as stated by the conference chairmen: *Carcinogenesis Testing of Chemicals*, Chap. 22, pp. 123-124. CRC Press, Cleveland, OH.

GREAVES, P. and FACCINI, J.M. (1981): Fibrous histiocytic neoplasms spontaneously arising in rats. *Br.J.Cancer, 43*, 402-411.

NAYLOR, D.C. (1978): The computerization of histopathological data in toxicological laboratories using SNOP. *Meth.Inform.Med., 17*, 272-279.

Table of contents

I. Integumentary system

SKIN/SUBCUTANEOUS TISSUE

Lesions in the skin and subcutaneous tissue may arise in or from the epidermis or epidermal appendages or from the mesenchymal (connective) tissues in the subcutis.

Non-neoplastic lesions

Inflammation/necrosis

Non-neoplastic inflammatory lesions may be seen in the skin and subcutaneous tissue of the rat. They may be related to trauma, but histologically they are non-specific, and include simple ulceration of the epidermis, and acute (acute necrotizing inflammation) and chronic inflammation of the dermis and subcutaneous tissue, sometimes associated with abscess formation and fibrosis. Granulation tissue may also form. Acute and subacute inflammatory foci around areas of necrosis due to subcutaneous or intravenous administration of compounds are not unusual. A foreign body type granulomatous inflammation may be also seen, presumably a reaction to sebaceous components which escape into the subcutaneous tissues. Inflammatory skin lesions may also be associated with reactive thickening of the horny layer (hyperkeratosis) or of the squamous cell layer (acanthosis and papillomatosis). Atrophy of the epidermis, sebaceous glands and hair follicles is occasionally seen in rats and may be associated with nutritional or hormonal factors (Platt, 1965). Oedema of the subcutaneous tissue may be associated with trauma, inflammation as well as nutritional disturbances. It can also be an agonal change.

Note:

Evaluation of possible local irritation by a test substance injected intravenously is best undertaken by specifically designed studies: segments of vein and surrounding tissue are taken from the site of injection and at two other points proximally and distally, sufficiently far enough away from the site of injection to indicate a primary irritant effect on the vascular endothelium.

Epidermoid cysts

Cystic lesions, lined by flattened squamous epithelium and containing inspissated keratin are found in the rat skin. If cellular proliferation is minimal or absent, they are grouped under the heading epidermoid cyst (epidermal cyst). However, it is clear that many of these may arise from dilated pilosebaceous units (hair follicle), and hair follicle differentiation may be visible in the edges of such simple cysts. These cysts are occasionally very inflamed and show a foreign body giant cell reaction (granulomatous inflammation) and residual epithelium may be sparse.

Fat necrosis

Fat necrosis may be seen in subcutaneous tissue or in any adipose tissue after trauma, enzymatic damage, injection of foreign material, or inflammation from any cause. It is characterized by the presence of macrophages, foreign body giant cells, fatty acid and cholesterol crystals, but there may be considerable inflammation, frank necrosis and fibrosis. In human pathology it can be mistaken for a neoplasm if cellular pleomorphism is marked.

Polyp (fibroepithelial)

Small, simple polyps may be found on the rat skin, composed of a fibromuscular connective tissue stroma covered by *normal* looking epidermis. As in the human counterpart, their structural appearances do not warrant grouping them with true neoplasms and they are best regarded as tumour-like lesions.

Skin tumours

Epidermal tumours can be divided into two groups:
(a) Tumours of the surface epidermis
(b) Tumours of the epidermal appendages

In each of the groups, benign and malignant neoplasms occur (Lever, 1975). As the rat possesses no apocrine sweat glands, and eccrine sweat glands are present only on the digital paws (Zackheim, 1973), most spontaneous tumours can be grouped simply in the following way:

Benign	Squamous cell papilloma
	Sebaceous adenoma (papilloma)
	Keratoacanthoma
Malignant	Basal cell carcinoma
	Sebaceous carcinoma
	Squamous carcinoma

Squamous cell papilloma (squamous papilloma, papilloma)

These are superficially located, benign tumours composed of squamous epithelium which show marked hyperkeratosis, acanthosis and papillomatosis (Fig. 1). In some cases the proliferation of epidermal cells is predominantly basaloid in appearance giving rise to a tumour very similar to that of the basal cell papilloma (seborrhoeic keratosis) observed in man (Lever, 1975). They show no histological evidence of true tissue invasion.

Inverted papilloma

This is similar to a squamous cell papilloma (Fig. 1) except that it is situated in a shallow cavity or depression in the dermis which is usually filled with keratin and cellular debris.

Sebaceous adenoma

Adenomas bear a close structural resemblance to normal sebaceous glands; they are well defined but not encapsulated, and many basal and intermediate-type cells are generally found (Figs 2 and 3). There is intensive formation of sebum with degeneration of many cells, whose nuclei may be preserved and seen in sebaceous masses;

as a result, many cavities are formed. Marked proliferation of epithelium occurs in these cavities giving the tumour a cystic papillary appearance. Incomplete sebaceous glands are sometimes formed. In some cases these lesions protrude like papillomas above the skin surface (sebaceous papilloma), and squamous metaplasia may be focally present.

Keratoacanthoma

Histologically, the keratoacanthoma is characterized by masses of basal and squamous epithelial cells with excessive keratin formation, either present within a crater or, as one or more superficial projections.

The term is used to embrace proliferating but *benign* epithelial tumours showing evidence of differentiation towards hair follicles. Many benign cutaneous neoplasms in experimental animals are believed to arise from the hair follicle. Ghadially (1961) has described the mode of evolution of this tumour from the hair follicle which, he suggests, produces a variety of types: the common bud-shaped keratoacanthoma (Type I) arising from the superficial part which may further develop into a cutaneous horn or papilloma, and two distinct morphological variants — the dome-shaped (Type II) and berry-shaped (Type III) — arising from the deeper part of the follicle. These tumours arise spontaneously in rodents and can also be produced by carcinogens. They do not appear to undergo spontaneous involution in the rat as they do in man (Zackheim, 1973) and the term is used in a wider sense than the specific diagnosis of human keratoacanthoma.

Carcinoma

Invasive carcinomas are grouped, where possible, according to the principal cell type present: basal cell carcinoma, squamous cell carcinoma (Fig. 4), sebaceous carcinoma. Some of these tumours do possess mixed appearances, especially some well-differentiated basal cell carcinomas (primordial epitheliomas) which may exhibit differentiation towards epidermal appendages. The sebaceous squamous cell carcinoma (Figs 56 and 164) may arise from squamous metaplasia in a sebaceous carcinoma or be a special tumour arising in the auditory sebaceous gland or Zymbal's gland (Zackheim, 1973).

Pigmented tumours of the skin

In pigmented rat strains, basal cell tumours, particularly the basal cell carcinoma, can contain melanin (Zackheim, 1973) similar to pigmented basal cell tumours in man. Malignant melanomas have also been described in the skin of pigmented rats and they may invade regional lymph nodes (Burek, 1978). Such pigmented tumours are not seen in albino strains, although pigment is present around some expanding skin tumours. Special stains in these cases usually reveal the presence of iron pigment (haemosiderin).

Subcutaneous tissue tumours (soft tissue tumors)

For convenience, and because mesenchymal (soft tissue) tumours are more commonly seen in the subcutaneous tissues in the rat, most of these tumours are described under this heading. However, tumours arising from connective tissue cells may naturally be found at any site where abundant connective tissue is found, including the

3

mediastinum, thoracic or abdominal cavity or even the orbit and cranial cavity. Thus, soft tissue tumour diagnoses, including those of skeletal muscle and peripheral nerve (see Muscle in Chapter III and Peripheral nerve, spinal nerve roots in Chapter XI) may be used at a variety of sites, other than subcutaneous tissue.

Experience in human pathology has shown that the interpretation of soft tissue lesions in general presents problems different from, and in many cases more difficult than, those encountered with epithelial disorders (MacKenzie, 1970). Mesenchymal cells can react in diverse ways and can give rise to a bewildering array of appearances. Although murine sarcomas have been studied experimentally for many years, few correlative morphological and behavioral studies have been performed, so that the question whether mesenchymal tumours behave in a truly benign or malignant fashion must sometimes remain unresolved. Although considerable effort is made at Amboise to define the nature of these tumours using special stains, enzyme histochemistry and electron microscopy, some tumours defy all attempts at classification. In addition, mixed appearances are also found and, although tumours are usually grouped according to the principal cell type present, in a number of cases the mixture of elements may preclude effective grouping. Thus it is appropriate to retain a group of unclassified tumours (sarcoma, undifferentiated sarcoma, unclassified sarcoma, cystic sarcoma) merely to avoid forcing unusual tumours into inappropriate categories.

Careful consideration of these rodent sarcomas and comparison with human soft tissue tumours is not merely an academic exercise, particularly since reports of a biological association between phenoxy herbicides or their contaminants and soft tissue sarcomas in man (Hardell and Sandström, 1979; Ericksson et al., 1981; Coggon and Acheson, 1982).

'Cystic' sarcoma

MacKenzie and Garner (1973) recorded nine undifferentiated sarcomas with a distinctive cystic appearance occurring in the subcutaneous tissue as well as salivary gland, uterus, mesentery and female genital tract. These have also been observed in the Sprague-Dawley rat at Amboise. These tumours possess both solid and cystic areas. They are quite cellular, being composed principally of small cells, either rounded, spindle or stellate in shape, lying in pale matrix. Generally, collagen and reticulin is minimal, although fibrous or fibroblastic areas may be focally apparent. Cavernous cystic spaces are characteristic, containing proteinaceous fluid as well as blood cells. These spaces are lined by ill-defined, rounded or cuboidal cells, suggestive of glandular structure or hyperplastic epithelium (Figs 5, 6 and 7). However, special stains reveal no well-defined basement membrane or any definite reticulin pattern associated with these gland-like structures. Large, dilated blood vessels with well-defined endothelial cells are also seen and may be focally abundant. Electron microscopic examination shows the stromal cell to be a rather primitive-looking mesenchymal cell with no diagnostic features (Fig. 8). Nuclei are oval to extremely irregular, and they contain abundant euchromatin and large nucleoli. The cytoplasmic margins are smooth but villous projections are present. The cytoplasm contains quite abundant rough endoplasmic reticulum and cysternae appear dilated with moderately electron-dense material. The Golgi apparatus is usually visible and lysosomal structures, lipid and mitochondria are focally present. Myelinoid bodies are occasionally seen. Small amounts of fibrillar substances are present, but desmosomes or well-defined cell junctions are not seen.

In summary, these tumours probably represent primitive mesenchymal sarcomas, and the cystic spaces may be degenerative in nature. Occasionally, this distinctive cystic appearance is found focally in sarcomas of well-defined type such as vascular and nerve sheath tumours, suggesting that it is not entirely a specific type of sarcoma. If no specific tissue differentiation is observed these tumours are grouped as undifferentiated sarcomas.

Fibroma

This term is reserved for a poorly cellular, subcutaneous mass composed principally of interwoven, dense collagen bands. These are fairly common tumours in rats exposed to ionizing radiation (Zackheim, 1973). It may not be possible to distinguish histologically between a fibrous mammary tumour lacking epithelial elements and a subcutaneous fibroma. These very fibrous lesions may not all be true neoplasms and may represent simple reactive fibrosis.

Fibrosarcoma

Grouped under this heading are the relatively rare, monomorphic, spindle cell sarcomas showing collagen formation but containing no other differentiated elements or features specific to other tumours such as the storiform pattern or smooth muscle differentiation. They characteristically exhibit a herring-bone cellular pattern.

Fibrous histiocytic tumours

These have recently been reviewed (Greaves and Faccini, 1981). They fall into four major histological groups, each associated with a particular biological behaviour:

    (a) Benign fibrous histiocytoma
    (b) Malignant fibrous histiocytoma
    (c) Malignant pleomorphic fibrous histiocytoma
    (d) Malignant histiocytoma (histiocytic sarcoma)

The characteristic storiform or cartwheel pattern is evident (Figs 9 and 10) in the first three types, and may be focally seen in the predominantly histiocytic type. It has been shown that the very fibrous tumours of this type showing little or no mitotic activity may be regarded as essentially benign tumours, whilst more cellular or pleomorphic types may metastasize (Greaves and Faccini, 1981). The term dermatofibroma is also used for superficial benign fibrous histiocytomas. The storiform pattern and histiocytic differentiation is usually evident in the pleomorphic type but the large cells in these tumours may be mistaken for myoblasts (see Rhabdomyosarcoma in Chapter III). This pleomorphic tumour is only occasionally seen in untreated aged rats but it can be induced in rats by the implantation of plastic discs (Figs 11 and 12) and by carcinogens (Konishi et al., 1982). The last type, the malignant histiocytoma, is clearly much more histiocytic or granulomatous in appearance. It is characterized by sheets of rounded histiocyte-like cells, areas of necrosis surrounded by palisaded cells as well as a scattering of fairly benign-looking multinucleated giant cells of foreign body or Langhans' type (Fig. 13). This tumour corresponds to the histiocytic sarcoma of other authors (Squire et al., 1981). Ultrastructural study has confirmed the histiocytic nature of this latter tumour type (Greaves et al., 1982). These histiocytic tumours (malignant histiocytoma, histiocytic sarcoma) may sometimes be very widely distributed in the tissues and form no obvious primary mass, and so appear lymphomatous or even leukaemic in character. The reticuloendothelial neoplasms induced predominantly in the rat liver by treatment with trypan blue appear to be of this type (Ford and Becker, 1982).

Note:
Fibrous histiocytic tumours may possess an immense variety of appearances. Recently, a myxoid variety has been reported in rats (Konishi et al., 1982) similar to that seen in man (Weiss and Enzinger, 1978). Ultrastructural study may be necessary to accurately classify these neoplasms (Herrera et al., 1982).

Lipoma
These lesions, considered as benign tumours, are nodules or masses composed of normal appearing fat cells, often arranged in lobules separated by connective tissue septa (Fig. 14). The fibrous component may be quite marked, blood vessels may be abundant and fat necrosis may also be seen. However, myxoid areas, stellate cells and anaplastic zones are not seen for these characterize the liposarcoma (see below).
Lipomas may occur in any fatty tissue, although they are most frequently observed in subcutaneous tissue, thorax and mesentery (Burek, 1978).

Hibernoma (brown fat tumour)
This rare tumour, believed to arise from brown fat, is seen occasionally in the rat, and has been observed in or on the posterior thorax (Coleman, 1980; Al Zubaidy and Finn, 1983). We have observed similar tumours in the mediastinum as well as on the posterior thorax (Figs 15 and 16). It is characterized histologically by a lobulated arrangement of round, oval or polygonal vacuolated cells (foamy cells) with small rounded nuclei. Too few hibernomas have been reported in the rat to draw firm conclusions about whether they are generally benign or malignant. Those reported in the literature have shown aggressive local infiltration, plentiful mitotic activity and necrosis, features suggesting malignancy (Coleman, 1980) (malignant hibernoma, liposarcoma).

Liposarcoma
This tumour is described in the rat (Carter, 1973) but it is rare and its differential diagnosis may be very difficult. It may be defined as a malignant tumour capable of forming fat as an integral part of its make-up (Enterline et al., 1960). Various cell types are described in liposarcomas including immature and mature lipocytes, foam cells ('brown fat' cells, see Hibernoma, above) giant cells and myxoid cells. The presence of immature cells, stellate myxoid cells and areas of anaplasia serve to separate the liposarcoma from the benign lipoma which is composed of well-differentiated mature fat cells (see above). A fat stain may be necessary to confirm the presence of lipocytes and lipoblasts.

Note:
Lipid-containing foam cells may also be observed in the fibrous histiocytoma, particularly the pleomorphic type, but the presence of other fibrous histiocytic components usually serves to make the diagnosis.

Adenocarcinoma

Occasionally an adenocarcinoma appears to arise from the skin, with no clear association with mammary tissue. It may not be evident whether these are in fact arising from aberrant mammary glandular tissue, or congenital rests (cysts), or whether they represent glandular differentiation in primordial epitheliomas (basal cell carcinomas).

Leiomyoma

Benign tumours of smooth muscle are found in the subcutaneous tissue of the rat (Carter, 1973), although they are found more commonly in organs which contain abundant smooth muscle such as the uterus and gastrointestinal tract. As the degree of mitotic activity is an important criterion in assessment of malignancy in smooth muscle tumours in man (Taylor and Norris, 1966), and as information concerning the biological nature of these tumours in the rat is scanty, it seems appropriate to regard undue mitotic activity and cellular pleomorphism in a smooth muscle tumour as an indication of potential malignancy (i.e. leiomyosarcoma).

Leiomyosarcoma

Occasional spindle cell sarcomas of the subcutaneous and soft tissues show definite smooth muscle differentiation, although this may only be apparent focally. Cells in other areas may exhibit considerable pleomorphism and mitotic activity. Reports of these tumours in the rat are very sparse (Carter, 1973), but they appear to be well described in the mouse (Stewart, 1979). They presumably arise from smooth muscle situated in the subcutis (blood vessels, erectores pilorum). Some leiomyomatous neoplasms show palisading of nuclei and other features found in tumours of nerve sheath origin, and it may sometimes be difficult to make the distinction between them (see Peripheral nerve, spinal nerve roots in Chapter XI). In this respect, ultrastructural study is helpful for smooth muscle tumours contain myofilaments with focal densities (Ghadially, 1980).

Haemangioma (angioma, haemangioendothelioma)

Haemangiomas are composed of benign proliferations of endothelial cells usually forming blood-containing channels (McAllister and Fenoglio, 1977). They may occur in the subcutaneous or soft tissues as well as in organs such as the liver, spleen, and lymph nodes (Carter, 1973). Microscopically, they vary in appearance. Common lesions are those composed of blood-filled spaces lined by a single layer of flat endothelial cells, with abundant connective tissue between the larger channels (cavernous haemangioma). These lesions are believed by some authors to be congenital malformations and not true neoplasms (Carter, 1973; Squire et al., 1978). Other tumours consist of more closely packed capillary structures with minimal stroma (capillary haemangioma). Haemangioendotheliomas resemble capillary haemangiomas, except that the vascular spaces are lined by benign looking, multi-layered endothelial cells. A reticulin stain outlines the vascular nature of this latter type and enables the distinction between it and the haemangiopericytoma to be made. The benign haemangioendothelioma is rare in the rat (Carter, 1973). For the sake of simplicity, these benign vascular tumours are grouped under the term haemangioma.

Haemangiosarcoma (angiosarcoma, haemangioendotheliosarcoma)

Malignant tumours of the vascular endothelium may occur in the soft tissues and organs of the rat (Carter, 1973). The vascular pattern is evident but solid masses may form. The cells are more pleomorphic than in benign vascular tumours, often swollen and mitoses may be abnormal and numerous. Various vascular patterns within these tumours may be present and undifferentiated or fibrosarcomatous areas may also be seen. Unless there are highly specific features of a sub-type, these tumours are grouped under the term haemangiosarcoma.

Note:

Lymphangiomas and lymphangiosarcomas are reported rarely in the rat (Squire et al., 1978). However, it is usually very difficult to be certain that vascular tumours are of purely lymphatic origin and, in doubtful cases, the simple terms angioma and angiosarcoma are preferred.

Haemangiopericytoma

This tumour is believed to arise from the pericytes of Zimmerman, which are normally arranged concentrically *outside* the vascular basement membrane. In haemangiopericytomas, this basic structure is preserved, the proliferating spindle or oval-shaped pericytes remaining outside of, but compressing capillaries. This architecture is best confirmed by a reticulin stain. The tumour cells are located outside the periendothelial ring of reticulin and some areas of individual tumour cells are also surrounded by a delicate network of reticulin fibres (Kuhn and Rosai, 1969). Less well-differentiated areas may be present in the same tumour and in the rat they are not infrequently malignant (malignant haemangiopericytoma, haemangiosarcoma).

Myxoma, myxosarcoma

Particular care must be taken with these diagnoses, for they have been the cause of considerable confusion and debate, particularly as myxoid areas may be found focally in a variety of soft tissue tumours. Stout (1948) defined a myxoma as a neoplasm composed of stellate cells set in a loose stroma through which course very delicate reticulin fibres, and in which if dense spindle shaped cells are present, they should not be too extensive. There must be no recognizable differentiated elements (Stout, 1948). If this definition is strictly adhered to, true myxomas are uncommon tumours in the rat. In general, we prefer not to utilize the diagnosis of myxosarcoma but rather that of sarcoma, undefined or undifferentiated sarcoma if there is no histological indication of histogenesis. A fat stain should be performed if possible in predominantly myxoid tumours to exclude liposarcoma.

MAMMARY GLAND

Introduction

The rat mammary gland is of considerable importance in experimental oncology and toxicology due to the fact that mammary tumours can be induced with relative ease and that considerable numbers of mammary neoplasms develop spontaneously in most rat strains. By contrast, non-neoplastic lesions are relatively uncommon. However, the rat mammary gland, along with ovarian and uterine tissue and the pituitary itself, is a highly sensitive indicator of functional activity of the hypothalamic-pituitary axis (see Uterus, Ovary and oviducts in Chapter IX). This tissue reflects, in the first instance, the artificial physiological state of laboratory animals. The rat, as maintained in toxicity studies, is undoubtedly kept in highly abnormal conditions when compared to its natural, wild habitat: males and females are housed in the same room and are, therefore, subject to the effects of pheromones, yet do not have the opportunity to mate; furthermore, they have free access to food without the necessity to forage. It is probable that the resultant 'unnatural' physiological status contributes to the high incidence of mammary tumours in this species when maintained under these conditions. In the second instance, it is a sensitive indicator of effects on dopamine-mediated pituitary function. A variety of compounds modulate this function, among the best known of which are neuroleptic agents and beta-blockers. These drugs increase both mammary hyperplasia and neoplasia in rats, principally through increased prolactin release (Tuchmann-Duplessis and Mercier-Parot, 1968; Nasrallah et al., 1977). Prolactin enhances the growth of rat mammary tumours, whether induced initially by carcinogens (Manni et al., 1977) or those occurring 'spontaneously' in certain strains, even in the absence of the ovaries, adrenals and the pituitary (Pearson et al., 1972). Conversely, as would be expected, suppression of prolactin secretion inhibits mammary carcinogenesis in rats (Welsch et al., 1979).

If an action on pituitary function is suspected, a careful assessment and grading of mammary changes in both sexes, taken into account with the incidence of ovarian cysts and endometrial hyperplasia (see Uterus, Ovary and oviducts in Chapter IX) proves a valuable indication of such hormonal effects.

The normal development, histology, ultrastructure and histochemistry of the rat mammary gland has been reviewed by Young and Hallowes (1973). The resting gland consists of a network of interconnecting ducts and alveolar buds surrounded by connective tissue and fat. In the lactating gland, there is considerable expansion of the alveoli and large clusters of secretory alveoli are seen. The involuting gland contains clusters of collapsed alveoli within a fatty stroma. Recent study of the rat mammary gland using the immunoperoxidase technique and antisera to several specific proteins has confirmed the presence of myoepithelial cells as a continuous layer around the epithelial cells, in turn surrounded by a continuous basement membrane (Warburton et al., 1982). In the same study, these authors demonstrated that basement membrane proteins are predominantly synthesized by the myoepithelial cells in vivo, confirming several previous in vitro studies (Warburton et al., 1981; Liotta et al., 1979).

These factors are of considerable importance in the understanding of changes in the mammary gland, for it has also been shown that synthesis of collagen Type IV, present in the lamina densa of the basement membrane (Yaoita et al., 1978), is under hormonal control (Liotta et al., 1979), and that an intact basement membrane is important in the maintenance of duct integrity (Wicha et al., 1980). Furthermore, disruption of the basement membrane by secretion of collagenases and other proteases may be necessary for the invasion of surrounding tissue by neoplastic mammary epithelial cells (Liotta et al., 1980; O'Grady et al., 1981).

Non-neoplastic changes

The female mammary gland may show a variety of changes suggestive of stimulation or hyperplasia. It should be noted, however, that males may also show similar changes. These changes are grouped under the following headings. However, it should be remembered that these changes may be found together in varying proportions.

Cystic change (cystic degeneration)
Grouped under this term are those mammary glands that show mild to moderate dilatation of ducts or ductules (ectasia) without evidence of epithelial or glandular proliferation (hyperplasia). The lumina of such dilated ducts may contain proteinaceous material or lipid and occasionally macrophages or lipophages (histiocytes) are also seen (Figs 17 and 18).

Galactocele
When the cystic dilatation of ducts is marked and the mammary gland contains greatly dilated cyst-like structures, the term galactocele is used. These cystic lesions may rupture and give rise to an inflammatory reaction in the adjacent adipose tissue (see below).

Hyperplasia
Hyperplasia of the acinar tissue (adenosis) or of the ductular epithelium (epitheliosis) or papillomatoid proliferation are grouped under the heading of hyperplasia. Some of these microscopic foci may show mild cellular pleomorphism and mitotic activity but no change in architecture to warrant the diagnosis of neoplasia. The term cystic hyperplasia is used if there is both cystic change and hyperplasia present.

Inflammation
Inflammation in the mammary glands is usually of a minor and non-specific nature (minimal focal chronic inflammation). Somewhat more severe inflammation may be seen in association with rupture of cysts and dilated ducts with leakage of secretions into the connective tissue (acute and chronic inflammation, granulomatous inflammation). An abscess may also form.

Fibrosis
Most marked fibrosis is observed in fibroadenomas but, occasionally, small foci of dense fibrous tissue are observed surrounding apparently otherwise normal ducts and acini.

Neoplasms

In assessing the biological significance of mammary tumours in a carcinogenicity study, a number of factors need to be taken into account. The housing of animals may be important, for singly caged rodents have a different hormonal status from those multiply housed (Chvédoff et al., 1980). Dietary factors can also have a considerable impact on the mammary tumour incidence in any study. Increased dietary fat enhances mammary tumorigenesis (Ip, 1980; Kollmorgen et al., 1981). The mere quantity of diet may have a profound effect, as food restriction alone reduces the spontaneous mammary tumour incidence in rats (Tucker, 1979).

The endocrinological milieu is known to be important (Ciocca et al., 1982), and some mammary carcinomas induced in female Sprague-Dawley rats do specifically bind estradiol (Capuco and Tseng, 1981).

It is also well known that there are considerable strain differences, and this is also true under laboratory conditions at Amboise, where female Sprague-Dawley rats develop more mammary carcinomas, but not fibroadenomas, than the Long Evans strain (Greaves and Rabemampianina, 1982). A high incidence of mammary adenocarcinomas in the Sprague-Dawley strain has been previously reported (Durbin et al., 1966). Although tumours develop mainly in female rats, similar neoplasms do occur occasionally in males. Furthermore, in our colonies, these tumours are occasionally found in untreated rats before 6 months of age (Chvédoff et al., 1979) and this fact has to be remembered in the evaluation of the pathology in shorter toxicity studies.

An effect by a test compound on mammary tumorigenesis can only be detected by carefully recording the time of appearance of every ventral swelling, the number of mammary tumours per animal, as well as the total incidence of animals with such tumours. If only the number of animals with mammary tumours is recorded, an effect on mammary neoplasia could be missed owing to the high incidence of mammary tumours in the rat.

Biological behaviour and classification of mammary neoplasia

It is of course essential that following macroscopic evaluation, there is subsequent microscopic correlation of every mammary mass, for not all mammary masses are neoplastic, nor are all ventral masses of mammary origin.

Several classifications of rat mammary neoplasms have been proposed and some are particularly complicated (Komitowski et al., 1982). There are, however, several good reasons why use of a fairly simple classification is advisable. One important reason is simply that no one classification is generally accepted. A simplified scheme may also help interlaboratory comparison (Young and Hallowes, 1973).

Terms such as fibroadenoma, lobular carcinomas, comedocarcinomas, and tubular carcinoma have been to some extent borrowed from human pathology, yet little rigorous correlative study has been undertaken. The so-called adenocarcinomas of the rat mammary gland are certainly not the exact counterparts of the more common mammary carcinomas occurring in man, although they may bear structural features in common with the more recently described rarer types of human tumour such as the so-called carcinoid or secretory carcinomas. The predominant carcinomas seen in women are scirrhous, medullary or colloid, types which are rarely observed in rodents. Whereas at least 50% of these human tumours produce distant metastases and 80% develop regional lymph node deposits (Symmers, 1978), metastatic spread of most rodent mammary neoplasia is uncommon. Furthermore, metastases from mammary cancers to the skeleton in humans are extremely common, whereas the haematogenous spread of a spontaneous rodent mammary tumour to bone has not been described. In this context, it is interesting to note that the surgical implantation of skin carcinomas into bones of small mammals produces a picture very similar to

11

that seen in humans (Faccini, 1974), so it does not appear that the bone tissue of rodents is especially resistant to tumour growth once the tumour is present. This highlights the difference in behaviour of the rodent primary mammary tumour.

Immunogenicity of chemically induced tumours is high, whereas spontaneous rat mammary tumour immunogenicity is low, factors which may also be important with respect to metastatic potential and transplantation behaviour (Middle et al., 1981).

A further feature of these rat tumours is the fact that mammary tumours are not histologically homogeneous and that examination of several blocks of tissue from any one tumour often reveals a highly variable glandular pattern.

All these factors tend to preclude a detailed morphological classification that is valid in a biological sense. However, the pathologist must, in the routine setting, make a general and pragmatic assessment of malignant potential in each individual case by cytological characteristics as well as the presence or absence of local tissue invasion. The presence of metastases may be helpful in a few cases.

To enable us to do this, we have adopted the approach of blocking adequate amounts of tumour tissue, particularly to include tumour margins. It is quite clear that one small block taken from the centre of a mass measuring several centimeters in diameter does not provide sufficient material to enable a reliable assessment of a tumour, particularly as variation within individual mammary tumours is often striking.

In our laboratory, mammary tumours are grouped in the following way, with the provision that distinction between groups is not always clear cut and that a spectrum of appearances from the very fibrous to the very cellular glandular tumours is observed.

Fibroadenoma

Rat fibroadenomas are not necessarily the exact counterparts of the human mammary tumour of the same name, except they are composed of fibrous and glandular tissue and they appear generally benign. Macroscopically, rat fibroadenomas are firm, whitish, mobile lobulated tumours that may be very small, or become so large as to be almost as heavy as the host rat.

Although these lesions can be very large, histologically they retain a remarkable overall likeness to normal mammary gland with well-defined lobules of glandular tissue being separated by varying amounts of dense collagen (Fig. 19).

Epithelial elements often resemble the normal acinus, the cells being arranged in clusters or groups of alveoli of fairly uniform cells (Figs 20, 21 and 22). These cells usually possess regular, rounded or oval nuclei showing little mitotic activity. The cytoplasm may be eosinophilic but it is mostly finely vacuolated or foamy or contains coarse vacuoles. A few glands in these areas may show what appears to be ductular differentiation, ducts being lined by a single layer of columnar or cuboidal cells. The PAS stain reveals only small amounts of mucopolysaccharide in these ducts and acini, although they often contain lightly staining concentric concretions, or protein plugs (Figs 20 and 21).

Some fibroadenomas contain areas composed principally of ductular components. In these cases a resemblance to the human fibroadenoma, either the intracanalicular or pericanalicular type is more apparent (Fig. 23). In those cases where there is dense and abundant fibrosis, atrophy of the glandular tissue often occurs (Fig. 24).

Overall, these tumours appear histologically benign, although some may show epithelial proliferation and atypia. If such atypia is marked, and there is evidence of stromal infiltration, these tumours with atypical foci are classed as carcinomas.

Fibroma

In some cases of fibroadenoma, the fibrous element is so marked and so dense that atrophy of glandular tissue is observed (see above). If there is no residual evidence of ducts or acini, the term fibroma is employed, although in many cases extensive search reveals evidence of glandular differentiation. In these purely fibrous masses, the connective tissue is poorly cellular and composed principally of wide, dense, eosinophilic-staining bands of collagen, unlike the very fibrous version of the fibrous histiocytoma which is somewhat more cellular and shows a storiform pattern (see Subcutaneous tissue, above).

Adenoma

Although, quite commonly, a fibroadenoma contains very glandular foci with little fibrous tissue stroma, in our experience benign tumours, in which the only cellular or proliferative elements are epithelial and the stroma is minimal and supportive in nature, are less common. However, adenomas composed of compactly arranged tubular structures (tubular adenomas) (Fig. 25) or showing a multicystic pattern (cystadenoma) are welll described (Komitowski et al., 1982). Mixed appearances are seen. There may be papillomatosis within dilated ducts (papillary adenoma) and a limited amount of mitotic activity and cellular pleomorphism may be present. However, the tumours remain well demarcated from the surrounding tissue and there is no evidence of tissue infiltration.

Intraduct papilloma

Neoplastic papillary growths may develop within ducts. They tend to have a central connective tissue framework covered by one or two layers of epithelial cells. If there are no invasive features to warrant the diagnosis of carcinoma, they are grouped as intraduct papillomas (Fig. 26).

Carcinoma

Spontaneous malignant tumours of the Sprague-Dawley rat mammary gland are predominantly adenocarcinomas (Durbin et al., 1966; Sher, 1982) and, like fibroadenomas, they grow to considerable size but they are more likely to ulcerate or undergo necrosis and are more often the cause of death of the rat than the fibroadenomas. Such ulcerated tumours are often associated with a leucocytosis or even a leukaemoid reaction (see under Haemopoietic and Lymphatic Systems, Chapter II).

Histologically, they present a wide variety of appearances, often within the same tumour. However, major features are the proliferating nature of the epithelial tissues, glands usually being arranged in a 'back-to-back' manner with little or no interspersed stroma (Fig. 27). Nuclei are quite large, usually moderately to markedly hyperchromatic, nucleoli may be prominent and mitoses numerous (Fig. 28). Often, malignant glands are lined by multi-layered epithelium. Cribriform, tubular, papillary or solid areas may be seen. Some tumours possess a fairly homogeneous and uniform pattern of glands, others are much more pleomorphic. Differentiation is also variable, ranging from well-differentiated to frankly anaplastic. Some anaplastic areas may even appear sarcomatous. Squamous metaplasia is also sometimes observed in otherwise unremarkable adenocarcinomas (adenosquamous carcinoma).

The edges of these tumours, when sufficient material has been sectioned, usually show fairly clear evidence of infiltrative behaviour, particularly into skeletal muscle. Perineural or intravascular invasion is even more convincing evidence of malignancy (Fig. 27). Less well-differentiated forms may metastasize, usually to the lungs (Fig. 29).

Carcinosarcoma

These are rare tumours of the rat mammary gland. Komitowski and his colleagues (1982) found only 10 carcinosarcomas out of 1,613 induced mammary tumours and none were recorded in a series of 170 spontaneous mammary neoplasms. We have seen occasional carcinosarcomas in untreated rats at Amboise. They are characterized by proliferating and malignant infiltrative growth of both glandular and spindle cell or sarcomatous elements. We feel that if representative and adequate material is examined, many of these tumours focally show convincing myoepithelial differentiation and the tumours are similar histologically to the malignant myoepithelioma in man (Figs 30, 31, 32 and 33). Recent studies, involving culture of rat mammary carcinomas in vitro, also support the concept that myoepithelial differentiation occurs in rat mammary neoplasms and that this can be controlled by the cell environment (Dulbecco et al., 1979; Rudland et al., 1982).

A poorly differentiated adenocarcinoma may also contain frankly sarcomatous areas (see above).

REFERENCES

AL ZUBAIDY, A.J. and FINN, J.P. (1983): Brown fat tumours (hibernomas) in rats: histopathological and ultrastructural study. *Lab.Anim., 17,* 13-17.

BUREK, J.D. (1978): Age-associated pathology. In: *Pathology of Aging Rats,* Chap. 4, pp. 29-167. CRC Press, West Palm Beach, FL.

CAPUCO, A.V. and TSENG, M.T. (1981): Estradiol binding by intact cells isolated from DMBA-induced mammary tumours of the rat. *Steroids, 37,* 649-662.

CARTER, R.L. (1973): Tumours of soft tissues. In: V.S. Turusov (Ed.), *Pathology of Tumours in Laboratory Animals, Vol. 1, Tumours of the Rat, Part 1,* pp. 151-168. IARC Scientific Publ. No. 5, Lyon.

CHVEDOFF, M., BUREAU, M. and MORTIER, G. (1979): Quelques données relatives à la maintenance des animaux témoins (rats, souris) dans les études de toxicologie chronique. *Sci.Tech.Anim.Lab., 4,* 227-231.

CHVEDOFF, M., CLARKE, M.R., IRISARRI, E., FACCINI, J.M. and MONRO, A.M. (1980): Effects of numbers of mice/cage on food intake, body weight and spontaneous lesions. A review of the literature and results of an 18-month study. *Food Cosmet.Toxicol., 18,* 517-522.

CIOCCA, D.R., PARENTE, A. and RUSSO, J. (1982): Endocrinologic milieu and susceptibility of the rat mammary gland to carcinogenesis. *Am.J.Pathol., 109,* 47-56.

COGGON, D. and ACHESON, E.D. (1982): Do phenoxy herbicides cause cancer in man? *Lancet, 1,* 1057-1059.

COLEMAN, G.L. (1980): Four intrathoracic hibernomas in rats. *Vet.Pathol., 17,* 634-637.

DULBECCO, R., BOLOGNA, M. and UNGER, M. (1979): Differentiation of a rat mammary cell line in vitro. *Proc.Natl Acad.Sci.USA, 76*, 1256-1260.

DURBIN, P.W., WILLIAMS, M.H., JEUNG, N. and ARNOLD, J.S. (1966): Development of spontaneous mammary tumors over the life-span of the female Charles River (Sprague-Dawley) rat: the influence of ovariectomy, thyroidectomy and adrenalectomy-ovariectomy. *Cancer Res., 26*, 400-411.

ENTERLINE, H.T., CULBERSON, J.D., ROCHLIN, D.B. and BRADY, L.W. (1960): Liposarcoma. A clinical and pathological study of 53 cases. *Cancer, 13*, 932-950.

ERICKSSON, M., HARDELL, L., BERG, N.O., MOLLER, T. and AXELSON, O. (1981): Soft tissue sarcomas and exposure to chemical substances: A case referent study. *Br.J.Ind.Med., 38*, 27-33.

FACCINI, J.M. (1974): The mode of growth of experimental metastases in rabbit femora. *Virchows Arch.A, 364*, 249-263.

FORD, R.J. and BECKER, F.F. (1982): The characterization of trypan blue-induced tumors in Wistar rats. *Am.J.Pathol., 106*, 326-331.

GHADIALLY, F.N. (1961): The role of the hair follicle in the origin and evolution of some cutaneous neoplasms of man and experimental animals. *Cancer, 14*, 801-816.

GHADIALLY, F.N. (1980): Is it a myosarcoma? A study of intracytoplasmic filaments. In: *Diagnostic Electron Microscopy of Tumours*, Chap. 10, pp. 116-139. Butterworths, London.

GREAVES, P. and FACCINI, J.M. (1981): Fibrous histiocytic neoplasms spontaneously arising in rats. *Br.J.Cancer, 43*, 402-411.

GREAVES, P. and RABEMAMPIANINA, Y. (1982): Choice of rat strain: A comparison of the general pathology and the tumour incidence in 2-year old Sprague-Dawley and Long-Evans rats. In: New Toxicology for Old. *Arch. Toxicol., Suppl. 5*, 298-303.

GREAVES, P., MARTIN, J.M. and MASSON, M.T. (1982): Spontaneous rat malignant tumours of fibrohistiocytic origin: An ultrastructural study. *Vet.Pathol., 19*, 497-505.

HARDELL, L. and SANDSTRÖM, A. (1979): Case control study: Soft tissue sarcomas and exposure to phenoxyacetic acids or chlorophenols. *Br.J.Cancer, 39*, 711-717.

HERRERA, G.A., REIMANN, B.E.F., SALINAS, J.A. and TURBAT, E.A. (1982): Malignant Schwannomas presenting as malignant fibrous histiocytomas. *Ultrastruct.Pathol., 3*, 253-261.

IP, C. (1980): Ability of dietary fat to overcome the resistance of mature female rats to 7,12-dimethylbenz(a)-anthracene-induced mammary tumorigenesis. *Cancer Res., 40*, 2785-2789.

KOLLMORGEN, G.M., KING, M.M., ROSZEL, J.F., DAGGS, B.J. and LONGLEY, R.E. (1981): The influence of dietary fat and non-specific immunotherapy on carcinogen-induced rat mammary adenocarcinoma. *Vet.Pathol., 18*, 82-91.

KOMITOWSKI, D., SASS, B. and LAUB, W. (1982): Rat mammary tumor classification: Notes on comparative aspects. *J.Natl Cancer Inst., 68*, 147-156.

KONISHI, Y., MARUYAMA, H., MII, Y., MIYAUCHI, Y., YOKOSE, Y. and MASUHARA, K. (1982): Malignant fibrous histiocytomas induced by 4-(hydroxyamino) quinoline 1-oxide in rats. *J.Natl Cancer Inst., 68*, 859-865.

KUHN, C. and ROSAI, J. (1969): Tumors arising from pericytes. Ultrastructure and organ culture of a case. *Arch.Pathol., 88*, 653-663.

LEVER, W.F. (1975): Tumours of the epidermal appendages. In: *Histopathology of the Skin*, 5th Ed., Chap. 26, pp. 498-561. Lippincott, Philadelphia.

LIOTTA, L.A., WICHA, M.S., FOIDART, J.M., RENNARD, S.I., GARBISA, S. and KIDWELL, W.R. (1979): Hormonal requirements for basement membrane collagen deposition by cultured rat mammary epithelium. *Lab.Invest., 41*, 511-518.

LIOTTA, L.A., TRYGGVASON, K., GARBISA, S., HART, I., FOLTZ, C.M. and SHAFIE, S. (1980): Metastatic potential correlates with enzymatic degradation of basement membrane collagen. *Nature (London), 284*, 67-68.

MacKENZIE, D.H. (1970): Preface. In: *The Differential Diagnosis of Fibroblastic Disorders*, pp. vii-viii. Blackwell Scientific, Oxford.

MacKENZIE, W.F. and GARNER, F.M. (1973): Comparison of neoplasms in six sources of rats. *J.Natl Cancer Inst., 50*, 1243-1257.

MANNI, A., TRUJILLO, J.E. and PEARSON, O.H. (1977): Predominant role of prolactin in stimulating the growth of 7,12-dimethylbenzanthracene-induced rat mammary tumor. *Cancer Res., 37*, 1216-1219.

McALLISTER, H.A. and FENOGLIO, J.J. (1977): Tumors of the Cardiovascular System. In: *Atlas of Tumor Pathology, Second Series, Fascicle 15*, pp. 46-52. AFIP, Washington, DC.

MIDDLE, J.G., ROBINSON, G. and EMBLETON, M.J. (1981): Naturally arising tumors of the inbred WAB/Not rat strain. I. Classification, age, sex distribution and transplantation behaviour. *J.Natl Cancer Inst., 67*, 629-636.

NASRALLAH, H.A., FREED, W.J., ROGOD, A. and WYATT, R.J. (1977): Propranolol and prolactin. *Lancet, 2*, 1175.

O'GRADY, R.L., UPFOLD, L.I. and STEPHENS, R.W. (1981): Rat mammary carcinoma cells secrete active collagenase and active latent enzyme in the stroma via plasminogen activator. *Int.J.Cancer, 28*, 509-515.

PEARSON, O.H., MURRAY, R.L.M., MOZAFFARIAN, G. and PENSKY, J. (1972): Prolactin and experimental breast cancer. In: A.R. Boyns and K. Griffiths (Eds), *Prolactin and Carcinogenesis*, pp. 154-157. Alpha Omega Alpha Publishing, Cardiff.

PLATT, B.S. (1965): Nutritional influences on the skin: experimental evidence. In: A.J. Rook and G.S. Walton (Eds), *Comparative Physiology and Pathology of the Skin*, pp. 245-260. Blackwell Scientific, Oxford.

RUDLAND, P.S., GUSTERSON, B.A., HUGHES, C.M., ORMEROD, E.J. and WARBURTON, M.J. (1982): Two forms of tumours in nude mice generated by a neoplastic rat mammary stem cell line. *Cancer Res., 42*, 5196-5208.

SHER, S.P. (1982): Tumours in control hamsters, rats and mice: Literature tabulation. *CRC Crit.Rev.Toxicol., 10*, 49-79.

SQUIRE, R.A., GOODMAN, D.G., VALERIO, M.G., FREDRICKSON, T.N., STRANDBERG, J.D., LEVITT, M.H., LINGEMAN, C.H., HARSHBARGER, J.C. and DAWE, C.J. (1978): Tumours. In: K. Benirschke, F.M. Garner and T.C. Jones (Eds), *Pathology of Laboratory Animals, Vol. 2*, Chap. 12, pp. 1051-1283. Springer-Verlag, New York.

SQUIRE, R.A., BRINKHOMS, K.M., PEIPER, S.C., FIRMINGER, H.I., MANN, R.B. and STRANDBERG, J.D. (1981): Histiocytic sarcoma with a granuloma-like component occurring in a large colony of Sprague-Dawley rats. *Am.J. Pathol., 105*, 21-30.

STEWART, H.L. (1979): Tumours of the soft tissues. In: V.S. Turusov (Ed.), *Pathology of Tumours in Laboratory Animals, Vol. 2, Tumours of the Mouse*, pp. 487-525. IARC Scientific Publ. No. 23, Lyon.

STOUT, A.M. (1948): Myxoma, tumour of primitive mesenchyme. *Ann.Surg., 127*, 706-719.

SYMMERS, W.St.C. (1978): The breasts. In: W.St.C. Symmers (Ed.), *Systemic Pathology, 2nd Ed., Vol. 4*, Chap. 28, pp. 1760-1861. Churchill Livingstone, Edinburgh.

TAYLOR, H.B. and NORRIS, H.J. (1966): Mesenchymal tumors of the uterus. *Arch.Pathol., 82*, 40-44.

TUCHMANN-DUPLESSIS and MERCIER-PAROT, L. (1968): Endocrine effects of some neurotropic drugs. In: S.B. de C. Baker, J.R. Boissier and W. Koll (Eds), *Toxicity and Side-Effects of Psychotropic Drugs, Vol. 9*, pp. 128-133. ICS No. 145, Excerpta Medica Foundation, Amsterdam.

TUCKER, M.J. (1979): The effect of long-term food restriction on tumours in rodents. *Int.J. Cancer, 23*, 803-807.

WARBURTON, M.J., ORMEROD, E.J., MONAGHAN, P., FERNS, S. and RUDLAND, P.S. (1981): Characterization of a myoepithelial cell line derived from a neonatal rat mammary gland. *J.Cell Biol., 91*, 827-836.

WARBURTON, M.J., MITCHELL, D., ORMEROD, E.J. and RUDLAND, P. (1982): Distribution of myoepithelial cells and basement membrane proteins in the resting, pregnant, lactating and involuting rat mammary gland. *J.Histochem.Cytochem., 30*, 667-676

WEISS, S.W. and ENZINGER, F.M. (1978): Malignant fibrous histiocytoma. *Cancer, 41*, 2250-2266.

WELSCH, C.W., BROWN, C.K., GOODRIGHT-SMITH, M., VAN, J., DENENBERG, B., ANDERSON, T.M. and BROOKS, C.L. (1979): Inhibition of mammary tumorigenesis in carcinogen-treated Lewis rats by suppression of prolactin secretion. *J.Ntl Cancer Inst., 63*, 5, 1211-1214.

WICHA, M.S., LIOTTA, L.A., VANDERHAAR, B.K. and KIDWELL, W.R. (1980): Effects of inhibition of basement membrane collagen deposition in rat mammary gland development. *Dev.Biol., 80*, 253-256.

YAOITA, H., FOIDART, J.M. and KATZ, S.J. (1978): Localization of the collagenous component in skin basement membrane. *J.Invest.Dermatol., 70*, 191-193.

YOUNG, S. and HALLOWES, R.C. (1973): Tumours of the mammary gland. In: V.S. Turusov (Ed.), *Pathology of Tumours in Laboratory Animals, Vol. 1, Tumours of the Rat, Part 1*, pp. 31-73. IARC Scientific Publ. No. 5, Lyon.

ZACKHEIM, H.S. (1973): Tumours of the skin. In: V.S. Turusov (Ed.), *Pathology of Tumours in Laboratory Animals, Vol. 1, Tumours of the Rat, Part 1*, pp. 1-30. IARC Scientific Publ. No. 5, Lyon.

17

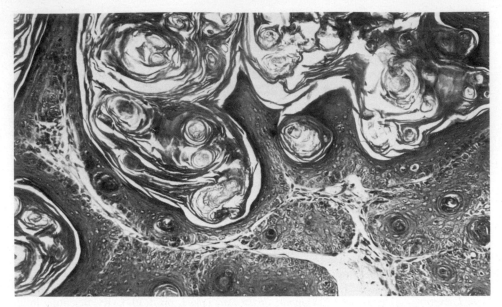

Fig. 1   A squamous papilloma occurring as a superficial, non-invasive skin nodule in a
26-month-old male Long-Evans rat. Papillomatosis, hyperkeratosis and acanthosis is marked.
A similar appearance is also seen in the inverted papilloma. (HE, × 105)

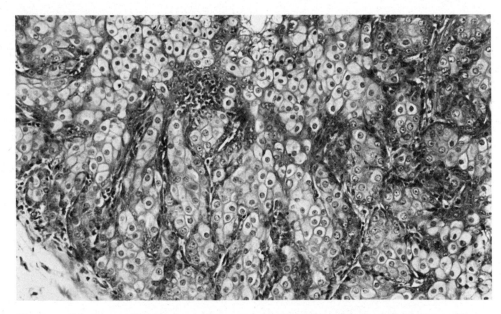

Fig. 2   Sebaceous adenoma presenting as a subcutaneous nodule 1 cm diameter on the posterior thorax of a 25-month-old male control Sprague-Dawley rat.   Note the well-defined
borders of the tumour which is composed of uniform eosinophilic cells resembling those found
in normal sebaceous glands. (HE, × 105)

18

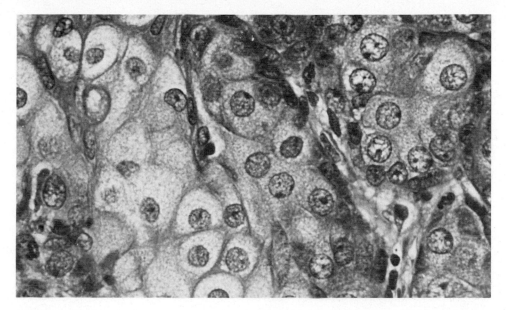

Fig. 3 Sebaceous adenoma, same case as in Figure 2, higher power view. (HE, ×450)

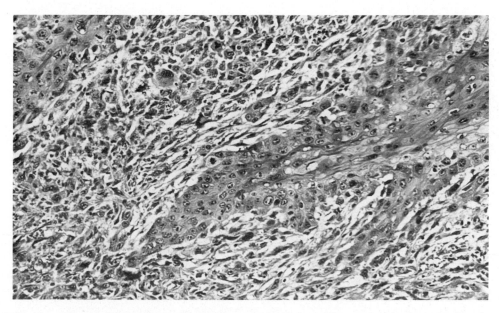

Fig. 4 Squamous carcinoma presenting as a mass 2.5 cm diameter on the face of a female Sprague-Dawley rat 25 months of age. It is only moderately differentiated and infiltrates the soft tissues with an accompanying inflammatory infiltrate. (HE, ×105)

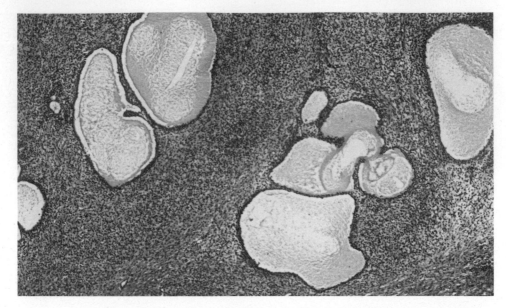

Fig. 5   Undifferentiated or cystic sarcoma found at scheduled sacrifice as a mass 2.5 cm diameter on the left side of the neck of a 26-month-old male Long-Evans rat. It is composed of solid and cystic areas, cells being mainly small and stellate in nature. Metastases were not found. (HE, × 26)

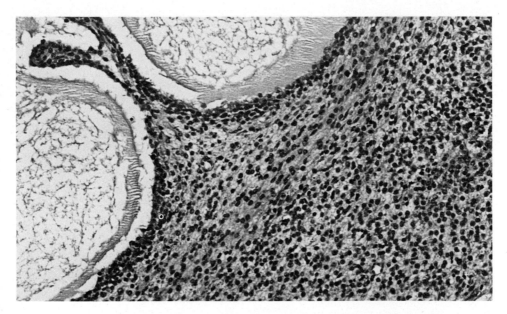

Fig. 6   Undifferentiated or cystic sarcoma, same case as in Figure 5. (HE, × 105)

20

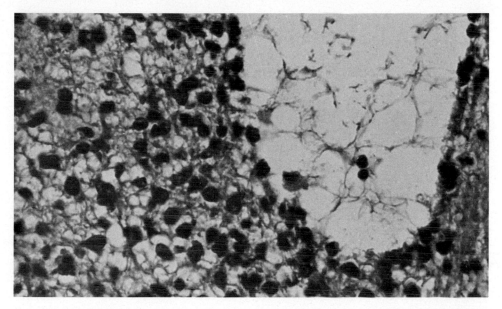

Fig. 7   Undifferentiated or cystic sarcoma, same case as in Figures 5 and 6. (HE, × 450)

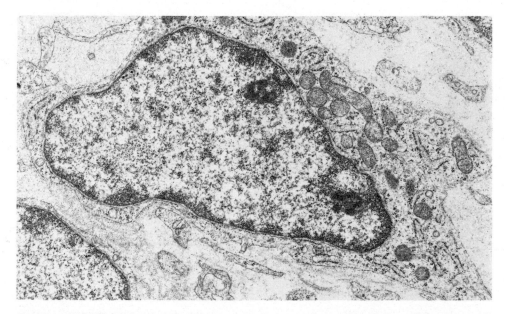

Fig. 8   Undifferentiated or cystic sarcoma, electron micrograph. These cells are the small stellate cells seen at light microscopic level (Figs 5, 6 and 7). Distinctive features are not seen, cells possessing oval, indented nuclei, with abundant chromatin with a moderate amount of cytoplasmic rough endoplasmic reticulum, mitochondria and lysosomes. The intercellular matrix is of low density. (E/M, × 13,500)

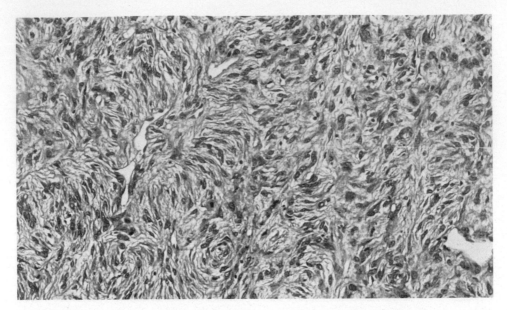

Fig. 9 Fibrous histiocytoma, presenting as an ulcerated mass 3 cm diameter on the left side of the abdomen of a 25-month-old female Sprague-Dawley rat. The typical cartwheel or storiform pattern of plump spindle cells is apparent, sometimes radiating around a small blood vessel. No metastases were found in this case. (HE, × 105)

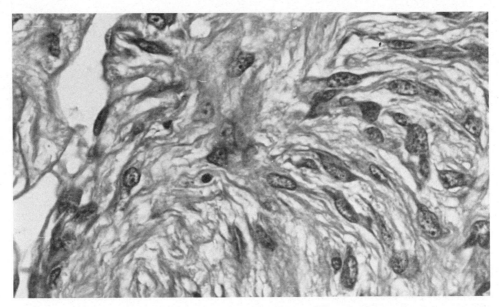

Fig. 10 Fibrous histiocytoma, same case as in Figure 9 but at a higher magnification. (HE, × 450)

22

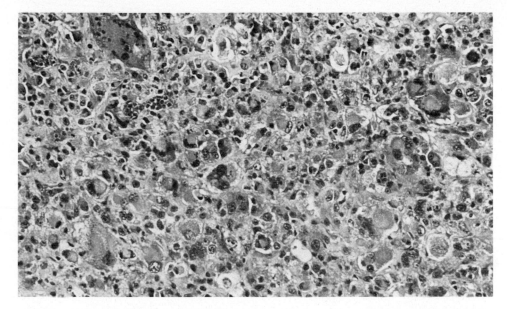

Fig. 11   Pleomorphic fibrous histiocytoma. A millipore filter 2.4 cm diameter, pore size 0.025 μm, was implanted beneath the dorsal skin of a 3-month-old Sprague-Dawley rat. By 20 months of age the filter was enveloped by an ulcerated but mobile mass 6 cm diameter. The pleomorphic nature of this tumour is evident, but a cell of foreign-body giant cell type can be seen in one corner. (HE, × 105)

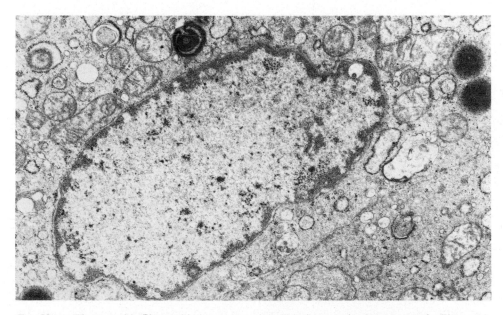

Fig. 12   Pleomorphic fibrous histiocytoma, electron micrograph, same case as in Figure 11. The nucleus of this cell contains marginated chromatin whilst numerous swollen mitochondria, some dilated short profiles of rough endoplasmic reticulum and lysosomal structures are present in the cytoplasm. (E/M, × 13,500)

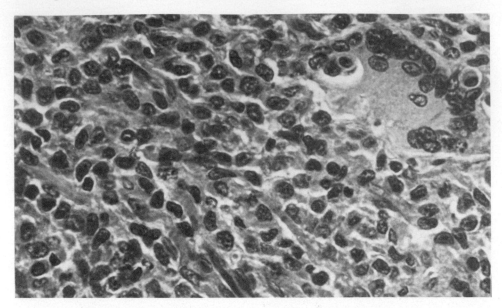

Fig. 13 Malignant histiocytoma (histiocytic sarcoma). This represents the more typical appearance of this type of tumour being composed of moderately uniform histiocytic cells and a scattering of fairly benign looking giant cells of foreign-body or Langhans' type. This tumour, a ventral in a 24-month-old Sprague-Dawley female rat, metastatized to mesenteric lymph nodes, lungs and liver. (HE, × 450)

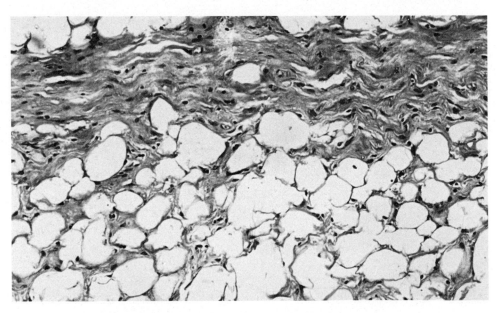

Fig. 14 Lipoma, occurring as soft, mobile, subcutaneous mass 4 cm diameter on the left side of the thorax in a male Sprague-Dawley rat 25 months of age. Typical mature fat cells and fibrous connective tissue are evident. (HE, × 105)

24

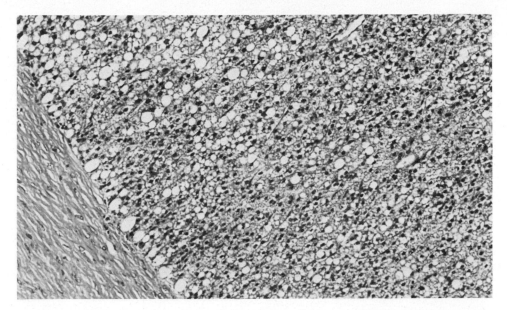

Fig. 15   Hibernoma presenting as a mobile, yellow, lobulated mass 4.5 cm diameter in the anterior part of the thoracic cavity and compressing the heart and lungs. This Sprague-Dawley male rat was sacrificed at the age of 10 months because of loss of weight and breathlessness. Histologically, it is characterized by the presence of uniform cells with vacuolated cytoplasm and small, dense, round nuclei surrounded by a thick fibrous capsule. Metastases or infiltrative appearances were not observed in this case. (HE, × 105)

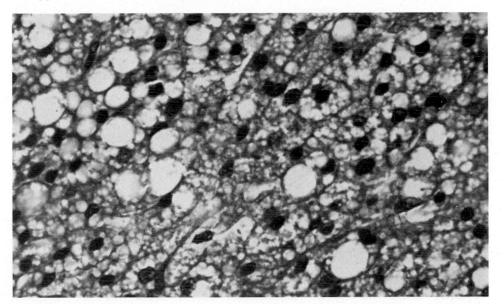

Fig. 16   Hibernoma, same case as in Figure 15, showing cellular architecture in more detail. (HE, × 450)

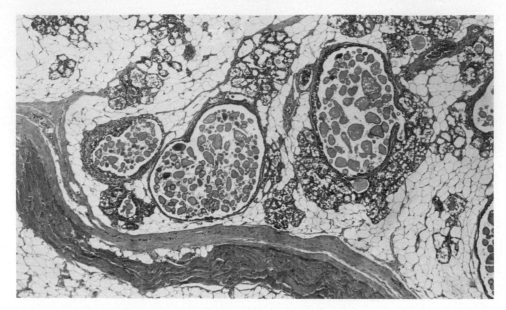

Fig. 17   Cystic change, mammary gland. An incidental finding in a 26-month-old female Long-Evans rat. Ducts show marked cystic dilatation and contain numerous rounded proteinaceous concretions. (HE, × 105)

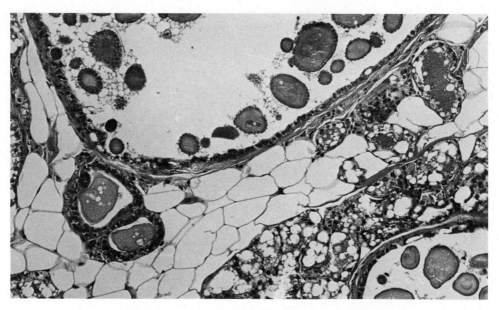

Fig. 18   Cystic change, mammary gland. Same case as in Figure 17. (HE, × 450)

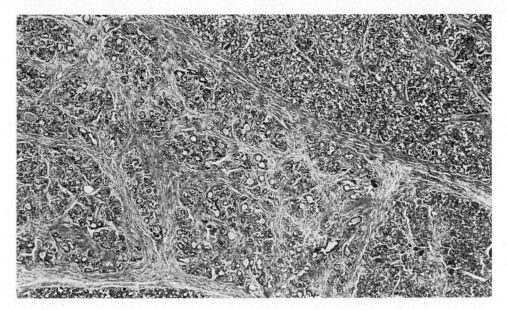

Fig. 19 Mammary fibroadenoma in a 26-month-old Sprague-Dawley female rat. The lobulated glandular pattern and fibrous tissue septa are apparent. (HE, ×26)

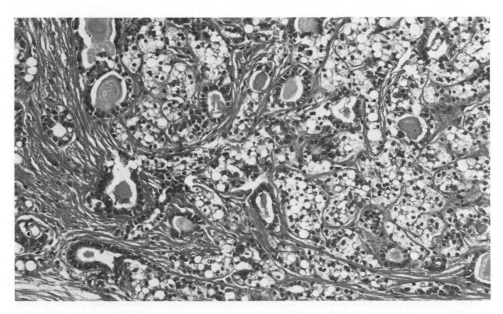

Fig. 20 Fibroadenoma, mammary gland, in a 26-month-old Long-Evans female rat showing both the coarsely and finely vacuolated acinar cells and the ducts containing concentric eosinophilic concretions. (HE, ×105)

27

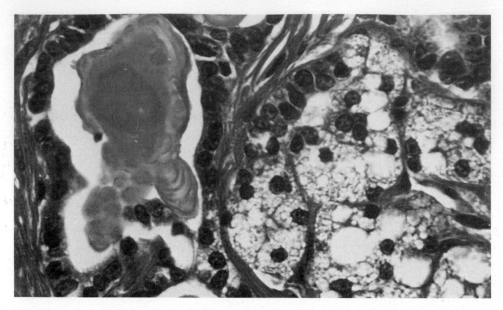

Fig. 21   Fibroadenoma, mammary gland, same case as in Figure 20, showing cellular detail. (HE, ×450)

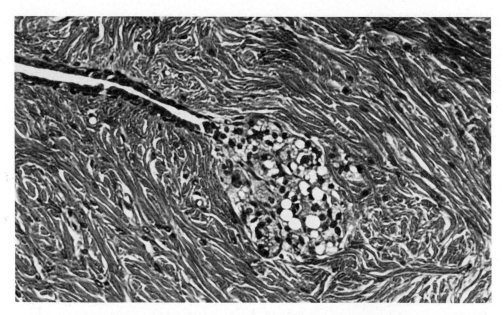

Fig. 22   Same case as in Figures 20 and 21, showing the typical coarse bands of poorly cellular collagen. There is a convincing demonstration of both duct and acinar differentiation in this microscopic field. (HE, ×165)

28

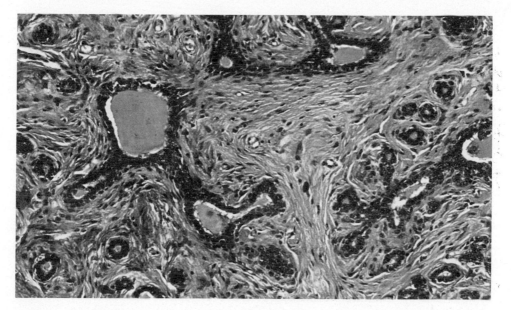

Fig. 23 Fibroadenoma in a 25-month-old Sprague-Dawley female rat. In this figure, glandular components are surrounded by dense concentric fibrous tissue, features similar to those found in the so-called pericanalicular fibroadenoma in man. (HE, × 105)

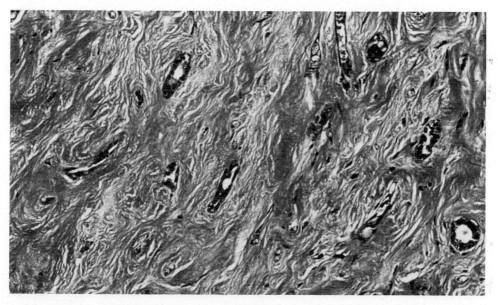

Fig. 24 Fibroadenoma in a 25-month-old female rat showing almost complete attenuation of epithelial elements by dense collagen. (HE, × 105)

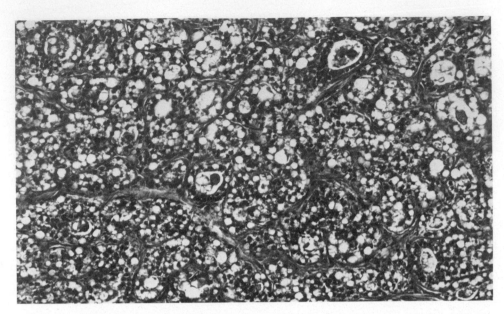

Fig. 25   Adenoma in the mammary gland of a 26-month-old Long-Evans rat. The lobulated structure is similar to that found in many fibroadenomas but the glandular tissue is predominant and connective tissue sparse. (HE, ×105)

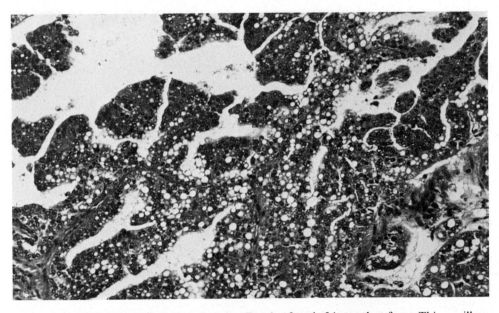

Fig. 26   Intraduct papilloma in a Sprague-Dawley female 24 months of age. This papillary lesion, although quite cellular, remained entirely localized within a dilated mammary duct. (HE, ×105)

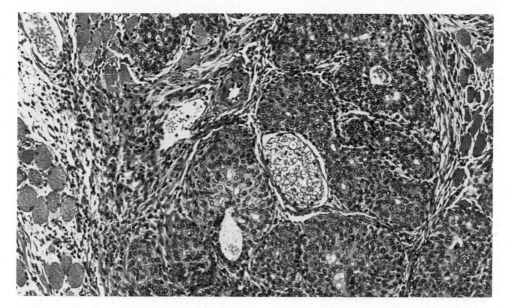

Fig. 27 Mammary carcinoma of typical appearance in a female Sprague-Dawley rat. In this section both the solid and cribriform glandular pattern are evident. There is infiltration of muscle, connective tissue and convincing perineural invasion. (HE, × 105)

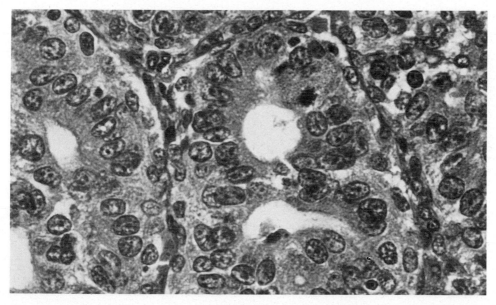

Fig. 28 Mammary carcinoma, same case as in Figure 27, showing moderately hyperchromatic tumour cells. There is little connective tissue stroma and a mitosis is evident. (HE, × 450)

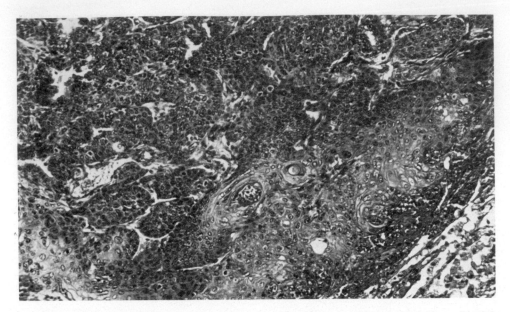

Fig. 29 Metastatic mammary carcinoma in a 25-month-old Sprague-Dawley rat. This large pulmonary metastasis shows squamous metaplasia at its periphery. The primary tumour was an unremarkable adenocarcinoma. (HE, × 105)

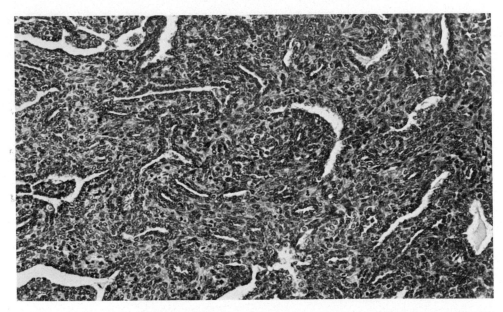

Fig. 30 Carcinosarcoma. Mammary mass 8 cm in diameter in a moribund Sprague-Dawley female rat aged 21 months. In this field, the biphasic glandular and myoepithelial components are apparent. Metastatic deposits were found in the lungs and myocardium. These neoplasms are commonly called carcinosarcomas, although a better term would be malignant myoepithelioma. (HE, × 105)

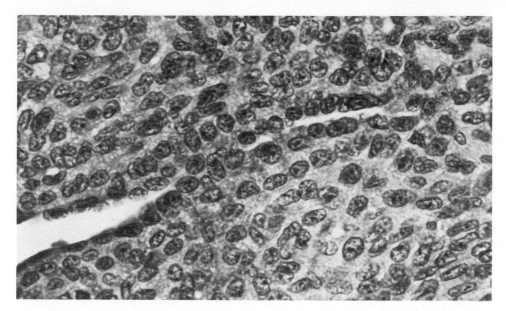

Fig. 31   Carcinosarcoma. Same case as in Figure 30, showing cellular detail of a biphasic zone. (HE, ×450)

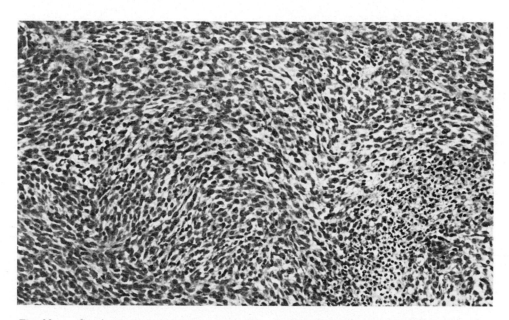

Fig. 32   Carcinosarcoma, same case as in Figures 30 and 31, showing the sarcomatous appearance. (HE, ×105)

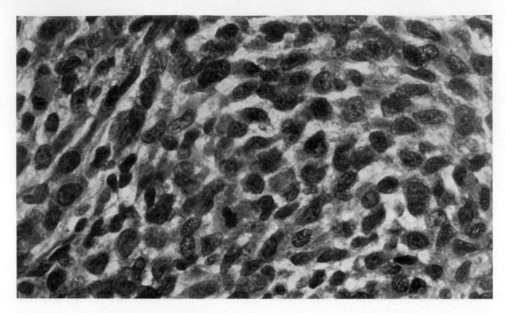

Fig. 33   Carcinosarcoma. Same case as in Figures 30, 31 and 32, showing cellular detail of the sarcomatous cells. (HE, × 450)

II. Haemopoietic and lymphatic systems

INTRODUCTION

The histological examination of the bone marrow and blood-forming cells naturally forms an integral part of the general haematological assessment of the test animal and, therefore, cannot be considered in total isolation from haematological findings.

For this reason a close cooperation should exist between the pathologist and the haematologist in the overall assessment of this system. As routine paraffin-embedded sections of bone marrow and lymphoid tissue often yield relatively poorly cytological detail, bone marrow smears and imprints of lymph nodes, thymus and spleen, stained with Romanovski stains are particularly useful in the assessment of these organs and this is, in our opinion, the method of choice for large numbers of animals. Others have used methacrylate-embedded semi-thin sections according to the method of Burkhardt routinely in toxicity tests (Burkhardt, 1966, 1970; Westen, 1974).

There has been a change in our understanding of the lymphoreticular and mononuclear phagocytic cell systems as a whole. These systems are now grouped into a stem cell compartment (bone marrow), the primary or central lymphoid organs (thymus, bursa of Fabricius or its equivalent) and the peripheral or secondary lymphoreticular tissue (lymph nodes, spleen, bronchial and gut associated lymphoid tissue, BALT or GALT – see review by Henry et al., 1978). The liver is also an integral part of the mucosal immune system (Kleinman et al., 1982).

The immense complexity of the immune system means that the initial screening for immunotoxicity can at best be crude and empirical (Davies, 1981). However, the pathologist is uniquely well situated for screening of the immune system because he can assess morphologically the various organs involved. Moreover, studies have shown that a certain relationship exists between function of the immune system and its morphology (Edwards et al., 1971; Patt et al., 1975; Tsakraklides et al., 1974).

Morphimetry and precise descriptive methods can also be used in the morphological assessment of lymphoid tissue (Cottier et al., 1972). In the future, this purely morphological assessment will be increasingly aided by more objective modern histochemical and immunohistochemical and cytochemical techniques (Davies, 1981). Surface marker analysis has already been used to define B and T cells in the rat (Koestner et al., 1982; Dijkstra and Döpp, 1983).

Note:
The neoplasms of the haemopoietic and lymphoid cells themselves are described together under the heading 'lymphoreticular neoplasms', and not under individual lymphoid and haemopoietic organs. However, tumours relating specifically to individual organs are described under the respective organ.

BONE MARROW/BLOOD

Under normal physiological conditions nearly all of the bone marrow space in the rat is occupied by haemopoietic tissue, except for a small number of scattered fat cells. Thus it appears that the reserve capacity of the rat bone marrow is rather limited and this may explain why extramedullary haematopoiesis is seen so readily under conditions of increased demand (Swaen and Van Heerde, 1973) – see Spleen and Lymph Nodes, below, and under Liver in Chapter VI, Kidney in Chapter VII and Adrenal Gland in Chapter X.

The generally reported myeloid erythroid ratio in the rat bone marrow is 1:1 and this concurs with our own experience, although normal variation is quite marked. In the peripheral circulation nucleated red cells are only occasionally seen (see below) although normal red cells show considerable anisocytosis (Sanderson and Phillips, 1981).

Note:

In our laboratory, the sternal bone marrow is that which is routinely sectioned for histological examination.

Non-neoplastic lesions

Fibrosis

Small foci of fibrosis (focal fibrosis) may occasionally be seen in the marrow space. These lesions are not associated with changes in the haemopoietic cells or peripheral blood and are presumably the result of inflammation and repair, but usually there are no specific features to denote histogenesis. More intense fibrosis may be associated with osteitis fibrosis or other skeletal conditions (see Bone in Chapter III). The term myelofibrosis is reserved for a myeloproliferative condition in which there is not only fibrosis but also proliferation of the haemopoietic cells (Swaen and Van Heerde, 1973).

Hyperplasia of the bone marrow (myeloid hyperplasia)

The bone marrow of the rat is usually quite cellular but blood-forming elements are usually interspersed with a few fat cells (see above). In a variety of reactive states, the marrow may become completely filled with normal haemopoietic tissue. Anaemia or increased red cell destruction may be associated with hyperplasia of the erythroid cell series in the bone marrow (erythroid hyperplasia).

Neutrophilia in the peripheral blood may be associated with hyperplasia of the myeloid elements (myeloid hyperplasia). A neutrophilia may be so intense as to mimic a frank leukaemia (leukaemoid reaction) and it may be quite difficult to distinguish between the two (Hardy, 1967). However, in bone marrow smears, myeloid hyperplasia is usually confined to the myelocytic stage (Thompson, 1977) and, in addition, a cause for hyperplasia and leukaemoid reactions, such as infection or necrosis in a large ulcerated tumour, is usually found.

Increased platelet consumption may also be characterized by increased megakaryocytic cells in the bone marrow (megakaryocytic hyperplasia). Very occasionally, hyperplasia of principally eosinophil or basophil cell series may be seen (eosinophilic or basophilic hyperplasia). Plasma cells may also be numerous in marrow smears or sections (plasma cell hyperplasia). Increased numbers of mast cells may be observed in smears in some cases of plasma cell hyperplasia.

Atrophy of the bone marrow (hypoplasia, aplasia, panmyelopathy)

Hypoplasia or aplasia of the marrow is best characterized in histological sections; hypocellularity of the marrow is observed, haemopoietic cells being replaced by adipose cells (fatty atrophy). Smears may be poorly cellular, containing only a few plasma cells and mast cells, and anaemia and neutropenia may be seen in the peripheral blood. However, significant reduction in marrow cellularity in the rat as a result of administration of toxic compounds may be observed in histological sections without concomitant reduction in cellularity in smear preparations (Blair et al., 1982).

Neoplasms

Haemopoietic neoplasms are treated under the heading 'lymphoreticular neoplasms'.

SPLEEN

The splenic parenchyma is composed of the so-called white and red pulp. Extensive study has shown that lymphocytes of thymic origin are located in the periarteriolar lymphoid sheaths (PALS) and those of B-cell origin, in the primary or secondary follicles (germinal centres) (Fig. 34).

The marginal or mantle zone (MZ), the border between the periarteriolar lymphoid sheaths and the red pulp also has special significance in the rat. It acts as the barrier which separates the white pulp from blood-borne material (Brelinska and Pilgrim, 1982) and cooperative interaction between B and T cells may begin in this area because the marginal zone is a prominent site of antigen localization in immune and non-immune animals (Nossal et al., 1966; Mitchell and Abbot, 1971; Van Rooijen, 1973). It is also the site at which lymphocytes emigrate from the circulation into the periarteriolar lymphoid sheaths. The location and temporal appearance of the different classes of lymphocytes in the rat spleen using immunocytochemical techniques have recently been described (Dijkstra and Döpp, 1983).

It is, therefore, important that pathologists evaluate these areas for changes because compounds that affect immune function have been shown to alter the morphology of these zones (Blair et al., 1982; Vos, 1977; Kociba, 1981).

Non-neoplastic lesions

Mild, non-neoplastic changes in the aged rat spleen are difficult to quantify, but are described when particularly prominent. Although it has been suggested that changes in splenic weight reflect changes in immune function (Vos, 1977), a variety of other factors may affect spleen weight, including changes in blood content, increases in connective tissue and mesenchymal cells, pigmentation and neoplasia. A recent study has in fact shown that there is an increase in splenic weight with advancing age in the F344 rat while there is a corresponding *decrease* in immune function with age (Tak Cheung, 1981). This paradox is probably explained by the increase in connective tissue elements and pigment-laden cells that increase with age (see below).

Extramedullary haemopoiesis (myeloid hyperplasia, myeloid metaplasia)

It should be remembered that the spleen of the rat only functions as an additional haemopoietic organ in times of stress (unlike the spleen of the mouse which routinely functions in a haemopoietic capacity) (Loeb et al., 1978). Splenic enlargement and extramedullary haemopoiesis have been observed frequently in female rats bearing mammary fibroadenomas (Berg, 1967). It may be marked when ulceration of large mammary tumours occurs. Histologically, extramedullary haemopoiesis is characterized by the presence of myeloid cells and more strikingly megakaryocytes.

Pigmentation

Pigment is commonly seen in the spleen of the aged rat. It may be situated diffusely throughout the red pulp, principally within sinusoidal macrophages and/or in large, dense extracellular clumps situated in the periarteriolar lymphoid sheaths (Fig. 34). In both sites, the pigment stains blue with Perls' stain and is, therefore, predominantly iron pigment. The ultrastructural appearances of this pigment within siderosomes in splenic macrophages suggests that erythrocyte degradation is principally responsible for pigment production (Ward and Reznik-Schüller, 1980). Iron accumulation in the spleen may also be dependent on the amount of iron in the diet and the manner of feeding (Richter, 1974).

Inflammation

The spleen may rarely become involved by an inflammatory process, usually extending from adjacent abdominal organs.

Congestion

Congestion of the splenic pulp and red blood cells may occur, but this may be an agonal phenomenon related to mode of death.

Lymphoid hyperplasia

In reactive states the amount of lymphoid tissue in the spleen may also be increased. This may take the form of hyperplasia of the periarteriolar lymphoid sheath (T-cell areas), follicular hyperplasia (B-cell zone), or marginal zone (MZ). The zone affected depends on the type of stimulus (Taylor, 1976).

Splenic atrophy

Marked lymphocyte depletion of the periarteriolar lymphoid sheaths and marginal zones has been observed in rats after the treatment with immunosuppressive compounds (Blair et al., 1982; Vos, 1977, 1981; Kociba, 1981). It may occur as a nonspecific reaction to stress or severe weight loss.

Splenic hamartoma (nodular hyperplasia of the spleen)

It can be extremely difficult to distinguish between bizarre hyperplasia and malignant lymphoma in the rodent spleen (Taylor, 1976). However, occasionally a well-defined, round, pale or white nodule may be found in the rat spleen. It is composed of a mixed population of mature lymphoid cells compressing but not infiltrating surrounding structures. It resembles the hamartomas described in the human spleen (Symmers, 1978).

Neoplasms (excluding lymphoid neoplasia)

Angioma and angiosarcoma are particularly prone to occur in the rat spleen. Histologically, they resemble those observed in other sites (see under Skin/Subcutaneous tissue in Chapter I). Various splenic sarcomas may also be seen (Goodman et al., 1979) – see also under Skin/Subcutaneous tissue.

LYMPH NODES

Lymph nodes are routinely examined in experimental toxicity and carcinogenicity studies but it is important to remember that they form only one part of the peripheral lymphoid system. The gastrointestinal tract is a major immune organ for it is intimately associated with lymphoid tissue, the so-called gut-associated lymphoid tissue – GALT (Shorter and Tomasi, 1982). The lungs and upper respiratory tract also normally contain lymphoid cells (bronchial-associated lymphoid tissue, BALT) – see under respective organs.

As in the spleen, certain parts of the lymph nodes are associated with different types of lymphoid cells. A standardized system for reporting of lymph node changes which can be correlated with immunological status has been proposed (Cottier et al., 1972) and has already formed the basis for more accurate histological assessment of the immune system in man (Kaufman et al., 1977; Patt et al., 1975; Tsakraklides et al., 1974).

The cortical area containing the germinal centres (Fig. 35) is formed principally of cells involved in humoral immunity, the germinal centres always being associated with humoral antibody production (B-lymphocytes). The paracortex (inner cortex, deep cortex) is the main site of proliferation of lymphocytes in a cell-mediated response (T-lymphocytes). It is in the paracortex that specialized vessels known as post-capillary venules are found and which represent an important site for lymphocyte traffic between the vascular and lymphatic compartments. In an inactive gland, they are inconspicuous but may become prominent in reactive lymph nodes (see review by Henry et al., 1978). Medullary cords are the main site of plasma cell proliferation, and subcapsular sinuses contain variable numbers of histiocytes and lymphocytes, the proportion of which is dependent on the site of the lymph node (Cottier et al., 1972).

The overall architecture and patterns of lymph flow in the rat lymph node have recently been well described (Sainte-Marie et al., 1982).

39

Non-neoplastic conditions

The lymph nodes show a variety of non-specific reactive changes as well as non-specific and specific inflammation.

Hypoplasia, atrophy

With increasing age, or after treatment with a number of immunosuppressive and cytotoxic agents, lymph nodes may become depleted of lymphoid cells. The zones in which the depopulation takes place may give a useful indication of the cell type affected (Kociba, 1981). Cervical and mesenteric lymph nodes of the germ-free rat, lacking normal antigenic stimulus, may also show atrophic change; their extrafollicular zone, follicles, deep cortex and medullary cords being all underdeveloped (Bélisle et al., 1982).

Hyperplasia (reactive hyperplasia, lymphoid hyperplasia, follicular hyperplasia, plasma cell hyperplasia)

This term embraces hyperplasia of the germinal centres (follicular hyperplasia) (Fig. 36) which may be associated with increased numbers of plasma cells in the sinusoids (plasma cell hyperplasia) (Figs 37 and 38). Both indicate a reaction of B-lymphocytes. These changes are usually observed accompanying spontaneous inflammatory disease. Normally, germinal centres are not prominent in the aged rat.

In certain circumstances, the deep cortex or paracortex may become very prominent, due to its larger area in histological sections and increased numbers of lymphoid cells, suggesting increased activity of the cell-mediated response (T-cell system).

Note:

In all hyperplastic states, the overall architecture of the lymph node is preserved and this can be confirmed by a reticulin stain. This is in contrast to neoplastic alterations which in general tend to disrupt normal lymph node architecture.

Reactive histiocytosis (sinus catarrh, sinus histiocytosis, sinus dilatation, sinus inflammation)

One of the commonest changes in lymph nodes is characterised by dilated sinuses which contain a variable number of histiocytic cells (sinus catarrh, dilatation) (Fig. 35). Depending on the type of stimulus, leucocytes, lymphocytes and plasma cells may also be present in the sinuses. Histiocytic cells may be abundant, and pack and distend the sinuses (sinus histiocytosis) (Fig. 37) – see Symmers (1978) for a detailed review. Large rounded histiocytic cells filled with ceroid or lipochrome pigment may also be seen, particularly in the mesenteric lymph nodes.

The presence of reactive but normal histiocytes within lymph node sinuses is to be distinguished from early neoplastic infiltration of lymph nodes, often observed in the peripheral sinuses. Hyperplastic histiocytes can look surprisingly pleomorphic and may cause the pathologist to think he is dealing with a malignant tumour.

Extramedullary haemopoiesis (myeloid metaplasia, granulocytic metaplasia)

Haemopoietic cells may be seen in the lymph nodes when there is increased haemopoietic demand. Usually, only cells of the granulocytic series are observed (granulo-cytic metaplasia) in smear preparations.

Inflammation/necrosis
Apart from the reactive changes observed in lymph nodes described above, the lymph nodes may themselves be the actual seat of the inflammatory process (adenitis, focal or diffuse inflammation). Cervical lymph nodes may show focal inflammation or necrosis (necrotizing inflammation) with associated hyperplasia (see above) in rats suffering from sialodacryoadenitis. Oedema of the surrounding tissues is usually observed in severe cases of sialodacryoadenitis (Jacoby et al., 1979). Focal inflammation (acute, necrotizing or granulomatous) may also be seen in mesenteric lymph nodes in rats suffering from Salmonella infections (Weisbroth, 1979).

Granuloma
Small granulomas may be found in lymph nodes. Although they may represent specific granulomatous infections, often they are merely aggregation of pigment or ceroid-laden macrophages in the lymph node parenchyma (Fig. 39).

Fibrosis
Any inflammatory process in the lymph node may be followed by healing and scarring (fibrosis).

Pigmentation
Histiocytes in lymph nodes may contain pale, brown ceroid pigment (see above), but lymph nodes may also contain dense clumps of dark pigment that show positive staining for iron (see review by Ward and Reznik-Schüller, 1980).

Congestion and haemorrhage
As the lungs, so may lymph nodes be heavily congested with blood or even frankly haemorrhagic. This seems also related to the mode of death and appears generally to be an agonal phenomenon. Blood vessels within lymph nodes may become prominent and dilated (telangiectasis).

Neoplasia (excluding lymphoid neoplasms)

Haemangioma (cavernous haemangioma, angioma)
These lesions occur in the lymph nodes of the rat. They consist of well-defined haemorrhagic nodules of small and large blood-filled spaces lined by flat endothelial cells (Fig. 40). The walls of the spaces are composed of fibrous tissue of variable thickness. These lesions are believed by some workers to be congenital malformations and not true neoplasms (Carter, 1973; Squire et al., 1978). Other tumours consist of more closely packed capillary structures with minimal stroma (capillary haemangioma). Haemangioendotheliomas resemble capillary haemangiomas, except that the vascular spaces are lined by benign-looking, multilayered endothelial cells. A reticulin stain outlines the vascular nature of this latter type and enables the distinction between it and the haemangiopericytoma to be made. The benign haemangioendothelioma is rare in the rat (Carter, 1973). For the sake of simplicity, these benign vascular tumours are grouped under the term haemangioma.

41

Metastatic tumours

Lymph nodes are sites of predilection for metastatic spread of a number of malignant tumours, particularly those of epithelial origin.

THYMUS

Careful inspection and weighing of the thymus at autopsy and subsequent histopathological examination has been used by Vos (1977) and Kociba (1981) as part of initial screening for effects of chemicals on the immune system. Certainly, histopathological study appears to reveal thymic effects of immune suppressants (Blair et al., 1982) and morphimetry of the thymic tissue may also increase the sensitivity of histopathological assessment (Papaioannou et al., 1978).

In general, the thickness of the thymic cortex is considered proportional to its lymphocyte content (Goldstein and Mackay, 1969). As the medulla, with its complement of epithelial cells, is responsible for the secretion of thymic hormones (Trainin, 1974), it has been suggested that a decrease in medullary size in man may indicate failure of thymic hormone secretion (Papaioannou et al., 1978).

Non-neoplastic changes

Atrophy

Atrophy of the thymus is a common age-related change in the rat, but it is sex and strain related. It is a physiologically normal process (age involution) but it can be accelerated by severe disease, trauma or stress (Rosai and Levine, 1976) as well as immune suppressant drugs (Vos, 1977; Blair et al., 1982) (Fig. 41).

Cystic change, cystic hyperplasia, (epithelial) hyperplasia

As age involution progresses, the amount of lymphatic tissue slowly decreases, the cortex becomes thinner, fatty replacement of the organ ensues, and Hassall's corpuscles become more prominent. Hassall's corpuscles may become cystic (cystic change) or even show proliferative features (cystic hyperplasia, epithelial hyperplasia). These spontaneous, non-neoplastic proliferative changes generally appear more commonly among female rats housed at Amboise.

Cysts

Large cysts also occur in the thymus. This term is restricted to large, simple, non-neoplastic cysts which may be lined by columnar, flattened or squamous epithelium. Some of these cysts may be derived from remnants of branchial endoderm (or ectoderm of the cervical sinus) (Henry et al., 1978).

Neoplasms

Practically all varieties of malignant lymphoma have been found in this organ either as a primary site or as the expression of generalized disease. Thus, all such tumours are grouped using the classification for lymphoid and haemopoietic tissue neoplasia (see under Lymphoreticular neoplasms, below). As suggested by Rosai and Levine (1976), the term thymoma is restricted to neoplasms of the thymic epithelial cells, regardless of the presence or absence of a lymphoid component or its relative abundance.

Thymoma

Large epithelial tumours, histologically resembling poorly differentiated adenocarcinomas, are occasionally observed in the mediastinum infiltrating around the major blood vessels issuing from the heart. These may arise from the epithelial cells of the thymus.

The term malignant thymoma is warranted in these infiltrative cases.

Recently, a metastasizing thymoma composed of spindle cell and squamous epithelial elements has been described in the rat (Abbott and Cherry, 1982). In our experience, thymomas may be localized or infiltrative, and can be predominantly epithelial in nature or mixed epithelial and lymphoid in type (Figs 42 and 43).

LYMPHORETICULAR NEOPLASMS

In some experimental situations a precise diagnosis of lymphoreticular and haemopoietic neoplasms is essential since each type of neoplasm may have a specific though still poorly understood biological significance (Della Porta et al., 1979). This may be particularly true in carcinogenicity studies for some carcinogens do seem to produce specific types of leukaemia (Huggins et al., 1982) and accurate classification may aid in interpretation of findings. In man, chemotherapy for lymphoma, particularly with alkylating agents, is associated with an increased risk of developing specific types of myeloproliferative disorders and non-lymphoblastic lymphomas (Pedersen-Bjergaard and Larsen, 1982). Unfortunately, knowledge of the morphology of rat lymphomas and leukaemias is still somewhat limited and most classifications used for the rat have been based on morphological criteria used in human material (Swaen and Van Heerde, 1973).

Even for lymphomas in man, numerous classifications have been proposed and none appear entirely satisfactory (Wintrobe et al., 1981). The subjective nature of histological evaluation limits its usefulness, particularly as reproducibility between pathologists is often not great (Wintrobe et al., 1981; Lennert and Stein, 1978; Magrath, 1981). Nonetheless, recent advances in immunology have led to important insights into leucocyte differentiation and the cellular origin of leukaemia and lymphomas. Increasingly, more objective criteria such as the demonstration of membrane markers are being used to assess these neoplasms in man (Foon et al., 1982). There is now considerable evidence that the phenotypes of most malignant leukaemic cells in man are not unique but can also be identified on a variety of mature and immature, but normal haemopoietic and lymphoid cells.

These newer immunological methods and marker studies are being applied to rat lymphoreticular cells (Koestner et al., 1982; Sminia and Plesch, 1982) and neoplasms (Krueger and Konorza, 1979). In the light of this rapidly advancing knowledge, it appears inappropriate to use a very detailed classification based on subjective morphological criteria alone.

For all these reasons we prefer to routinely use a fairly simple morphological classification, using both histological and cytological material for assessment. However, where possible and where necessary, an effort is made to class these neoplasms according to modern pathological and functional criteria as used in the Kiel classification (Gérard-Marchant et al., 1974) or that of Lukes and Collins (1975).

These rat neoplasms, therefore, are grouped into the principal cell type present, recognizing that mixtures of cell types are seen. Although leukaemias and lymphomas are not entirely distinct entities in the rat, the term *leukaemia* is used for neoplasms in which there is primary involvement of the bone marrow and malignant cells usually in the peripheral blood, and the term *lymphoma* for predominantly localized lymphoreticular growth patterns.

The causation of the generally infrequent, spontaneous lymphoreticular neoplasms in the rat remains uncertain, although the application of the murine leukaemia virus to rats has proved an effective method of producing lymphatic tumours (Swaen and Van Heerde, 1973). Recent study in man and animals does, however, suggest that viruses are implicated in man and rodents more commonly than previously believed (Gallo and Wong-Staal, 1982).

Lymphoma

Introduction

A variety of cell types are found in rat lymphomas. Some lymphomas are composed of fairly monomorphic cell types, others are mixtures of different lymphoid cells. In general, however, cells found in rat lymphomas are similar to those found in normal lymphoid tissue, except that lymphomas with a follicular (or nodular) growth pattern are seldom seen.

Lymphocytic lymphoma (lymphosarcoma, lymphoplasmacytic lymphoma, small cell lymphoma, lymphocytic lymphoma well- and intermediate-differentiated)

Many of these lymphomas are composed of small, round lymphocytes (well-differentiated lymphocytes) similar to those observed in lymphatic leukaemia (Fig. 44). Plasmacytoid differentiation is also occasionally observed (lymphoplasmacytoid) suggesting B-cell origin. A rare occurrence at Amboise is a rat lymphoma composed principally of plasma cells (plasmacytoma, plasma cell sarcoma).   Other lymphocytic lymphomas contain slightly larger cells (intermediate differentiation) with somewhat larger, irregular nuclei, corresponding to the small cleaved follicular centre cell lymphoma described by Lukes and Collins (1975), or centroblastic/centrocytic lymphoma of the Kiel classification (Gérard-Marchant et al., 1974).

Lymphoblastic lymphoma (lymphoblastic lymphosarcoma, poorly differentiated lymphocytic lymphoma)

Some lymphomas are composed principally of large 'lymphoblast'-like cells similar to those observed in lymphoblastic leukaemia (see below).

Other large cell lymphomas (reticulum cell sarcoma)

Other large cell lymphomas may be of several types. Previously, the term reticulum cell sarcoma has often been used to designate lymphomas of large cell type. This group of lymphomas contains cells resembling the large cells seen normally in germinal centres. Large, irregular ('cleaved' or 'centroblastic') cells may be seen (Fig. 45) or they may be large, rounded cells (immunoblasts or large non cleaved cells). These latter cells possess large, rounded nuclei with marginated chromatin and prominent nucleoli, as well as basophilic or pyrinophilic cytoplasm (immunoblastic sarcoma).

The malignant histiocytoma or histiocytic sarcoma (see under Skin/Subcutaneous tissue in Chapter I) can also infiltrate in a lymphomatous manner and, therefore, in some cases will resemble a true histiocytic lymphoma.

Note:

Very occasionally, the leukaemias of myeloid type (see below) present as tissue masses, i.e. granulocytic sarcoma (myeloid sarcoma, chloroma).

When only a few isolated cases of lymphoma are observed in a study, we group all these tumours together as malignant lymphoma.

Leukaemia

Introduction

Rats are less liable to develop leukaemia than mice (Hardy, 1967), although in most carcinogenicity studies several cases are found. The fact that some leukaemias develop at a quite early age means that an occasional young rat in toxicity studies of less than 6-month duration develops leukaemia, and this is disquieting for the pathologist, when such a case is found only in a treated group. They are divided into classical groups according to the principal cell type present.

Lymphocytic leukaemia

In a typical case, there is an increase in the absolute lymphocytic count in the peripheral blood to between 60 and 140,000 per mm³ (usual range in the aged Sprague-Dawley rat: approximately 10 to 15,000 per mm³; Chvédoff et al., 1982). Usually, a high proportion of the circulating leukaemic cells are small lymphocytes, differing little, if at all, from the normal circulating lymphocyte (Fig. 44). Nuclear chromatin is densely clumped and a narrow rim of cytoplasm is usually visible. Although occasional cells may be more immature, usually there is no confusion with leukaemia of lymphoblastic type (see below).

Extensive visceral infiltration may occur and in fact these small lymphocytes are similar to those observed in typical lymphocytic lymphoma (see above).

Note that aleukaemic cases of lymphocytic leukaemia are observed, in which the blood count is normal but the marrow is unequivocally infiltrated by neoplastic lymphocytes (Chignard, unpublished observations).

Lymphoblastic leukaemia

In our experience, lymphoblastic leukaemia occurs only half as frequently in the rat as lymphocytic leukaemia (Chignard, unpublished observations). The peripheral blood contains large numbers of lymphoblasts, in numbers ranging from about 90 to over 200,000 per mm³, generally somewhat higher counts than observed in lymphocytic leukaemia. The principal cell type is a large, lymphoid cell with a high nu-

45

clear-cytoplasmic ratio, the nucleus being round and generally not indented or twisted. The nucleus is surrounded by a narrow rim of blue or basophilic cytoplasm with few, if any, granulations.

Granulocytic leukaemia (myeloid leukaemia)

This form of leukaemia is relatively common in the aged rat and it has been observed to arise spontaneously in rats of less than 6 months of age in our series. It is associated with particularly variable but often very high white cell counts in the peripheral blood (20,000 to 1 million cells per mm³; Chignard, unpublished observations). Splenic involvement is often very striking and enormous spleens are sometimes seen at autopsy.

Primitive forms of granulocytic cells, such as blast cells and promyelocytes, are not prominent in smear preparations, increases being mainly myelocytes and apparently mature neutrophils. Eosinophils are occasionally very prominent in smear preparation so as to suggest the diagnosis of eosinophilic leukaemia, although we have not observed basophilic proliferation in the rat.

Note:

Granulocytic leukaemia must be distinguished from leukaemoid reaction associated with infections and other neoplasms. Careful review of all the pathological and haematological data is often necessary to exclude causes of reactive hyperplasia (see above).

Myeloblastic leukaemia

The cells of myeloblastic leukaemia in the rat resemble normal myeloblasts, the cells being a little more irregular and possessing somewhat more abundant cytoplasm than lymphoblasts. The nuclei contain prominent nucleoli and azurophilic granules are frequently present in the cytoplasm. These granules may be particularly prominent or abnormally large. In addition to these blast cells, which are sometimes relatively agranular, variable numbers of promyelocytes are seen, a feature of diagnostic importance. The promyelocyte also shows prominent nucleoli and occasionally they dominate in the peripheral blood and bone marrow smears, so that the appearances are of a promyelocytic leukaemia. Few other cells, intermediate in maturity between blasts or promyelocytes and mature neutrophils, are seen ('hiatus leucaemicus' of Naegeli (1931)), another point of diagnostic interest.

In our experience, the peripheral white cell counts in rats with myeloblastic leukaemia vary between 20 and 700,000 per mm³ (Chignard, unpublished data).

Monocytic, myelomonocytic leukaemia

Very occasionally, leukaemic cells possess lobulated or twisted nuclei with a fine chromatin pattern and prominent nucleoli as well as fine cytoplasmic azurophilic granules, features suggestive of monocytoid differentiation. Such cells are usually accompanied by other cells showing more classical myeloid differentiation. The terms myelomonocytic or monocytic leukaemia are used in these rare instances.

Other types of leukaemia

No cases of erythroleukaemia or mast cell tumours have been observed spontaneously arising in our rat population during the last ten-year period. Certain chemical carcinogens, however, do appear to specifically elicit erythroleukaemia in high incidence in rats (Huggins et al., 1982). Acute stem cell leukaemia, reported to occur in young rats and involving not only bone marrow but particularly the central nervous system, was reported by Richter and his colleagues (1972). These leukaemic cells showed *no* specific cytological features to suggest a particular progenitor cell and for this reason the term stem cell leukaemia was used. In fact, very occasionally, leukaemias showing no clear cytological differentiation are seen to which this term can be applied. The heterogeneous morphological patterns seen in large granular lymphocytic leukaemia common in the F344 rat (Ward and Reynolds, 1983) are not commonly observed at Amboise.

REFERENCES

ABBOT, D.P. and CHERRY, C.P. (1982): Mixed malignant tumor with metastases in a rat. *Vet.Pathol., 19*, 721-723.

BELISLE, C., SAINTE-MARIE, G. and PENG, F.S. (1982): Tridimensional study of the deep cortex of the rat lymph node. IV. The deep cortex units of the germ-free rat. *Am.J. Pathol., 107*, 70-78.

BERG, B.N. (1967): Longevity studies in rats. II. Pathology of aging rats. In: E. Cotchin and F.J.C. Roe (Eds), *Pathology of Laboratory Rats and Mice*, Chap. 23, pp. 749-786. Blackwell Scientific, Oxford.

BLAIR, J.T., THOMSON, A.W., WHITING, P.H., DAVIDSON, R.J.L. and SIMPSON, J.G. (1982): Toxicity of the immune suppressant cyclosporin A in the rat. *J.Pathol., 138*, 163-178.

BRELINSKA, R. and PILGRIM, C. (1982): The significance of the subcompartments of the marginal zone for directing lymphocyte traffic within the splenic pulp of the rat. *Cell Tissue Res., 226*, 155-165.

BURKHARDT, R. (1966): Präparative Voraussetzungen zur klinischen Histologie des menschlichen Knochenmarkes. 2. Mitteilung: Ein neues Verfahren zur histologischen Präparation von Biopsien aus Knochenmark und Knochen. *Blut, 14*, 30-46.

BURKHARDT, R. (1970): *Farbatlas der klinischen Histopathologie von Knockenmark und Knochen*, pp. 1-19. Springer-Verlag, Berlin.

CARTER, R.L. (1973): Tumours of soft tissues. In: V.S. Turusov (Ed.), *Pathology of Tumours in Laboratory Animals, Vol. 1, Tumours of the Rat, Part 1.*, pp. 151-167. IARC Scientific Publ. No. 5, Lyon.

CHVEDOFF, M., CHIGNARD, G., DANCLA, J.L., FACCINI, J.M., LOYEAU, F., PERRAUD, J. and TARADACH, C. (1982): Le rongeur âgé: Observations recueillies au cours d'essais de carcinogénicité. *Sci.Tech.Anim.Lab., 7*, 87-97.

COTTIER, H., TURK, J. and SOBIN, L. (1972): A proposal for a standardized system of reporting human lymph node morphology in relation to immunological function. *Bull. WHO, 47*, 375-408.

DAVIES, G.E. (1981): Toxicology of the immune system. *Histochem.J., 13*, 879-884.

DELLA PORTA, G., CHIECO-BIANCHI, L. and PENNELLI, N. (1979): Tumours of the haemopoietic system. In: V.S. Turusov (Ed.), *Pathology of Tumours in Laboratory Animals, Vol. 2, Tumours of the Mouse*, pp. 527-575. IARC Scientific Publ., No. 23, Lyon.

DIJKSTRA, C.D. and DÖPP, E.A. (1983): Ontogenetic development of T- and B-lymphocytes and non-lymphoid cells in the white pulp of the rat spleen. *Cells Tissue Res., 229*, 351-363.

EDWARDS, A.J., SUMNER, M.R., ROWLAND, G.F. and HURD, C.M. (1971): Changes in lymphoreticular tissues during growth of a murine adenocarcinoma. 1. Histology and weight of lymph nodes, spleen and thymus. *J.Natl Cancer Inst., 47*, 301-311.

FOON, K.A., SCHROFF, R.W. and GALE, R.P. (1982): Surface markers on leukaemia and lymphoma cells: Recent advances. *Blood, 60*, 1-19.

GALLO, R.C. and WONG-STAAL, F. (1982): Retroviruses as etiological agents of some animal and human leukemias and lymphomas and as tools for elucidating the molecular mechanism of leukemogenesis. *Blood, 60*, 545-557.

GERARD-MARCHANT, R., HAMLIN, I., LENNERT, K., RILKE, F., STANSFELD, A.G. and VAN UNNIK, J.A.M. (1974): Classification of the non-Hodgkin's lymphoma. *Lancet, 2*, 406-408.

GOLDSTEIN, G. and MACKAY, R. (1969): The thymus and experimental pathology. In: *The Human Thymus*, Chap. 3, pp. 86-127. Heinemann, London.

GOODMAN, D.G., WARD, J.M., SQUIRE, R.A., CHU, K.C. and LINHART, M.S. (1979): Neoplastic and non-neoplastic lesions in aging F344 rats. *Toxicol.Appl. Pharmacol., 48*, 237-248.

HARDY, J. (1967): Haematology of rats and mice. In: E. Cotchin and F.J.C. Roe (Eds), *Pathology of Laboratory Rats and Mice*, Chap. 16, pp. 501-536. Blackwell Scientific, Oxford.

HENRY, K., BENNETT, M.H. and FARRER BROWN, G. (1978): Classification of the non-Hodgkin's lymphomas. In: P.P. Anthony and N. Woolf (Eds), *Recent Advances in Histopathology, Vol. 10*, Chap. 13, pp. 275-302. Churchill Livingstone, Edinburgh.

HUGGINS, C.B., GRAND, L. and UEDA, N. (1982): Specific induction of erythroleukemia and myelogenous leukemia in Sprague-Dawley rats. *Proc. Natl Acad. Sci. (USA), 79*, 5411-5414.

JACOBY, R.O., BHATT, P.N. and JONAS, A.M. (1979): Viral diseases. In: H.J. Baker, J.R. Lindsey and S.H. Weisbroth (Eds), *Laboratory Rat, Vol. 1, Biology and Diseases*, Chap. 11, pp. 272-306. Academic Press, New York.

KAUFMAN, M., WIRTH, K., SCHEURER, J., ZIMMERMAN, A., LUSCIETI, P. and ST. JERNSWARD, J. (1977): Immunomorphological lymph node changes in patients with operable bronchiogenic squamous cell carcinoma. *Cancer, 39*, 2371- 2377.

KLEINMAN, R.E., HARMATZ, P.R. and WALKER, W.A. (1982): The liver: An integral part of the enteric mucosal immune system. *Hepatology, 2*, 379-384.

KOCIBA, R.J. (1981): Morphological considerations in the detection of immune suppression in routine toxicity studies. In: R.P. Sharma (Ed.), *Immunological Considerations in Toxicology, Vol. 2*, Chap. 6, pp. 123-132. CRC Press, Boca Raton, FL.

KOESTNER, A.W., KOESTNER, A., KRAKOWA, S. and RINGLER, S.S. (1982): Identification of rat T and B lymphocytes by surface marker analysis. *Lab. Anim., 16*, 20-26.

KRUEGER, G.R.F. and KONORZA, G. (1979): Classification of animal lymphomas: The implications of applying Rappaport's classification for human lymphomas to experimental tumors. *Exp.Hematol., 7*, 305-314.

LENNERT, K. and STEIN, H. (1978): Personal points of view on the Kiel classification. *Recent Results Cancer Res., 64*, 31-37.

LOEB, W.F., BANNERMAN, R.M., RININGER, B.F. and JOHNSON, A.J. (1978): Haematological disorders. In: K. Benirschke, F.M. Garner and T.C. Jones (Eds), *Pathology of Laboratory Animals, Vol. 1*, Chap. 11, pp. 889-1050. Springer-Verlag, New York.

LUKES, R.J. and COLLINS, R.D. (1975): New approaches to the classification of the lymphomata. Symposium on non-Hodgkin's lymphomata. *Br.J.Cancer, 31, Suppl. 2*, 1-28.

MAGRATH, I.T. (1981): Lymphocyte differentiation: An essential basis for the comprehension of lymphoid neoplasia. *J.Natl Cancer Inst., 63*, 501-514.

MITCHELL, J. and ABBOT, A. (1971): Antigens in immunity. XVI. A light and electron microscope study of antigen localization in the rat spleen. *Immunology, 21*, 207-224.

NAEGELI, O. (1931): *Blutkrankheiten und Blutdiagnostik, 5th Ed.*, p. 469. Julius Springer, Berlin.

NOSSAL, G.J.V., AUSTIN, C.M., PYE, J. and MITCHELL, J. (1966): Antigens in immunity. XII. Antigen trapping in the spleen. *Int.Arch.Allergy, 29*, 368-383.

PAPAIOANNOU, A.N., TSAKRAKLIDES, V., CRITSELIS, A.N. and GOOD, R.A. (1978): The thymus in breast cancer. *Cancer, 41*, 790-796.

PATT, D.J., BRYNES, R.K., VARDIMAN, J.W. and COPPLESON, L.W. (1975): Mesocolic lymph node histology is an important prognostic indicator for patients with carcinoma of the sigmoid colon: An immunomorphological study. *Cancer, 35*, 1388-1397.

PEDERSEN-BJERGAARD, J. and LARSEN, S.O. (1982): Incidence of acute non-lymphocytic leukemia, preleukemia and acute myeloproliferative syndrome up to 10 years after treatment of Hodgkin's disease. *New Engl.J.Med., 307*, 965-971.

RICHTER, G.W. (1974): Effects of cyclic starvation-feeding and of splenectomy on the development of hemosiderosis in rat livers. *Am.J.Pathol. 74*, 481-506.

RICHTER, C.B., ESTES, P.C. and TENNANT, R.W. (1972): Spontaneous stem-cell leukaemia in young Sprague-Dawley rats. *Lab.Invest., 26*, 419-428.

ROSAI, J. and LEVINE, G.D. (1976): *Tumors of the Thymus, Fascicle 13, 2nd Series*, pp. 34-37. AFIP, Washington, DC.

SAINTE-MARIE, G., PENG, F-S. and BELISLE, D. (1982): Overall architecture and pattern of lymph flow in the rat lymph node. *Am.J.Anat., 164*, 275-309.

SANDERSON, J.H. and PHILLIPS, C.E. (1981): *An Atlas of Laboratory Animal Haematology*, Chap. 3, pp. 38-87. Clarendon Press, Oxford.

SHORTER, R.G. and TOMASI, T.B. Jr (1982): Gut immune mechanisms. *Adv.Int.Med., 27*,247-280.

SMINIA, T. and PLESCH, E.C. (1982): An immunohistochemical study of cells with surface and cytoplasmic immunoglobulins in situ in Peyer's patches and lamina propria of rat small intestine. *Virchows Arch.Cell.Pathol., 40*, 181-189.

SQUIRE, R.A., GOODMAN, D.G., VALERIO, M.G., FREDRICKSON, T.N., STRANDBERG, J.D., LEVITT, M.H., LINGEMAN, C.H., HARSHBARGER, J.C. and DAWE, C.J. (1978): Tumours. In: K. Benirschke, F.M. Garner and T.C. Jones (Eds), *Pathology of Laboratory Animals, Vol. 2*, Chap. 12, pp. 1051-1283. Springer- Verlag, New York.

SWAEN, G.J.V. and VAN HEERDE, P. (1973): Tumours of the haemopoietic system. In: V.S. Turusov (Ed.), *Pathology of Tumours in Laboratory Animals, Vol. 1*, pp. 185-214. IARC Scientific Publ. No. 5, Lyon.

SYMMERS, W.St.C. (1978): The lymphoreticular system. In: W.St.C. Symmers (Ed.), *Systemic Pathology, 2nd Ed.*, Chap. 9, pp. 504-891. Churchill Livingstone, Edinburgh.

TAK CHEUNG, H. (1981): Age- and maturation-dependant changes in the immune system of Fischer F344 rats. *J.Reticuloendothelial Soc., 30*, 563-572.

TAYLOR, C.R. (1976): Immuno-histological observations upon the development of reticulum cell sarcoma in the mouse. *J.Pathol., 118*, 201-219.

THOMPSON, R.B. (1977): The leucocytes. I. The granulocytes and monocytes. In: *Disorders of the Blood*, Chap. 29, pp. 448-488. Churchill Livingstone, Edinburgh.

TRAININ, N. (1974): Thymic hormones and the immune response. *Physiol.Rev., 54*, 272-315.

TSAKRAKLIDES, V., OLSON, P., KERSEY, J.H. and GOOD, R.A. (1974): Prognostic significance of the regional lymph node histology in cancer of the breast. *Cancer, 34*, 1259-1267.

VAN ROOIJEN, H. (1973): Mechanism of follicular antigen trapping. Migration of antigen-antibody complexes from marginal zone towards follicle centres. *Immunology, 25*, 847-852.

VOS, J.G. (1977): Immune suppression as related to toxicology. *CRC Crit.Rev. Toxicol., 5*, 67-101.

VOS, J.G. (1981): Screening and function tests to detect immune suppression in toxicity studies. In: R.P. Sharma (Ed.), *Immunologic Considerations in Toxicology, Vol. 2*, Chap. 5, pp. 109-122. CRC Press, Boca Raton, FL.

WARD, J.M. and REYNOLDS, C.W. (1983): Large granular lymphocyte leukemia. A heterogeneous lymphocyte leukemia in F344 rats. *Am.J.Pathol., 111,* 1-10.

WARD, J.M. and REZNIK-SCHÜLLER, H. (1980): Morphological and histochemical characteristics of pigments in aging F344 rats. *Vet.Pathol., 17,* 678-685.

WEISBROTH, S.H. (1979): Bacterial and mycotic diseases. In: H.J. Baker, J.R. Lindsey and S.H. Weisbroth (Eds), *The Laboratory Rat, Vol. 1, Biology and Diseases*, Chap. 9, pp. 193-241. Academic Press, New York.

WESTEN, H. (1974): Bone marrow examination in experimental animals. In: W.A.M. Duncan (Ed.), *Proceedings of the European Society for the Study of Drug Toxicity, Vol. XV*, pp. 313-316. Excerpta Medica, Amsterdam.

WINTROBE, M.M., LEE, G.R., BOGGS, D.R., BITHELL, T.C., FOERSTER, J., ATHENS, J.W. and LUKENS, J.N. (1981): Lymphomas other than Hodgkin's disease. In: *Clinical Hematology, 8th Ed.*, Chap. 69, pp. 1681-1685. Lea and Febiger, Philadelphia.

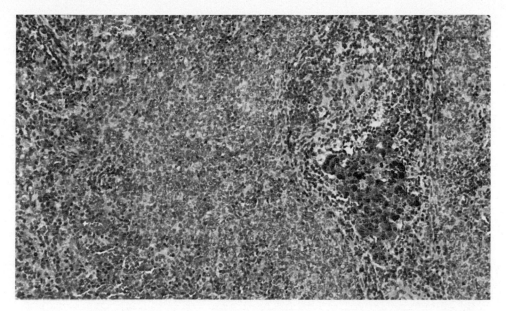

Fig. 34   Normal spleen from an aged (25 months) Sprague-Dawley rat showing the periarteriolar lymphoid sheaths (PALS) and prominent marginal zones (MZ). Prominent germinal follicles are not commonly observed in this strain. A mass of dark pigment is present within the periarteriolar lymphoid sheath. (HE, × 105)

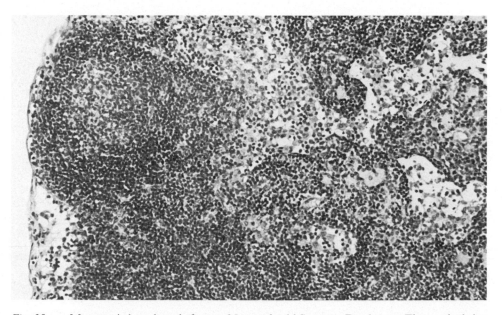

Fig. 35   Mesenteric lymph node from a 25-month-old Sprague-Dawley rat. The cortical sinus is dilated and the germinal follicle is only moderately developed. The sinusoids are also dilated and contain moderate numbers of histiocytes (sinus catarrh or mild sinus histiocytosis). (HE, × 105)

51

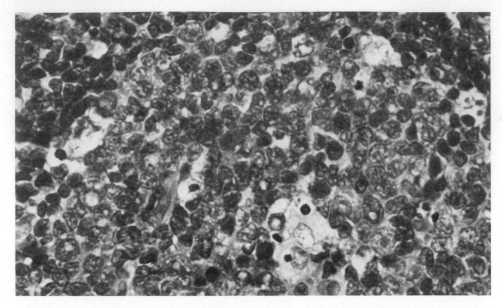

Fig. 36   Germinal centre in a reactive mesenteric lymph node from a 25-month-old Sprague-Dawley rat. Small lymphocytes are present around the germinal centre. Larger, round and irregular lymphoid cells are situated within the germinal centre. Note the presence of pale-staining macrophages ('Tingible bodies'). (HE, ×450)

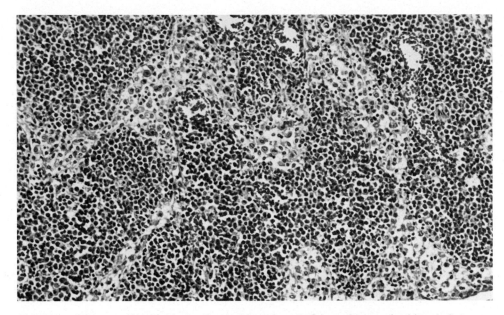

Fig. 37   Plasma cell hyperplasia. Cervical lymph node from a 25-month-old male Sprague-Dawley rat. The medullary cords contain numerous plasma cells (plasma cell hyperplasia). Sinusoids contain abundant reactive histiocytes (moderate sinus histiocytosis). (HE, ×105)

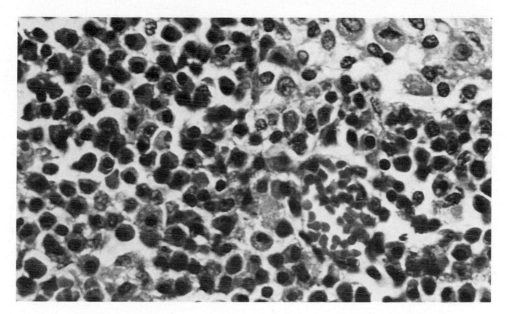

Fig. 38　Plasma cell hyperplasia. Same cervical lymph node as in Figure 37, showing numerous plasma cells. (HE, × 450)

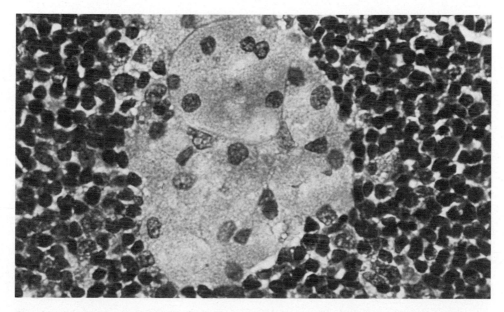

Fig. 39　Mesenteric lymph node from a 25-month-old Sprague-Dawley male showing an aggregate of foamy, ceroid-laden macrophages, commonly found in aged rats. (HE, × 450)

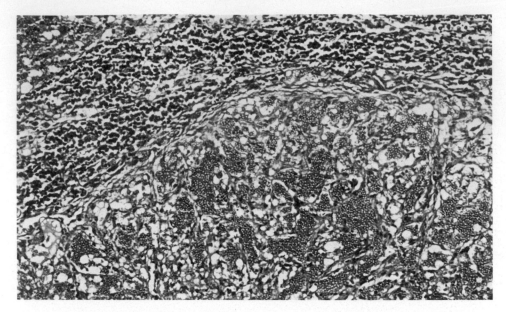

Fig. 40   Haemangioma, an incidental finding in a mesenteric lymph node of a 26-month-old Sprague-Dawley rat. The lesion is well circumscribed and composed of blood-filled spaces lined by flattened endothelial cells separated by connective tissue stroma. (HE, × 105)

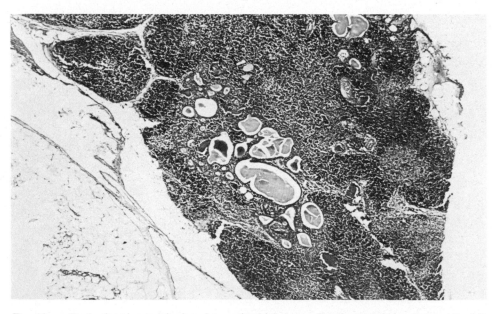

Fig. 41   Early thymic atrophy in a 3-month-old Sprague-Dawley rat. There is considerable loss of both cortical and medullary lymphoid tissue and mild proliferation of epithelial tissue. (HE, × 105)

54

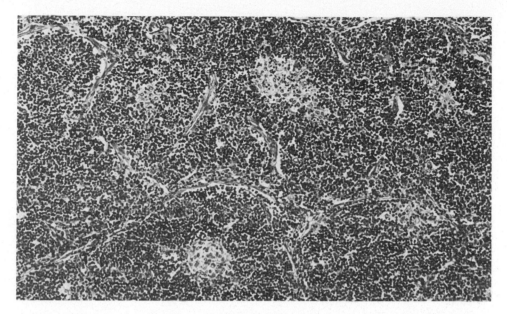

Fig. 42   Thymoma presenting as a large, mobile mass in the anterior mediastinum of a Sprague-Dawley rat, 25 months of age. The tumour is lobulated and composed of both small lymphoid cells and pale foci of epithelial cells. (HE, × 105)

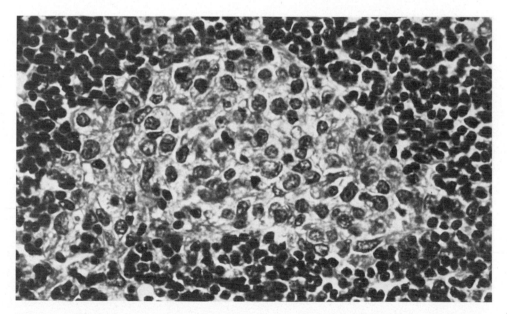

Fig. 43   Thymoma. Same case as in Figure 42 at a higher magnification, showing cellular detail of both epithelial and lymphoid cells. (HE, × 450)

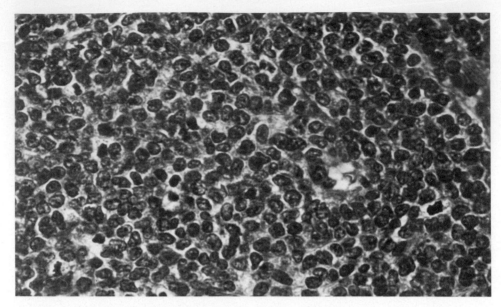

Fig. 44   Lymphocytic leukaemia in a 19-month moribund, Long-Evans female rat. The neoplastic cells are predominantly small lymphocytes and are similar in appearance to those found in lymphocytic lymphoma. (HE, × 450)

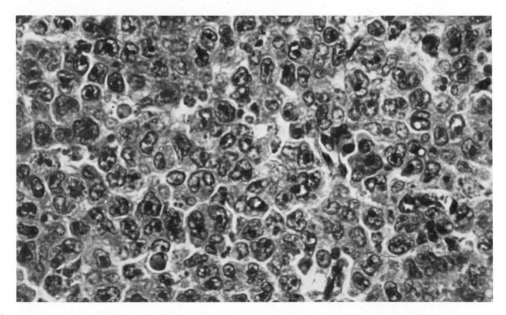

Fig. 45   Large cell lymphoma (reticulum cell sarcoma) found in a 25-month-old Sprague-Dawley male. The cells are pleomorphic with generally irregular nuclei, reminiscent of irregular lymphoid cells in normal germinal centres of lymph nodes. (HE, × 450)

III. Musculoskeletal and soft tissue systems

BONE

A considerable body of information is available on the structure and growth of rodent bone and yet this tissue remains little used as an indicator of toxicity. Rats grow throughout their lives and so the epiphyses do not close. The length of the femur, therefore, is possibly a better indication of the growth rate in life time studies using rats than the body weight: the latter can be confounded by large benign tumours such as mammary fibroadenomas, for example. Furthermore, because the proximal and distal epiphyses of long bones are the growth centres from which metaphyseal and ultimately diaphyseal bone is formed, histological examination of the columns of cells in the growth cartilage can give an indication of an adverse effect on bone growth. Similarly, by labelling periosteal and endochondrial bone formation with radioactive phosphorus (Leblond et al., 1950), calcium (Comar et al., 1953), or tetracyclines (Faccini, 1969), precise measurement of bone formation can be made. The bone that is incorporated into the shaft is lamellar whereas that which forms after repair or secondary resorption is woven in type. Simple examination of cortical bone in decalcified haematoxylin and eosin sections in polarised light clearly identifies the type of bone and, therefore, for example the characteristic changes seen in hyperparathyroidism (Faccini and Teotia, 1974).

Non-neoplastic lesions

Osteomyelitis
An inflammation of bone and bone marrow that usually arises by direct spread of infection from an adjacent abscess or erosive tumour allowing ingress of pathogenic organisms. It is consequently more likely to be seen in those bones that are close to the exterior of the animal such as the jaws, tibiae or foot bones. The medullary spaces are occupied by an inflammatory exudate which may or may not have progressed to pus formation. The cellular exudate is principally polymorphonuclear in type with occasional lymphocytes and plasma cells. The osteoblasts bordering the adjacent trabeculae are generally necrotic and the osteocyte lacunae are empty, the resultant necrotic bone usually shows evidence of osteoclastic resorption. With progression of the lesion, the surrounding viable subperiosteal cortical bone reveals new bone formation, producing eccentrically radiating trabeculae of woven bone lined by plump osteoblasts.

Osteitis fibrosa
Excessive secretion of parathyroid hormone, the result of secondary hyperparathyroidism from chronic renal disease can produce characteristic osteitis fibrosa cystica similar to that seen in man – von Recklinghausen's disease of bone. The bone lesions comprise excessive bone resorption by osteoclasts and replacement of bone and bone marrow by fibrous tissue (Fig. 46). New bone formation is evident and

cortical bone is replaced by non-lamellar woven bone easily recognised in polarised light. The severity and incidence of glomerulonephrosis is higher in the OFA rats at Lyon than in those at Amboise, consequently the degree of osteitis fibrosa is more pronounced in this colony.

Neoplasia

In strong contrast to man, rat skeletal neoplasms appear to be only represented by osteosarcoma (Litvinov and Soloviev, 1973).

Osteosarcoma

Knowledge of rodent osteosarcomas comes largely from work with ionizing radiation. Litvinov and Soloviev (1973) consider spontaneous tumours to be so rare in all laboratory strains of rats thay they need not be taken into account. We have seen occasional osteosarcomas in untreated rats at Amboise.

Osteosarcomas are composed of primitive osteoid and bone forming from a pleomorphic and clearly malignant stroma comprising tumorous osteoblasts and spindle cells (Fig. 47). The differential diagnosis is from an anaplastic tumour growing in a region adjacent to bone and inducing secondary periosteal new bone formation which intermingles with the cells of the tumour. Metastasis to the lungs is usual in induced tumours (Litvinov and Soloviev, 1973) and was apparent in a spontaneous case observed at Amboise.

MUSCLE (STRIATED OR SKELETAL)

Non-neoplastic lesions

Chronic inflammation

Myositis (chronic inflammation diffuse) in laboratory animals is usually a result of infectious agents, but may also be related to administration of toxic agents, stress and corticosteroid administration (see review by Montgomery, 1978). Mild non-specific inflammation is occasionally seen in rats used at Amboise (Fig. 48); this is usually *focal*.

Atrophy

Certain individual muscles display a decrease in mass with advancing age, although in general, total lean body mass remains stable in the rat until just before death (Yu et al., 1982). Histologically, however, minor changes are not evident in routine histological sections. Atrophy of the skeletal muscle becomes prominent principally in association with spontaneous degeneration of the peripheral nerves in aged rats (see under Peripheral nerves, spinal nerve roots in Chapter XI). Histologically, there is focal degeneration of the skeletal muscle fibres and this may be accompanied by focal inflammation.

Neoplasia

Rhabdomyosarcoma

This diagnosis is made in rodent tumour pathology often without sufficient evidence of skeletal muscle origin. Even in human pathology, the diagnostic accuracy remains lower for rhabdomyosarcoma than any other neoplastic group (Enterline, 1981). The presence of large or giant cells with abundant eosinophilic cytoplasm, or strap-like cells alone is not sufficient evidence to make the diagnosis of rhabdomyosarcoma, for cells of other origin, particularly neoplastic histiocytes, may exhibit this appearance (Greaves and Faccini, 1981). In addition, many soft tissue sarcomas infiltrate skeletal muscle, and degenerating but pleomorphic muscle cells can be found deep within sarcomas of different type. Despite these reservations, occasional rhabdomyosarcomas are seen in which there is at least focally some convincing evidence of striated muscle differentiation including the pathognomonic presence of cross striations (Glaister, 1981). In the current state of knowledge of rat sarcomas, it is best not to make the diagnosis of rhabdomyosarcoma unless convincing cross striations are seen, although this may necessitate special stains such as Heidenhain's haematoxylin or phosphotungstic acid-haematoxylin or even electron microscopic examination. This is also the approach of Carter (1973).

They may occur in both skeletal and cardiac muscle (see under Cardiovascular System, Chapter V).

REFERENCES

CARTER, R.L. (1973): Tumours of soft tissues. In: V.S. Turusov (Ed.), *Pathology of Tumours in Laboratory Animals, Vol. 1, Tumours of the Rat, Part 1*, pp. 151-167. IARC Scientific Publ. No. 5, Lyon.

COMAR, Cl., VISEK, W.J., LOTZ, W.E. and RUST, J.M. (1953): Effects of fluorine on calcium metabolism and bone growth in pigs. *Am.J.Anat., 92*, 361-389.

ENTERLINE, H.T. (1981): Histopathology of sarcomas. *Semin.Oncol., 8*, 133-155.

FACCINI, J.M. (1969): Fluoride and bone – a review. *Calcif.Tissue Res., 3*, 1-16.

FACCINI, J.M. and TEOTIA, S.P.S. (1974): Histopathological assessment of endemic skeletal fluorosis. *Calcif.Tissue Res., 16*, 45-57.

GLAISTER, J.R. (1981): Rhabdomyosarcoma in a young rat. *Lab.Anim., 15*, 145-146.

GREAVES, P. and FACCINI, J.M. (1981): Fibrous histiocytic neoplasms spontaneously arising in rats. *Br.J.Cancer, 43*, 402-411.

LEBLOND, C.P., WILKINSON, G.W., BELANGER, L.F. and ROBICHOU, E.J. (1950): Radioautographic visualization of bone formation in the rat. *Am.J.Anat., 86*, 289-341.

LITVINOV, N.N. and SOLOVIEV, Ju.N. (1973): Tumours of the bone. In: V.S. Turusov (Ed.), *Pathology of Tumours in Laboratory Animals, Vol. 1, Tumours of the Rat, Part 1*, pp. 169-184. IARC Scientific Publ. No. 5, Lyon.

MONTGOMERY, C.A. (1978): Muscle diseases. In: K. Benirschke, F.M. Garner and T.C. Jones (Eds), *Pathology of Laboratory Animals, Vol. 1*, Chap. 10, pp. 821-887. Springer-Verlag, New York.

YU, B.P., MASORO, E.J., MURATA, I., BERTRAND, H.A. and LYND, F.T. (1982): Life span study of SPF Fischer 344 male rats fed ad libitum or restricted diets: Longevity, growth, lean body mass and disease. *J.Gerontol., 37*, 130-141.

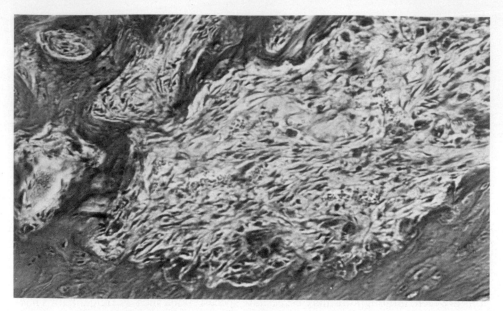

Fig. 46   Osteitis fibrosa. Sternum from a 25-month-old rat with severe renal disease (nephrosis). The marrow space is replaced by proliferating fibrous tissue; osteoblasts and osteoclasts are present. (HE, × 130)

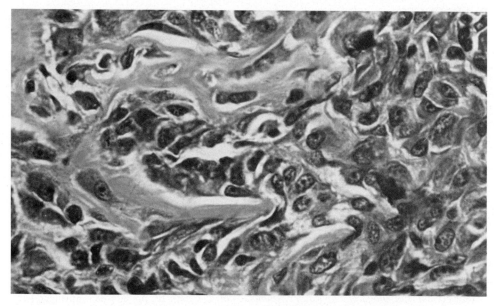

Fig. 47   High power view of a well-differentiated osteosarcoma found on the hindleg of a 26-month-old female Long-Evans rat. Pulmonary metastases were found. The entire tumour including metastatic deposits was composed of the osteoblastic tissue as seen in this photomicrograph. (HE, × 450)

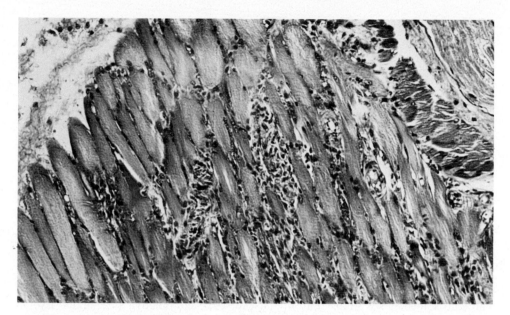

Fig. 48   Focal chronic inflammation in skeletal muscle found incidentally in the neck of a 26-month-old female Long-Evans rat. (HE, × 105)

IV. Respiratory tract

NOSE, NASAL SINUSES, NASOPHARYNX

Non-neoplastic lesions

Inflammation (rhinitis, sinusitis, pharyngitis)

Respiratory inflammatory disease may affect both the upper and lower respiratory tract. Infective agents causing pulmonary inflammation in the rat (see below) may also cause inflammatory change of variable severity in the upper respiratory tract. Acute and/or chronic inflammation may be found in the epithelium of the nose and nasal sinuses (acute and chronic rhinitis, and sinusitis) or the pharynx (pharyngitis). Inflammation may also spread to adjacent sites such as the Eustachian tube, middle ear (otitis media, see under Ear in Chapter XI), conjunctiva (see under Eye in Chapter XI), or downwards to involve the larynx, trachea, bronchi and lung parenchyma (see below).

Aetiological agents are similar to those implicated in lower respiratory tract inflammatory disease, particularly *Corynebacterium kutscheri* (pseudotuberculosis), *Streptococcus pneumoniae*, *Pasteurella pneumotropica*, *Klebsiella pneumoniae* as well as *Mycoplasma pulmonis*, and viruses such as the sialodacryoadenitis virus and rat coronavirus (Weisbroth, 1979; Cassell et al., 1979; Jacoby et al., 1979).

Submucosal aggregates of lymphoid cells without evidence of mucosal inflammation are not uncommon in untreated rats.

Neoplasia

Carcinoma

Pour et al. (1976) claim to have found no reports of spontaneously occurring neoplasms in the upper respiratory tract. We have not found any examples at Amboise or Lyon. It should be emphasized, however, that the nasal sinuses are not routinely examined histologically in toxicological studies.

Squamous carcinoma can be induced in the anterior nasal cavity, septum and ethmoturbinates in the rat; local invasion of the orbit and brain may occur but distant metastases are generally rare (Pour et al., 1976).

LARYNX AND TRACHEA

Inflammation

Small, non-specific acute and chronic inflammatory foci are sometimes observed in the laryngeal and tracheal mucosa. The larynx and trachea may also be involved as part of an upper or lower respiratory tract infection (acute or chronic inflammation, laryngitis, tracheitis).

Submucosal aggregates of lymphoid cells without evidence of mucosal inflammation are not uncommon in conventionally housed rats, although inflammatory cells are not usually found in the larynx of the germ-free or specific pathogen-free rat (Lewis, 1982).

The laryngeal mucosa in the rat is particularly sensitive to inhaled irritants and it responds by undergoing squamous metaplasia. It has, therefore, been suggested that the rat larynx provides a good model for the bioassay of inhaled particles (Coggins et al., 1980).

Calcification, ossification

The laryngeal cartilage may become focally calcified or ossified in the rat. This is seen at all ages.

Cystic change

Submucosal glands lining the trachea may show marked cystic dilatation (cystic change). This appears to be a spontaneous change, observed in young and older rats unassociated with inflammation or disease process.

BRONCHI/LUNGS

Non-neoplastic lesions

Inflammation (acute inflammation, bronchitis, bronchopneumonia, pneumonia)

Although lower respiratory tract infection is generally not now a major health problem in most rat colonies, it remains a potential hazard of which the pathologist must be aware (Lamb, 1975). There may be considerable strain differences in susceptibility to infectious agents, and environmental factors are particularly important with regard to respiratory tract infection (Davis and Cassell, 1982). Viral infection may have considerable impact on inhalation toxicology experiments (Jakab, 1977), and complex interactions between viral and bacterial agents in the murine lung have also been reported (Jakab, 1981). Immune suppressive agents can also lead to unusual types of pneumonia (Chandler et al., 1979). The actual infective agents involved, whether bacterial, mycoplasmal or viral are to some extent reflected by the type of inflammatory process seen in histological sections.

Typically, bacterial agents such as *Streptococcus pneumoniae* produce acute inflammation in the bronchial mucosa and lumen (bronchitis), usually associated with acute inflammation in the lung parenchyma (i.e. bronchopneumonia). Involved alveolar spaces contain neutrophils and proteinaceous exudate and blood vessels are congested. The lesions may become organized with ensuing chronic inflammatory change (chronic inflammation), fibroblastic proliferation and fibrosis. Reactive focal hyperplasia, metaplasia of alveolar epithelium may also be seen. Squamous metaplasia of bronchial mucosa may occur in cases of long-standing bronchial inflammation such as occurs in murine respiratory mycoplasmosis. Classical confluent lobar pneumonia has been described following infection with *Streptococcus pneumoniae* (Weisbroth, 1979).

Viral agents, such as the rat coronavirus or Sendai virus, typically produce interstitial pneumonia. Histologically, this is characterized by diffuse or focal inflammation, predominantly of mononuclear cells, in the alveolar septa. Mononuclear cells, macrophages and neutrophils may be seen in air spaces in acute cases. Peribronchial lymphoid tissue may also be hyperplastic (see below).

As in man, immune suppression in the rat also may lead to pneumocystis pneumonia, also characterized by thickened alveolar walls infiltrated by mononuclear cells (interstitial pneumonia) but in which the alveoli are filled with foamy eosinophilic material composed of *Pneumocystis carinii* (Chandler et al., 1979). The organism may be visualized by PAS, toluidine blue or methenamine silver stains.

Despite the great variety of potential inflammatory changes that can occur in the rodent lung, the most common are in fact small aggregates of lymphocytes around small blood vessels and airways (minimal focal chronic inflammation). The cause of these minor changes are often not clear, although an infectious agent may be involved (Lamb, 1975; Burek, 1978).

Lymphoid hyperplasia

Respiratory tract inflammation with *Mycoplasma pulmonis* (murine respiratory mycoplasmosis) and some viruses produces a characteristic histological picture. Normally small aggregates of lymphocytes are seen around more proximal parts of major bronchi and this is regarded as normal bronchial-associated lymphoid tissue (BALT) involved in the mucosal immune defense system (see review by Johnson et al., 1979). This tissue has recently been more precisely characterized in rats and it comprises large and small lymphocytes, of which, in the F344 rat at least, 25% are of T cell origin, 25% of B cell type and the remainder carry no membrane markers (Val et al., 1971; Cassell et al., 1979; see also Haemopoietic and Lymphatic Systems, Chapter II). In mycoplasma infection, proliferation of the bronchial-associated lymphoid tissue (lymphoid hyperplasia) is one of the earliest and most pronounced changes with increases both in T lymphocytes and B lymphocytes producing IgA (Cassell et al., 1979). Peribronchial lymphoid hyperplasia has also been observed in Sendai and rat coronavirus infection (Jacoby et al., 1979).

Bronchiectasis

When a bronchus is subjected to prolonged inflammation as during chronic mycoplasma infection, various elements in its wall may become disorganized and degenerate. The subsequent bronchial dilatation of the lumen is known as bronchiectasis. On microscopic examination, bronchial walls are inflamed, the lumen may be filled with acute and chronic inflammatory cells and there may be increased mucin production (mucus retention). Squamous metaplasia of the bronchial mucosa may also be seen.

Goblet cell hyperplasia

This phenomenon can be produced by chronic inflammatory disease of the lung or be induced by inhalation of irritant substances, including cigarette smoke (Coggins et al., 1980). It is characterized histologically by an increase in the number of mucus-laden bronchial goblet cells (Fig. 49).

Abscess

An occasional pulmonary abscess may be seen even in well-housed rat colonies (Kroes et al., 1981).

Granuloma (granulomatous inflammation)

Granulomas or granulomatous inflammation may occur under a variety of circumstances. Pseudotuberculosis *(Corynebacterium kutscheri)* of the rat lung, however, does *not* produce a classical granulomatous appearance (Weisbroth, 1979). The most common spontaneous granulomatous change in the aged rat is the formation of cholesterol granulomas in association with foam cell accumulation (see below). Foreign bodies, either inhaled or injected may induce a foreign-body granuloma or granulomatous inflammation (see Foreign body, below) (Figs 49 and 51).

Foreign body

A variety of foreign bodies may be found in the lungs of rats. Microscopic fragments of bone unaccompanied by an inflammatory reaction are occasionally seen in the alveoli of untreated rats. It has been suggested that these fragments are the result of inhalation of bone particles in powdered diet (Innes et al., 1956), although they appear very large in some instances and do contain viable osteocytes. The term osseous metaplasia may be more appropriate. Vegetable particles are also seen (Fig. 49).

Fragments of hair and keratin may embolise from tail vein injection sites to the pulmonary vasculature (Fig. 50) and provoke a granulomatous reaction (see Granuloma, above) (Tekeli, 1974). Intravenous injection of insoluble products, compounds with high molecular weights or high viscosity may also be deposited in the pulmonary vasculature and excite a foreign body reaction (Provost, 1982) (Fig. 51).

Foam cells (histiocytosis, lipidosis)

Accumulations of foam cells are quite commonly seen in alveoli in aged rats (Fig. 52), and they are regarded as alveolar macrophages. These cells invariably contain lipid (Yang et al., 1966) and may be associated with the presence of cholesterol granulomas and foci of fibrosis. Aetiology is unknown. They are unassociated with any specific infective agent (Stookey and Moe, 1978). As they accompany obstructive pulmonary lesions in both rat (Fig. 55) and man, they may be the result of stasis of secretions and exudate. They are not infrequently increased in numbers in rats used in inhalation studies.

A wide variety of cationic amphiphilic drugs will induce characteristic changes in alveolar macrophages known as drug-induced lipidosis or phospholipidosis. The alveolae are filled with large, foamy macrophages which, on electron microscopy, are seen to contain many lysosomes as dense bodies or myelin figures (see review by Reasor, 1981).

Fibrosis

Focal fibrosis is seen in the lungs of rats associated with chronic focal inflammation (i.e. focal pneumonia) or cholesterol granulomas. The pleura may become involved if the fibrosis is situated in the peripheral parts of the lung (see under Pleura, below).

Emphysema

Focal compensatory emphysema may be found in association with pulmonary destruction and fibrosis. Mild spontaneous emphysematous changes have also been described in the edge of the upper lobes of the rat lung (Lauche, 1958).

There is some evidence that certain rats develop more widespread emphysema spontaneously, and this has functional consequences (Palecek and Holusa, 1971). It is not clear whether such changes are merely degenerative in nature and age-related or whether they are the more direct consequences of pulmonary inflammatory disease. Exposure of rats to hypoxia can cause an over-inflation of alveoli (Hislop and Reid, 1976).

Collapse (atelectasis)

Although normal lungs collapse on removal from the thoracic cavity, true collapse (atelectasis) occurs in the rat, generally as the result of obstructive bronchial disease, or the presence of neoplasms.

Congestion and haemorrhage

Congestion and haemorrhage in the lungs of laboratory animals is often an agonal phenomenon related to mode of death (Innes et al., 1967), and it may be particularly severe in rats found dead rather than sacrificed. Rats dying with myocardial disease or severe endocardial disease may also develop congestion of the lungs (Burek, 1978). Drugs and chemicals causing cardiac damage which leads to death may also produce severe pulmonary congestion as a result of cardiac failure. Pulmonary infections can give rise to congestion and haemorrhage.

Oedema

Pulmonary oedema is often associated with congestion of the lungs and, therefore, may be the result of congestive cardiac failure or an agonal change. Oedema may be associated with pulmonary infection, metastatic pulmonary tumours or inhalation of toxic substances. Histologically, oedema is characterized by the presence of a pale proteinaceous, cell-poor exudate in the alveoli and sometimes in the septa and perivascular connective tissue.

Pigmentation

Pigment-laden macrophages may aggregate in the pulmonary air spaces, and these usually contain iron (haemosiderin). They commonly accompany congestion and haemorrhage.

Focal adenomatous hyperplasia (pulmonary adenomatosis, focal hyperplasia)

This is a proliferative lesion of the alveolar epithelium, consisting of a fairly localized, unencapsulated focus of hyperplastic alveolar cells (Figs 53 and 54). The specific cell type involved is disputed. The abnormal cells invest apparently normal alveolar walls and there is no definite solid growth as seen in unequivocal neoplasia. It may or may not be accompanied by frank inflammation. This lesion is produced by a variety of different agents and it occurs spontaneously in aged rats. Its relationship to neoplasia remains unclear, but there is no evidence that the common, non-specific hyperplasia is a precursor of carcinoma (see review by Stookey and Moe, 1978; and Pour et al., 1976).

Neoplasia

Adenoma and carcinoma (bronchiolo-alveolar neoplasms)

Primary neoplasms of the lung are uncommon in untreated rats although certain strains have a higher incidence than that usually observed (Pour et al., 1976). The occasional tumour encountered appears analogous to the commonly occurring pulmonary tumour of the mouse.

These neoplasms are generally discrete nodules within the lung parenchyma composed of fairly uniform eosinophilic cells arranged in various patterns. They may be solid (or alveolar) tubular, papillary or combinations of these patterns. The localized and closely packed nature of these cellular formations helps to distinguish them from the more diffuse pulmonary hyperplasia. They also displace lung tissue by compression and may protrude from the pleural surface. Loss of differentiation, and unequivocal tissue invasion with spread to adjacent organs is distinctly uncommon, but when such features are present the terms adenocarcinoma or carcinoma are used (Fig. 55). Localized non-aggressive growths are regarded as adenomas.

Precise histogenesis of these fairly uncommon spontaneous rat neoplasms is not entirely clear. For this reason, in the Carcinogenesis Testing Program of the National Cancer Institute, they have been grouped as alveolar/bronchiolar adenomas and carcinomas (Goodman et al., 1979). Recent study of histologically similar tumours in the mouse has suggested that the solid or alveolar growths arise from Type II alveolar cells, whilst tubular and papillary differentiation indicates origin from a non-ciliated bronchiolar cell, the Clara cell (Kauffman, 1981). Mixed growths may indicate the presence of a variety of different cell lines within individual tumours but phenotypic modification of a common stem cell cannot be excluded at the present time.

Squamous carcinoma is only rarely observed as a spontaneous tumour in the rat lung (Goodman et al., 1979; Altman and Goodman, 1979).

Metastatic tumours

The lungs are an important site for metastatic deposits which should be looked for diligently in all cases in which primary tumours in other organs are of disputed malignancy (Figs 29, 56 and 143).

PLEURA

Non-neoplastic lesions

Most pleural lesions in the rat are a result of pathological processes in the underlying lung or surrounding tissues.

Inflammation of the pleural surfaces commonly accompanies pneumonia. Rupture of the oesophagus either spontaneously or as a result of trauma gives rise to intense inflammation in the pleural cavity (acute and chronic inflammation, empyema).

Scarring and fibrosis follows inflammatory damage. Fibroblastic proliferation and reactive hyperplasia of the mesothelium (mesothelial hyperplasia) may be very marked and care must be taken to distinguish such change from neoplasia. Florid mesothelial hyperplasia can also simulate a malignant process in man (Rosai and Dehner, 1975).

Rupture of a major thoracic blood vessel may produce haemorrhage into the pleural sac.

Neoplasia

Mesothelioma (mesothelial sarcoma)

This tumour has not been seen in the pleura of rats that we have examined. Mesotheliomas are known to occur on other serosal surfaces, for example in the testis, but are exceptionally rare in the pleura (Squire et al., 1978).

However, it should be noted that mesotheliomas can be induced in the rat by intrapleural injection of asbestos and polycyclic hydrocarbons and that histologically, the induced tumours resemble mesotheliomas found in man (Davis, 1979; Wagner et al., 1982; Pour et al., 1976).

Other tumours

Although we have not observed primary pleural tumours in our rat populations, the pleural cavity is infiltrated by a variety of metastatic neoplastic cells.

REFERENCES

ALTMAN, N.H. and GOODMAN, D.G. (1979): Neoplastic diseases. In: H.J. Baker, J.R. Lindsey and S.H. Weisbroth (Eds), *The Laboratory Rat, Vol. 1*, Chap. 13, pp. 333-376. Academic Press, New York.

BUREK, J.D. (1978): Age-associated pathology. In: *Pathology of Aging Rats*, Chap. 4, pp. 29-167. CRC Press, West Palm Beach, FL.

CASSELL, G.H., LINDSEY, J.R., BAKER, H.J. and DAVIS, J.K. (1979): Mycoplasmal and rickettsial diseases. In: M.J. Baker, J.R. Lindsey and S.H. Weisbroth (Eds), *The Laboratory Rat, Vol. 1*, Chap. 10, pp. 243-269. Academic Press, New York.

CHANDLER, F.W.Jr, FRENCKEL, J.K. and CAMPBELL, W.G.Jr (1979): Animal model: *Pneumocystis carinii* pneumonia in the immunosuppressed rat. *Am.J.Pathol., 95*, 571-574.

COGGINS, C.R.E., FOUILLET, X.L.M., LAM, R. and MORGAN, K.T. (1980): Cigarette smoke induced pathology of the rat respiratory tract: a comparison of the effects of the particulate and vapour phases. *Toxicology, 16*, 83-101.

DAVIS, J.M.G. (1979): The histopathology and ultrastructure of pleural mesotheliomas produced in the rat by injections of crocidolite asbestos. *Br.J.Exp.Pathol., 60*, 642-652.

DAVIS, J.K. and CASSELL, G.H. (1982): Murine respiratory microplasmosis in LEW and F344 rats: Strains differences in lesion severity. *Vet.Pathol., 19*, 280-293.

GOODMAN, D.G., WARD, J.M., SQUIRE, R.A., CHU, K.C. and LINHART, M.S. (1979): Neoplastic and non-neoplastic lesions in aging F344 rats. *Toxicol.Appl. Pharmacol., 48*, 237-248.

HISLOP, A. and REID, L. (1976): New findings in pulmonary arteries of rats with hypoxia-induced pulmonary hypertension. *Br.J.Exp.Pathol., 57*, 542-554.

INNES, J.R.M., YEVICH, P. and DONATI, E.J. (1956): Note on origin of some fragments of bone in lungs of laboratory animals. *Arch.Pathol., 61*, 401-406.

INNES, J.R.M., GARNER, F.M. and STOOKEY, J.L. (1967): Respiratory diseases in rats. In: E. Cotchin and F.J.C. Roe (Eds), *Pathology of Laboratory Rats and Mice*, Chap. 9, pp. 229-257. Blackwell Scientific, Oxford.

JACOBY, R.O., BHATT, P.N. and JONAS, A.M. (1979): Viral diseases. In: H.J. Baker, J.R. Lindsey and S.H. Weisbroth (Eds), *The Laboratory Rat, Vol. 1, Biology and Diseases,* Chap. 11, pp. 271-306. Academic Press, New York.

JAKAB, G.J. (1977): Adverse effect of a cigarette smoke component, acrolein, on viral-bacterial interactions in the lung. *Am.Rev.Resp.Dis., 115,* 33-38.

JAKAB, G.J. (1981): Interactions between Sendai virus and bacterial pathogens in the murine lung: A review. *Lab.Anim.Sci., 31,* 170-177.

JOHNSON, K.J., CHAPMAN, W.E. and WARD, P.A. (1979): Immunopathology of the lung. *Am.J.Pathol., 95,* 794-844.

KAUFFMAN, S.L. (1981): Histogenesis of the papillary Clara cell adenoma. *Am.J.Pathol., 103,* 174-180.

KROES, R., GARBIS-BERKVENS, J.M., DE VRIES, T. and VAN NESSELROOY, J.H.J. (1981): Histopathological profile of a Wistar rat stock including survey of the literature. *J.Gerontol., 36,* 259-279.

LAMB, D. (1975): Rat lung pathology and quality of laboratory animals: The user's view. *Lab.Anim., 9,* 1-8.

LAUCHE, A. (1958): Trachea, Bronchien, Lungen und Pleura. In: P. Cohrs, R. Jaffé and H. Meessen (Eds), *Pathologie der Laboratoriumstiere, Vol. 1,* pp. 28-58. Springler-Verlag, Berlin

LEWIS, D.J. (1982): A comparison of the pathology of the larynx from SPF, germ-free, conventional, feral and mycoplasma-infected rats. *J.Comp. Pathol., 192,* 149-160.

PALECEK, F. and HOLUSA, R (1971): Spontaneous occurrence of lung emphysema in laboratory rats, a quantitative functional and morphological study. *Physiol.Bohemoslov., 20,* 335-344.

POUR, P., STANTON, M.F., KUSCHNER, M., LASKIN, S and SHABAD, L.M. (1976): Tumours of the respiratory tract. In: V.S. Turusov (Ed.), *Pathology of Tumours in Laboratory Animals, Vol. 1, Tumours of the rat, Part 2,* pp. 1-40. IARC Scientific Publ. No. 6, Lyon.

PROVOST, J-P. (1982): *Toxicité de Différents Polymères de Synthèse Destinés à Servir de Support à des Médicaments.* Mémoire, Conservatoire National des Arts et Métiers, Tours.

REASOR, M.J. (1981): Drug-induced lipidosis and the alveolar macrophage. *Toxicology, 20,* 1-38.

ROSAI, J. and DEHNER, L.P. (1975): Nodular mesothelial hyperplasia in hernia sacs. *Cancer, 35,* 165-175.

SQUIRE, R.A., GOODMAN, D.G., VALERIO, M.G., FREDRICKSON, T.N., STRANDBERG, J.D., LEVITT, M.H., LINGEMAN, C.H., HARSHBARGER, J.C. and DAWE, C.J. (1978): Tumours. In: K. Benirschke, F.M. Garner and T.C. Jones (Eds), *Pathology of Laboratory Animals, Vol. 2,* Chap. 12, pp. 1051-1283. Springer-Verlag, New York.

STOOKEY, J.L. and MOE, J.B. (1978): The respiratory system. In: K. Benirschke, F.M. Garner and T.C. Jones (Eds), *Pathology of Laboratory Animals, Vol. 1,* Chap. 2, pp. 71-113. Springer-Verlag, New York.

TEKELI, S. (1974): Occurrence of hair-fragment emboli in the pulmonary vascular system of rats. *Vet.Pathol., 11,* 482-485.

VAL, F., FOURNIER, M. and PARIENTE, R. (1971): Bronchial lymphoepithelial nodules in the rat. Definition and morphological characteristics in optical and electron microscopy. *Biomedicine, 26,* 130-137.

WAGNER, J.C., JOHNSON, N.F., BROWN, D.G. and WAGNER, M.M.F. (1982): Histology and ultrastructure of serially transplanted rat mesotheliomas. *Br.J. Cancer, 46,* 294-299.

WEISBROTH, S.H. (1979): Bacterial and mycotic diseases. In: H.J. Baker, J.R. Lindsey and S.H. Weisbroth (Eds), *The Laboratory Rat, Vol. 1, Biology and Diseases,* Chap. 9, pp. 191-241. Academic Press, New York.

YANG, Y.H., YANG, C.Y. and GRICE, H.C. (1966): Multifocal histiocytosis in the lungs of rats. *J.Pathol.Bacteriol., 92,* 559-561.

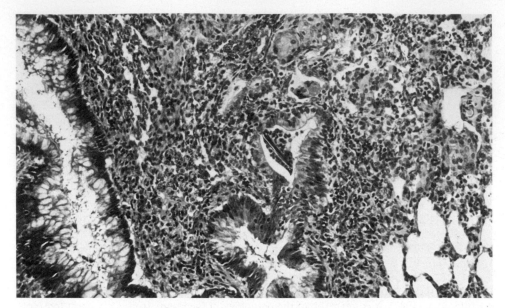

Fig. 49   Chronic granulomatous pulmonary inflammation in a female Sprague-Dawley rat aged 25 months at schedule sacrifice. Intense granulomatous inflammation involves the peribronchial lung parenchyma. A fragment of vegetable matter is visible in a small bronchus. The larger bronchus to the left of the picture shows marked goblet cell hyperplasia. (HE, × 105)

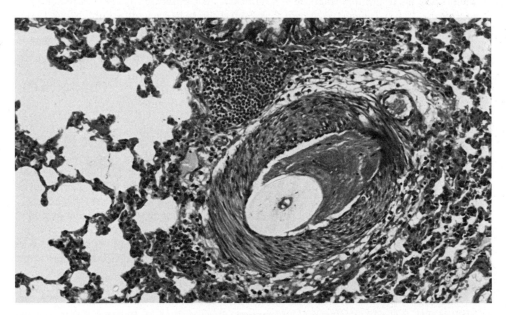

Fig. 50   A foreign body (hair fragment) is lodged in a medium-sized branch of the pulmonary artery in the lungs of a male Sprague-Dawley rat from a 1-month intravenous toxicity study. A small amount of thrombus is also present in the vessel lumen. (HE, × 105)

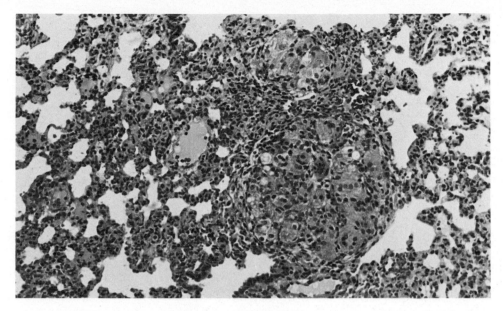

Fig. 51   Lung granuloma in a Sprague-Dawley male rat occurring after repeated intravenous injection with a soluble synthetic polymer for 6 months. The material appeared to be deposited in small pulmonary blood vessels and excited a focal granulomatous reaction (Provost, 1982). (HE, × 105)

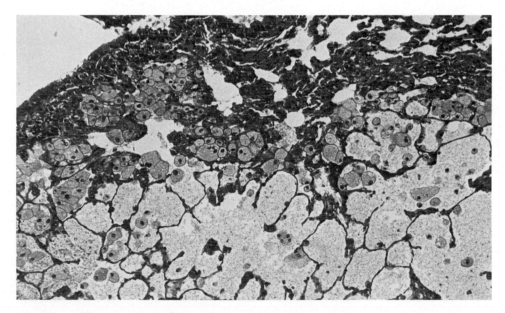

Fig. 52   Histiocytosis, lipidosis. Foam cells are present in the alveoli of a 26-month-old Sprague-Dawley male rat. (HE, × 105)

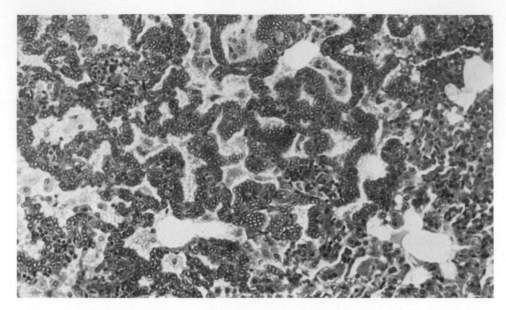

Fig. 53   Pulmonary adenomatosis (focal adenomatous hyperplasia) found in a Long-Evans male rat at scheduled sacrifice at the age of 26 months. It is composed of an unencapsulated focus of hyperplastic cells lining pulmonary alveoli. (HE, × 105)

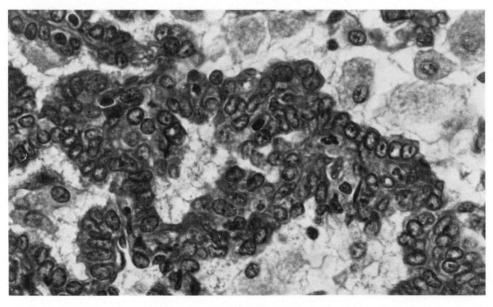

Fig. 54   Pulmonary adenomatosis. Same case as in Figure 53. (HE, × 450)

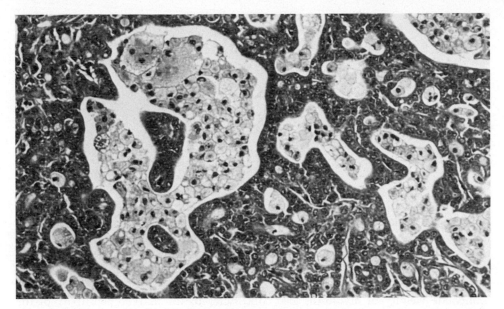

Fig. 55   Primary adenocarcinoma of the lung in a moribund Long-Evans male aged 24 months. Foamy macrophages (foam cells) have accumulated in the glandular spaces of this neoplasm. (HE, × 130)

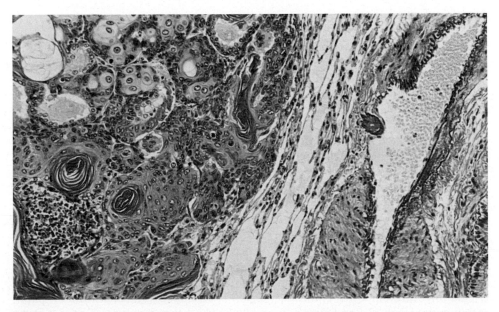

Fig. 56   Metastatic sebaceous squamous carcinoma found in the lungs of a 16-month-old moribund Sprague-Dawley male. Note the alterations in the nearby branch of the pulmonary artery, which shows focal thickening of the media and focal mineralization. Both changes are quite common spontaneous findings in rats of this age. Same case as in Figure 164. (HE, × 105)

V. Cardiovascular system

HEART

Introduction

The heart is an exceedingly complex organ designed to pump blood through the lungs and systemic circulation to provide oxygen and nutrients to the tissues. Its function is dependent not only on a good supply of oxygen but also on complex ionic balances at the cellular and sub-cellular level. Disturbances in these delicate balances may result in cardiac cellular damage. A large number of drugs and chemicals can mediate cardiac cellular damage by a variety of different mechanisms (Ferrans, 1981). The dependence of myocardial fibres on a supply of free calcium ions in the immediate vicinity of myofibrils also contributes to the marked sensitivity of the heart to exogenous chemicals (Durrett and Adams, 1981). Although changes induced by chemicals are seldom specific, characterization of myocardial pathology both at light and ultrastructural level may provide some indication of the mode of action of a given agent (Ferrans, 1981).

Non-neoplastic lesions

Myocardial necrosis, inflammation and fibrosis, myocardial degeneration
Cardiac necrosis (coagulation necrosis) is characterized histologically by dense eosinophilic staining of muscle fibres, and their subsequent fragmentation (degeneration). A notable feature is pyknosis or total loss of cell nuclei. Condensation of contractile material into bands or granules (contraction bands) may also be seen. Following necrosis, an acute inflammatory reaction occurs, manifested by oedema, vascular dilatation and infiltration by polymorphonuclear cells (focal acute inflammation). During this acute inflammatory phase, nuclear debris may accumulate in larger areas of necrosis. The accumulation of macrophages and lymphocytes and the appearance of granulation tissue (focal subacute or chronic inflammation) follows, and this is in turn followed by the appearance of fibroblasts and fibrosis. A given zone of necrosis may be to some extent dated by the stage reached in this inflammatory and repair process. The presence of fibrosis with a few mononuclear cells and pigment-laden macrophages indicates old myocardial damage.

Mild focal myocardial necrosis, inflammation (necrotizing inflammation) or fibrosis is found quite commonly in the aged rat heart. It is usually present in the left ventricular myocardium, often in the inner region or subendocardial zones and the papillary muscles (Figs 57 and 58). It is generally believed that this type of change is the result of local ischaemia produced by myocardial vascular disease (Ayers and Jones, 1978). The subendocardial zone of the left ventricle is certainly a site of predisposition for ischaemic injury. This is probably due to the fact that capillary pressure decreases through the thick wall of the left ventricle and is lowest in the subendocardial zone (Balazs, 1981). Any adverse influence on vascular perfusion will, therefore, preferentially affect this area.

Bacillus piliformis (Tyzzer's disease) may also give rise to focal myocardial necrosis and inflammation. This organism may be demonstrated in these cardiac lesions (Weisbroth, 1979).

Myocarditis

Although inflammatory cells are observed focally in the myocardium in association with focal necrosis, diffuse inflammation of the myocardium (myocarditis) is uncommon. When observed, it is probably the result of an infectious process but it has been described following administration of drugs and chemicals (Ferrans, 1981).

Metaplasia

Cartilagenous and osseous metaplasia may be seen focally in areas of myocardial degeneration in aged rats, particularly in subendocardial and papillary tissue. A rounded or oval focus of cartilage is also observed in the rat heart, localized to the root of the aorta and base of the aortic valve.

Valvular lesions

Non-specific valvular lesions occur in the valve cusps of the rat heart, and these are most commonly myxomatous degenerative changes (myxoid/mucoid degeneration or change) (Burek, 1978). Vegetations or inflammatory valvular lesions (grouped as focal inflammation) are often found in association with a suppurative process elsewhere in the body (Ayers and Jones, 1978). These uncommon lesions are composed of clumps of fibrin, platelets, and inflammatory cells, in which bacterial colonies may be seen.

Subendocardial proliferation (subendocardial fibrosis)

First described by Boorman et al. (1973), this lesion is characterized by proliferation of mesenchymal cells in the subendocardial zone (Figs 59 and 60). It is usually confined to the left ventricle, but mild involvement of other chambers may be seen. Recent electron microscopic study has shown the lesion to be composed of proliferating fibroblasts only (Lewis, 1980). It remains localized to the endocardium, a point of distinction between subendocardial proliferation and a true infiltrative neoplasm. Its aetiology is unknown, although its incidence increases with age.

Subendocardial fibrosis can be induced by a variety of chemicals and infectious processes (Frith et al., 1977).

Cardiac (myocardial) hypertrophy

The weight of the normal rat heart depends mainly on the sex, age and weight of the individual animal. Recent study of heart weights in a number of inbred rat strains has shown, however, that genetic factors are of major importance in the determination of heart weight in rats (Tanase et al., 1982). Absolute heart weight shows a progressive increase with age in our Sprague-Dawley rat population. However, heart size is dependent on the demands made on it by the circulation. If circulatory demand is raised (as in hypertensive rats) heart weight increases and if demand is later reduced it reverts to its former normal value (see review by Payling Wright, 1976).

Cardiac hypertrophy is defined as an increase in the mass of the heart beyond the limits of normal for age, sex and body weight (Ferrans, 1981). In general, when the heart undergoes diffuse hypertrophy, there is usually no increase in the number of its cells, the change being due solely to enlargement of cells. However, it may not always be possible to confirm this microscopically without morphimetric techniques. It has, in fact, been shown that when the heart becomes very large, some hyperplasia may also occur (Porter, 1976).

Some drugs and chemicals may also produce a real increase in heart weight in experimental animals (Greaves et al., 1983). Care must be taken, using appropriate special techniques, to define whether such increases in heart weight are the result of true muscle hypertrophy (with or without hyperplasia), or whether such increases are due to increased accumulation of lipid, interstitial collagen or mucopolysaccharide. For example, administration of alcohol to experimental animals has been shown to increase interstitial collagen accumulation in the myocardium (Regan and Moschos, 1981).

It may be necessary to not only weigh the whole heart but to measure the thickness of the wall of each chamber and weigh the left and right ventricles separately to distinguish between hypertrophy and simple dilatation of the chambers and the presence of right ventricular hypertrophy. Right ventricular hypertrophy in the rat can result from chronic hypoxia (Heyrick and Reid, 1981).

Degenerative changes tend to develop in the myocardium in long-standing cases of cardiac hypertrophy (Ferrans, 1981).

Fatty change (lipid droplet accumulation)

Special stains for fat (e.g. oil red O stain) demonstrate lipid droplet accumulation in the rat myocardium under certain circumstances. This occurs particularly after short periods of fasting (Adams et al., 1981) and, in our experience, some drugs affecting lipid metabolism can produce similar changes (Greaves et al., 1983).

Focal hypertrophy

Foci of surviving heart muscle fibres in areas of myocardial fibrosis may show reactive hypertrophy (Fig. 58).

Neoplasia

Spontaneous primary cardiac neoplasms are rare in rats, being reported with incidences of 0.05 to 0.29% (Robertson et al., 1981). This does mean, however, that an occasional primary cardiac tumour can be expected in the usual rat carcinogenicity study.

Various spindle cell sarcomas are reported to occur in the rat heart, and these infiltrating neoplasms have to be distinguished from the subendocardial spindle cell proliferation, although this differential diagnosis may not always be straightforward. MacKenzie and Garner (1973) reported two spontaneously arising fibrosarcomas in the rat myocardium. The Anitschkow cell sarcoma, described originally in a carcinogen treated rat (Morris et al., 1961), and since reported occasionally in untreated rats (Vesselinovitch and Mihailovich, 1968; Goodman et al., 1979) is a spindle cell sarcoma characterized by the presence of elongated nuclei possessing a dense central core of chromatin which gives rise to an owl's eye appearance. Ivankovic (1976) described 16 spindle cell tumours of the rat heart which he regarded all as of neurogenic origin (neurinoma, neurilemmoma, neurosarcoma) on the basis of light microscopic study. Whether these different names represent the same or different neoplasms is unclear. Certainly, the Anitschkow cell can be observed in a wide variety of neoplasms metastatic to the myocardium (Ragsdale, 1973) and cannot be regarded as indicating a specific cell type.

More recently, ultrastructural study of these myocardial spindle cell sarcomas has revealed the presence of desmosomes and basement membrane around individual tumour cells (Berman et al., 1980). This and the presence of Verocay bodies suggested that these sarcomas were of Schwann cell origin (schwannoma). However, myofibroblasts also exhibit desmosome-like structures and surface material resembling basal lamina (Ryan et al., 1974), so that other cell types may be involved. Schwannomas are only rarely reported in the human heart and those occurring have arisen in the right atrium close to the site of vagal innervation of the heart (McAllister and Fenoglio, 1977). This suggests that these rat and human tumours are not strictly comparable.

Histologically, spindle cell sarcomas of the heart are characterized by infiltrating and sometimes nodular growth of spindle cells, showing moderate nuclear pleomorphism and mitotic activity. Whorling and nuclear palisading may be present. Anitschkow nuclei may be seen but collagen and reticulin is minimal (Robertson et al., 1981), and elastic fibres are not seen (Berman et al., 1980). We prefer the terms sarcoma or undifferentiated sarcoma for these tumours.

In our experience, myocardial metastases of neoplasms with totally unrelated histogenesis can produce similar histological appearances.

The distinction between a sarcoma and the benign subendocardial proliferation has to be made on the presence or absence of true tissue invasion.

Other tumours are occasionally observed in the rat myocardium and these include angiomas, angiosarcomas, and very occasionally rhabdomyosarcomas, all with histological features similar to those occurring elsewhere in the soft tissues. Primary tumours developing at other sites in the mediastinum (particularly thymus), or neoplasms metastatic to thoracic lymph nodes may infiltrate the myocardium, particularly in the region of the great vessels.

PERICARDIUM

Primary pathology of the pericardium is seldom observed although it is involved by inflammation and neoplasia arising from the myocardium and nearby structures. A reactive papillomatous hyperplasia of the pericardium may result from inflammatory lesions (see Pleura in Chapter IV).

SYSTEMIC BLOOD VESSELS

Non-neoplastic lesions

Arteriosclerosis

Aged rats develop a variety of non-specific changes in the arterial tree. These comprise intimal plaque formation (intimal proliferation), medial degeneration (mucoid degeneration), medial hypertrophy and mineralization (calcium deposition, calcification focal). The term hyaline degeneration is used where hyaline change, not thought to be fibrinoid necrosis, occurs in a vessel wall.

The coronary arteries in some rat colonies may be the site of preference for such changes such as medial degeneration or hypertrophy associated with intimal proliferation.

Medial degeneration and calcification may also occur in the wall of the aorta in aged rats (Fairweather, 1967). Badly diseased aortas may rupture (tear) completely. There may also be partial rupture and blood may dissect into the media and along the wall of the aorta.

Severe degenerative changes are not commonly seen in the rat populations at Amboise. However, the incidence and severity of vascular degenerative changes does appear to vary between strains. Certains strains are more resistant (Wexler and McMurtry, 1982), and dietary factors are also important (Durand et al., 1964). Similar pathology appears to be exacerbated in both female and male rats by repeated breeding (Wexler, 1964).

It should be noted that, although the term arteriosclerosis is commonly employed for these arterial changes in the rat, the lesions are morphologically somewhat dissimilar to arteriosclerosis observed commonly in man (Bishop, 1980). This is particularly due to the general absence of lipid deposition (atheroma, atherosclerosis) in the rat lesions, although dietary induced hypercholesterolaemia may induce lipid deposition in certain arteries in certain strains of rat (Okomoto et al., 1972; Bishop, 1980; Coutard and Osborne-Pellegrin, 1982).

Arteritis (periarteritis, polyarteritis nodosa, perivasculitis)

Although the aetiology of arteritis in aged rats is obscure, it is a well-described lesion and usually affects small muscular arteries (Fairweather, 1967). It is characterized by an inflammatory infiltrate in all layers of the vessel wall and necrosis with accumulation of fibrin (fibrinoid necrosis, focal necrotizing inflammation). Older lesions show fewer acute changes (focal chronic inflammation) and an end-stage is reached in which there is fibrosis only. Although it is not generally severe among rats housed at Amboise, it may occasionally give rise to aneurysms and frank rupture (tear) of the vessel wall.

Lesions are most commonly seen in testes and pancreas in our experience (Figs 61 and 86). The coronary arteries are only occasionally involved. Food restriction may reduce the incidence of periarteritis in the rat (Yu et al., 1982).

PULMONARY BLOOD VESSELS

Medial hypertrophy of pulmonary arteries

Fairweather (1967) remarked that the major pulmonary arteries of the aged rat were particularly liable to show marked medial hypertrophy and this concurs with our own experience. Although other authors do report medial hypertrophy of the pulmonary arteries in aged rats, the incidence appears generally low (Coleman et al., 1977; Anvar et al., 1982).

In our Sprague-Dawley rat population, the major branches of the pulmonary arteries quite often show striking medial hypertrophy unaccompanied by any other changes such as intimal thickening, fibrosis or mineralization (Figs 56 and 62). Smaller side branches of these pulmonary arteries appear normal, which is unlike pulmonary artery hypertrophy induced in rats by chronic hypoxia, in which the more peripheral branches of the pulmonary vasculature characteristically show muscular thickening (Meyrick and Reid, 1981).

Although these changes are striking, no pathological significance can be clearly attached to them.

Thrombosis

Occasional pulmonary veins may be occluded and distended by thrombus. The origin of such thrombi is obscure and some may be associated with left atrial thrombosis or tumour emboli.

Mineralization

Isolated subendothelial deposits of calcium salts are sometimes seen in the pulmonary arteries of aged rats, although their causation is not clear (Figs 56 and 63).

REFERENCES

ADAMS, M.G., BARAR, R., JOSEPH, S. and OM'INIABOHS, F. (1981): Fat accumulation in the rat heart during fasting. *J.Pathol., 135,* 111-126.

ANVAR, M.R., COHEN, B.J., LATTUADA, C.P. and FOSTER, S.J. (1982): Age-associated lesions in barrier-reared male Sprague-Dawley rats: A comparison between Hap:(SD) and Crl:COBS-CD(SD) stocks. *Exp.Aging Res., 8,* 3-24.

AYERS, K.M. and JONES, S.R. (1978): The cardiovascular system. In: K. Benirschke, F.M. Garner and T.C. Jones (Eds), *Pathology of Laboratory Animals, Vol. 1,* Chap. 1, pp. 1-69. Springer-Verlag, New York.

BALAZS, T. (1981): Cardiotoxicity of adrenergic bronchodilator and vasodilating antihypertensive drugs. In: T. Balazs (Ed.), *Cardiac Toxicology, Vol. 2,* Chap. 6, pp. 61-73. CRC Press, Boca Raton, FL.

BERMAN, J.J., RICE, J.M. and REDDICK, R. (1980): Endocardial schwannomas in rats. *Arch.Pathol.Lab.Med., 104,* 187-191.

BISHOP, S.P. (1980): Cardiovascular research. In: H.J. Baker, J.R. Lindsey and S.H. Weisbroth (Eds), *The Laboratory Rat, Vol. 2, Research Applications,* Chap. 8, pp. 161-179. Academic Press, New York.

BOORMAN, G.A., ZURCHER, C., HOLLANDER, C.F. and FERON, V.J. (1973): Naturally occurring endocardial disease in the rat. *Arch.Pathol., 96,* 39-45.

BUREK, J.D. (1978): Age-associated pathology. In: *Pathology of Aging Rats*, Chap. 4, pp. 29-167. CRC Press, West Palm Beach, FL.

COLEMAN, G.L., BARTHOLD, S.W., OSBALDISTON, G.W., FOSTER, S.J. and JONAS, A.M. (1977): Pathological changes during aging in barrier-reared Fischer 344 male rats. *J.Gerontol., 32, 258-278.*

COUTARD, M. and OSBORNE-PELLEGRIN, M.J. (1982): Spontaneous lesions in the rat caudal artery. *Atherosclerosis, 44*, 245-260.

DURAND, A.M.A., FISHER, M. and ADAMS, M. (1964): Histology in rats as influenced by age and diet. I. Renal and cardiovascular systems. *Arch.Pathol., 77*, 268-277.

DURRETT, L.R. and ADAMS, H.R. (1981): Myocardial function and drug actions. In: T. Balazs (Ed.), *Cardiac Toxicology, Vol. 1*, Chap. 2, pp. 15-37. CRC Press, Boca Raton, FL.

FAIRWEATHER, F.A. (1967): Cardiovascular disease in rats. In: E. Cotchin and F.J.C. Roe (Eds), *Pathology of Laboratory Rats and Mice*, Chap. 8, pp. 213-226. Blackwell Scientific, Oxford.

FERRANS, V.J. (1981): Overview of morphologic reactions of the heart to toxic injury. In: T. Balazs (Ed.), *Cardiac Toxicology, Vol. 3*, Chap. 4, pp. 83-109. CRC Press, Boca Raton, FL.

FRITH, C.H., FARRIS, H.E. and HIGHMAN, E. (1977): Endocardial fibromatous proliferation in a rat. *Lab.Anim.Sci., 27*, 114-117.

GOODMAN, D.G., WARD, J.M., SQUIRE, R.A., CHU, K.C. and LINHART, M.S. (1979): Neoplastic and non-neoplastic lesions in aging F344 rats. *Toxicol.Appl. Pharmacol., 48*, 237-248.

GREAVES, P., MARTIN, J., MICHEL, M.C. and MOMPON, P. (1983): Cardiac hypertrophy in dogs and rats induced by oxfenicine, an agent which modifies muscle metabolism. Paper presented at: 24th Congress of the European Society of Toxicology, Rome. *Arch. Toxicol., Suppl. 7*, in press.

IVANKOVIC, S. (1976): Tumours of the heart. In: V.S. Turusov (Ed.), *Pathology of Tumours in Laboratory Animals, Vol. 1, Tumours of the Rat, Part 2*, pp. 313-319. IARC Scientific Publ. No. 6, Lyon.

LEWIS, D.J. (1980): Subendocardial fibrosis in the rat: A light and electron microscopical study. *J.Comp.Pathol., 90*, 573-583.

MacKENZIE, W.F. and GARNER, F.M. (1973): Comparison of neoplasms in six sources of rats. *J.Natl Cancer Inst., 50*, 1243-1257.

McALLISTER, H.A. and FENOGLIO, J.J. (1977): *Tumors of the Cardiovascular System. Atlas of Tumor Pathology, Second Series, Fascicle 15*, pp. 102-104. AFIP, Washington, DC.

MEYRICK, B. and REID, L. (1981): The effect of chronic hypoxia on pulmonary arteries in young rats. *Exp.Lung Res., 2*, 257-271.

MORRIS, H.P., WAGNER, B.P., RAY, F.E., SNELL, K.C. and STEWART, H.L. (1961): Comparative study of cancer and other lesions of rats fed N,N-2,7-fluorenzylene-bisacetamide or N-2-fluorenzylacetamide. *Natl Cancer Inst.Monograph, 5*, 1-53.

OKOMOTO, K., YAMORI, Y., OOSHIMA, A. and TANAKA, T. (1972): Development of substrains in spontaneously hypertensive rats: Geneology, isoenzymes and effect of hypercholesterolemic diet. *Jpn Circ.J., 36*, 461-470.

PAYLING WRIGHT, G., revised by CRAWFORD, T. (1976): The heart. In: W.St.C. Symmers (Ed.), *Systemic Pathology, 2nd Ed., Vol. 1*, Chap. 1, pp. 1-72, Churchill Livingstone, Edinburgh.

PORTER, K.A. (1976): Hypertension. In: W.St.C. Symmers (Ed.), *Systemic Pathology, 2nd Ed., Vol. 1*, Chap. 3B, pp. 170-189. Churchill Livingstone, Edinburgh.

RAGSDALE, B.D. (1973): Anitschkow nuclear structure in cardiac metastases. *Am.J. Clin. Pathol., 59*, 798-802.

REGAN, T.J. and MOSCHOS, C.B. (1981): Cardiac toxicity of ethanol. In: T. Balazs (Ed.), *Cardiac Toxicology, Vol. 2*, Chap. 2, pp. 15-28. CRC Press, Boca Raton, FL.

ROBERTSON, J.L., GARMAN, R.H. and FOWLER, E.H. (1981): Spontaneous cardiac tumors in eight rats. *Vet.Pathol., 18*, 30-37.
RYAN, G.B., CLIFF, W.H., GABBIANI, G., IRLE, C., MONTANDON, D., STAKOV, R.R. and MAJNO, G. (1974): Myofibroblasts in human granulation tissue. *Hum. Pathol., 5*, 55-67.
TANASE, H., YAMORI, Y., HANSEN, C.T. and LOVENBERG, W. (1982): Heart size in inbred strains of rats. Part 1. Genetic determination of the development of cardiovascular enlargement in rats. *Hypertension, 4*, 864-872.
VESSELINOVITCH, S.D. and MIHAILOVICH, N. (1968): Development of neurogenic neoplasms, embryonal kidney tumors, Harderian gland adenomas, Anitschkow cell sarcomas of the heart and other neoplasms in urethan-treated newborn rats. *Cancer Res., 28*, 888-897.
WEISBROTH, S.H. (1979): Bacterial and mycotic diseases. In: H.J. Baker, J.R. Lindsey and S.H. Weisbroth (Eds), *The Laboratory Rat, Vol. 1, Biology and Diseases*, Chap. 9, pp. 191-241. Academic Press, New York.
WEXLER, B.C. (1964): Spontaneous arteriosclerosis in repeatedly bred male and female rats. *J.Atheroscler.Res., 4*, 57-80.
WEXLER, B.C. and McMURTRY, J.P. (1982): Genetically mediated resistance to naturally occurring aortic sclerosis in spontaneously hypertensive as against Sprague-Dawley and Wistar-Kyoto breeder rats. *Br.J.Exp.Pathol., 63*, 66-81.
YU, B.P., MASORO, E.J., MURATA, I., BERTRAND, H.A. and LYND, F.T. (1982): Life span study of SPF Fischer 344 male rats fed ad libitum or restricted diets: Longevity, growth, lean body mass and disease. *J.Gerontol., 37*, 130-141.

Fig. 57   Spontaneous myocardial fibrosis in the left ventricle in a 25-month-old, clinically normal male Sprague-Dawley rat. There is a loss of myocytes, and their replacement by loose connective tissue. Some residual muscle cells show hypertrophy. Similar changes may be precipitated by administration of cardioactive compounds. (HE, × 105)

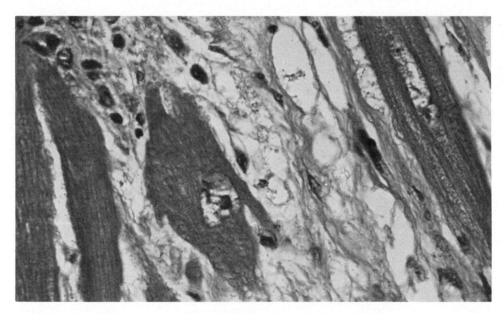

Fig. 58   Myocardial fibrosis. Same case as in Figure 57. Loose connective tissue and hypertrophy of residual myocytes is visible. (HE, × 450)

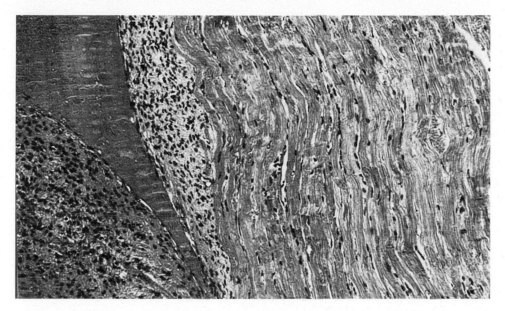

Fig. 59 Subendocardial proliferation (fibrosis) in the left ventricle of a 26-month-old male Long-Evans rat. The endocardium is covered by a layer of uniform, spindle cells with fusiform nuclei. (HE, × 105)

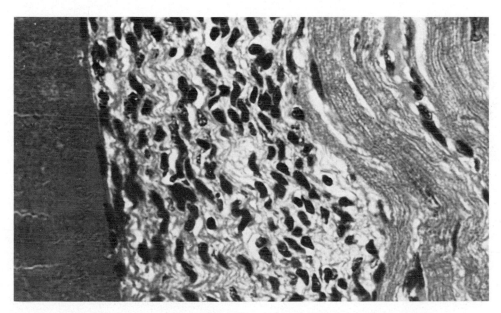

Fig. 60 Subendocardial proliferation. Same case as in Figure 59. (HE, × 450)

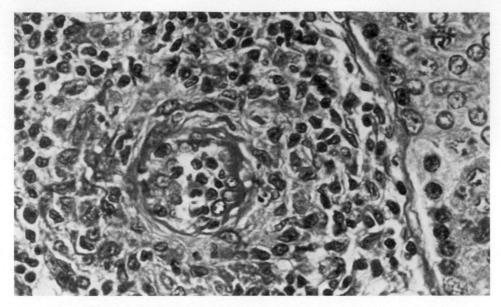

Fig. 61   Arteritis (periarteritis, polyarteritis nodosa) found incidentally in an otherwise normal testis of a 26-month-old Sprague-Dawley rat. Fibrin is visible in the inner part of the vessel wall and both the artery itself and the surrounding connective tissue contain numerous inflammatory cells. (HE, × 450)

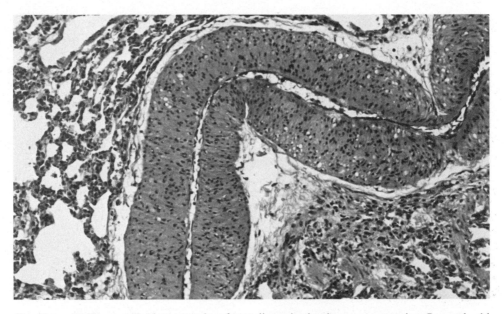

Fig. 62   Striking medial hypertrophy of a medium-sized pulmonary artery in a 7-month-old male Sprague-Dawley rat. This is seen quite frequently among control rats housed at Amboise. (HE, × 105)

84

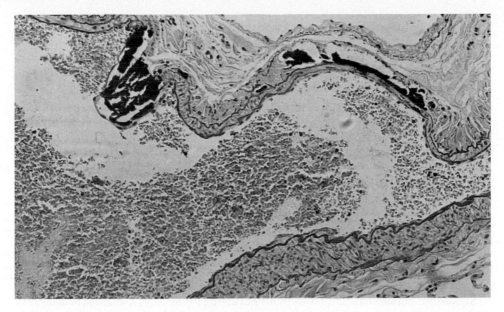

Fig. 63   Mineralization (calcification) in a large branch of the pulmonary artery in a 25-month-old Sprague-Dawley male. (HE, × 105)

VI. Digestive system

Non-neoplastic lesions

Minor non-specific inflammation may be observed in the buccal cavity. Few other spontaneous non-neoplastic lesions are observed in our rat populations and this appears to be the experience of others (Anver et al., 1982).

Neoplasia

Squamous papilloma
Squamous papillomas, similar to those occurring in the forestomach, are occasionally seen in the buccal cavity (see below and Goodman et al., 1979).

Squamous carcinoma
Squamous carcinomas arise from the buccal epithelium of aged rats and they usually are highly invasive (Burek, 1978). They may widely infiltrate the surrounding mandibular and maxillary structures, and may occasionally metastatize to lungs and lymph nodes.

Mesenchymal tumours
The usual soft tissue neoplasms may arise in the head or neck region (see under Skin/Subcutaneous tissue in Chapter I).

SALIVARY GLANDS

Non-neoplastic lesions

Inflammation and fibrosis
Innes and Stanton (1961) were the first to describe acute sialodacryoadenitis (sialoadenitis) in rats and many reports have since followed (see Utsumi et al., 1980). It is most commonly associated with the sialodacryoadenitis virus (Bhatt et al., 1972), although other viruses such as rat parvovirus and cytomegalovirus may cause inflammatory disease in the rat salivary tissue (Jacoby et al., 1979).

Infection with the sialodacryoadenitis virus is widespread in rat colonies and this RNA virus has a particular affinity for the ducts and glands of salivary and other glandular tissue. In the acute stages, infection is characterized by necrosis of the ductular and alveolar epithelium of the salivary glands and generally marked acute and chronic inflammation. Oedema, congestion, and swelling of the glands and surrounding connective tissue may be prominent in severe cases (Figs 64 and 65). Regeneration of the glandular tissue occurs rapidly, although squamous metaplasia of the ductular epithelium and fibrosis can occur. Usually, resolution is surprisingly complete for what is often severe inflammatory damage.

The sialodacryoadenitis virus may also cause inflammation of the harderian gland and keratoconjunctivitis (see under Eye and adnexa in Chapter XI) (Weisbroth and Peress, 1977).

Among other viruses which produce inflammation of the salivary glands, cytomegalovirus, a herpes virus, causes intranuclear inclusion body formation but only relatively minor non-suppurative inflammation.

Minimal focal chronic inflammation, minimal focal fibrosis

The small foci of chronic inflammation and fibrosis seen sporadically in otherwise normal salivary tissue may be the result of previous sialodacryoadenitis, although such changes cannot be taken as specifically indicating this (Carthew and Slinger, 1981).

Calculi (concretions, mineralization)

Mineral deposits are occasionally found within the ducts of rat salivary glands.

Atrophy

Atrophy of salivary tissue is occasionally seen. There is loss (atrophy) of acinar tissue and dilatation of ducts which are lined by flattened epithelium. Glandular tissue may be replaced by fat (fatty atrophy). A mild chronic inflammatory infiltrate may also be present. These changes are possibly the result of previous sialodacryoadenitis.

Neoplasia

Neoplasms of the rat salivary glands are rare and only a few spontaneous tumours have been reported (Squire et al., 1978). Tumours can, however, be induced in the rat (Glucksman and Cherry, 1973).

Squamous carcinomas

Classical, well-differentiated keratinizing squamous carcinomas have been induced in the rat salivary gland. We have not observed an unequivocal primary squamous tumour developing spontaneously in the rat salivary gland, although squamous carcinomas arising from other sites in the head and neck region may infiltrate the salivary glands (Fig. 4).

Sarcoma

Tumours of the soft tissues do arise in and around the salivary gland. The most common sarcoma in our experience is of undifferentiated type, showing characteristically a cystic appearance. This tumour was first described in 1973 by MacKenzie and Garner (see under Skin/Subcutaneous tissue in Chapter I).

A variety of other sarcomas have been induced in the salivary gland, including fibrous and vascular tumours as well as rhabdomyosarcomas (Glucksman and Cherry, 1973).

LIVER

Non-neoplastic lesions

A variety of morphological changes reflect hepatic injury by chemical or biological agents (Zimmerman, 1978). In addition to defining the type of alteration, the pathologist must try to define the distribution of any changes. The principal sites described are periportal (peripheral), midzonal and centrilobular (centriacinar) corresponding to the functional zones 1, 2 and 3 of Rappaport. These zones of Rappaport are defined in terms of their proximity to the afferent (portal tract) blood supply (Rappaport, 1963).

The term focal is used for isolated lesions or changes showing no well-defined regional distribution, and diffuse for alterations involving all parts of the hepatic lobule.

Inflammation

Acute inflammation (acute necrotizing inflammation, necrosis) Sporadically, the rat liver may contain occasional small, well-defined zones of acute inflammation and/or necrosis (focal acute inflammation, focal acute necrotizing inflammation, focal necrosis, coagulative necrosis). Such lesions are sometimes associated with inflammatory disease of the gastrointestinal tract, notably Tyzzer's disease (*Bacillus piliformis*) and salmonellosis. Foci of hepatic inflammation have also been occasionally seen in pseudotuberculosis infection (*Corynebacterium kutscheri*) (Weisbroth, 1979). The diagnosis of Tyzzer's disease remains principally a histopathological one, by the demonstration of generally centrilobular sharply defined zones of necrotizing inflammation at the edge of which *Bacillus piliformis* can be demonstrated using Giemsa, P.A.S. or a silver impregnation technique (Warthin-Starry or Levaditi). Drug-induced hepatic injury may also elicit an acute inflammatory response although it is fairly unusual (Zimmerman, 1978). However, cytotoxic injury induced by drugs and chemicals may occasionally lead to a chronic inflammatory response or granuloma formation in man (Weinbren, 1978).

Chronic inflammation Chronic inflammation is to be distinguished from extramedullary haemopoiesis seen normally in the foetal liver and also in the adult animal under conditions of increased haemopoietic demand (see Haemopoietic and Lymphatic Systems, Chapter II). The various haemopoietic cell types are usually recognizable, including occasional megakaryocytes. Leukaemia and lymphoma may also be observed in the liver and should be distinguished from inflammation.

Necrosis (coagulative necrosis, infarction)

Infarction or necrosis of liver parenchyma may occur under a variety of circumstances. Small foci of necrosis in the centrilobular areas may be seen in Tyzzer's disease (see above). Large hepatic nodules or tumours may also undergo necrosis. Occlusion of the hepatic artery leads to necrosis in man and rat. In the rat, massive necrosis (marked necrosis) occurs and involves the portal structures. Necrosis tends not to occur with simple hepatic or portal vein obstruction (see Weinbren, 1978 for review). In our experience, extensive infiltration of the liver with metastatic tumour or lymphoma may produce hepatic necrosis. Such necrosis can be massive. Centrilobular necrosis can also result from neoplastic growth and thrombosis in the hepatic veins.

Some chemical agents produce hepatic necrosis and depending on the agent this may be diffuse, massive (marked) or zonal, involving central, midzonal or periportal parts of the lobule (Zimmerman, 1978). The zonality of necrosis appears to be often related to the mechanism of toxicity.

Degeneration

Several types of cytologic degenerative changes may be observed in hepatocytes. They may be seen in cells prior to the development of necrosis or in non-necrotic cells surrounding zones of necrosis. Administration of subnecrogenic doses of toxins or only mildly toxic agents may produce hepatocyte degeneration in the absence of necrosis.

'Ballooning' or hydropic degeneration of the hepatic cytoplasm, often associated with viral hepatitis in man, represents the distortion, dilatation and fragmentation of the rough endoplasmic reticulum observed at ultrastructural level and, when it is marked, it is regarded as early manifestation of irreversible cell damage (David, 1978).

Eosinophilic degeneration (acidophilic bodies, Mallory's hyalin) may also be seen in viral hepatitis as well as following hepatic injury following alcohol ingestion in man (Weinbren, 1978). Acidophilic or eosinophilic bodies may also be seen after the administration of a number of other drugs and chemicals. The cytoplasm contains dense acidophilic, hyaline material that is composed of randomly orientated fibrils probably arising from intracytoplasmic filaments (Ghadially, 1982). They are observed in rodents and this subject has been reviewed by Denk et al. (1979).

Pigmentation

As in other organs, a variety of pigments may be seen. Lipofuscin (ceroid) may be observed in hepatocyte cytoplasm. Bile pigment (bile, casts or thrombi, cholestasis) is occasionally present in bile ducts or caniculi in untreated aged rats. Some drugs and chemicals may cause principally bile stasis (cholestasis) without cell damage (Zimmerman, 1978). In cases of doubt, the Van Gieson stain may be helpful in that bile is stained bright green. Iron pigment (haemosiderin) can be seen after cell damage and haemorrhage, and this occurs principally in Kupffer cells.

Considerable evidence exists to suggest that dietary deficiencies or dietary manipulation can greatly influence the accumulation of iron in the liver of rats. Dietary iron content and such factors as frequency of feeding may affect the amount of stainable iron in the liver (Richter, 1974).

Fibrosis

Chronic hepatic injury induced by any agent may lead to increased hepatic fibrous tissue. Small foci of fibrosis (focal fibrosis) may be observed in the liver parenchyma of untreated rats presumably the result of healing and fibrosis of small inflammatory foci. Occasionally, active necrotizing inflammation (see above) is also associated with

89

fibrosis, although a highly proliferative, but non-neoplastic, fibroblastic reaction can also be seen.

Parasites

Cysticercus fasciolaris is the larval stage of *Taenia taeniaeformis* which, as an adult tapeworm, occurs in the cat and other related carnivores. It is fairly common in rats and mice, and is found in cystic cavities with dense fibrous walls attached to the liver. Sarcomas occasionally develop in the surrounding liver (Stewart et al., 1980).

Fatty change

The fatty liver is associated with a variety of different conditions including nutritional disturbances, metabolic disease, hormonal balance, as well as the ingestion of toxic substances (see review by Newberne, 1978; Sherlock, 1975). In rat studies, spontaneous fatty change may be occasionally very severe and diffuse, particularly in aged, sick animals or when the liver is infiltrated by metastatic neoplastic cells (Figs 66 and 67), but generally it is mild and there is evidence of zonal or regional distribution. Thus, fatty change of this type is described under the following headings:

(a) diffuse
(b) centrilobular
(c) midzonal
(d) periportal

This is distinguished from fatty change of irregular distribution forming part or all of a focus of cellular alteration or hyperplastic nodule. Fatty change as a focus of cellular alteration is described as vacuolated focus. If such a focal lesion possesses the features of a hyperplastic nodule, then the term hyperplastic nodule is used and fatty change disregarded (see below).

Fatty change (focal minimal)

The normal liver contains lipocytes (fat-storing cells, Ito cells), and with aging isolated hepatocytes may also normally contain increased amounts of lipid. These minor changes, unrelated to foci of cellular alteration (see below) are grouped as minimal focal fatty change.

Clear cell change

This alteration is characterized by hepatocytes with clear cytoplasm, a densely staining eosinophilic cytoplasmic membrane and a centrally placed nucleus (Fig. 68). Special stains show that these cells contain glycogen. Diffuse clear cell change may be seen in normal, well-fed rodents but disappears quickly with starvation. A glycogen storage disorder has also been described in an inbred strain of rat, thought to be due to a specific deficiency of liver phosphorylase kinase (Clark et al., 1980; Haynes et al., 1983). The term clear cell focus is, however, reserved for those foci of cellular alteration consisting largely of clear cells (see below).

Note:

The PAS stain performed on the formalin or Bouin fixed rodent liver may be misleading for this is frequently negative or only slightly positive staining even in livers that are replete with glycogen. In our experience, the PAS stain performed on unfixed cryostat sections is usually convincingly positive in such cases.

90

Atrophy

Atrophy of the hepatocyte may occur under some conditions, particularly as a result of ligation of the portal vein (Weinbren, 1978). Atrophic hepatic cell cords also form in the rat liver after administration of hepatotoxins, nutritionally deficient diets, or as a result of bile duct ligation (Stewart et al., 1980).

Liver enlargement (hypertrophy, enzyme induction)

A large number of chemical compounds of different chemical structure and biological activity produce liver enlargement in the rat (Crampton et al., 1977a). In some cases, no structural changes are visible at light microscopic level. Some compounds such as phenobarbitone will produce regional hypertrophy of the hepatocytes characterized histologically by simple enlargement of the cells, unaccompanied by accumulation of lipid or other evidence of cellular damage, such as increased mitotic activity or cell proliferation (hyperplasia) (Fig. 69). In enzyme induction, the hepatocyte cytoplasm may exibit a 'ground glass' appearance, and this may provide a diagnostic hint (Klinge, 1973) (Figs 70 and 71).

In such cases, electron microscopic, histochemical and biochemical study of the hepatocytes can be particularly useful in helping to define the mechanism involved in producing liver enlargement. Liver enlargement may be simply accompanied by induction of the hepatic microsomal drug metabolizing system which enhances metabolism and thus prevents the accumulation of the repeatedly administered chemical compound. Such an effect is characterized by reversibility after cessation of treatment, and at ultrastructural level, proliferation of the smooth endoplasmic reticulum in the absence of damage to other subcellular organelles. Histochemical study reveals concurrent and sustained increase in the activity of the microsomal drug metabolizing enzyme system (Crampton et al., 1977a).

Compounds that give rise to simple adaptive change should be distinguished from those that produce liver enlargement with only a transient rise or loss in drug metabolizing enzyme activity. Agents such as safrole and Ponceau MX produce proliferation of the smooth endoplasmic reticulum but with only transient increases in drug metabolizing activity. Such changes may be early manifestations of frank toxicity and also may signal different long-term effects (Crampton et al., 1977b).

The significance and function of peroxisomes (microbodies) in the liver cell is uncertain. It is unfortunately also uncertain whether proliferation of peroxisomes, induced by a number of disease processes and chemical agents such as hypolipidaemic agents, is an adaptive response or evidence of injury (Jezequel and Orlandi, 1972). From the available data, it appears that hepatic peroxisomal proliferation is an important stage that precedes liver cancer induced by hypolipidaemic agents in rodents, but it is unlikely that this indicates liver cancer risk in man (Cohen and Grasso, 1981).

Note:

Not all increases in liver weight result from hypertrophy. For instance, an increase in relative liver weight follows experimental bile duct ligation in the rat, but this is accompanied by a *decrease* in hepatocyte size (Vital et al., 1982).

Congestion (dilatation of sinusoids)

The liver sinusoids may become dilated or congested with blood and this appears often related to the mode of death. It is usually centrilobular in distribution and presumably is the result of venous stasis. Such changes may become more marked after treatment with cardiotoxic compounds which produce an element of cardiac failure. However, these changes can be misleading for they become accentuated after death if there has been any delay between death and fixation (Weinbren, 1978).

A simple dilatation of the periportal sinusoids has been described in the livers of man and rodents treated with oral contraceptive agents and oestrogens (Winkler and Poulsen, 1973; Ishak, 1981; Furth and Boon, 1945; Beaconsfield, 1974). Although simple periportal sinusoidal dilatation may proceed to peliosis hepatis (see below) it should be distinguished from it by the fact that the dilated spaces conform in position and shape to sinusoids rather than to the rounded blood-filled, unlined cavities of peliosis hepatis.

Peliosis hepatis

A condition first described in man more than a century ago and now with the administration of androgens, anabolic hormones, and oral contraceptives (Sherlock, 1975). It is characterized by numerous blood-filled spaces in the liver not lined by endothelium but occasionally lined by a thin band of fibrous tissue. The lesions appear to commence as dilated sinusoids and to progress with concomitant necrosis of hepatic cells. The lesion, as observed in the rat, is of the order of size of one to several lobules, but does progress to the widespread honeycomb appearance seen in the human liver. The pathogenesis is uncertain but it is generally accepted to be associated with hepatic degeneration.

Cirrhosis

This term is reserved for a characteristic change in the liver that comprises nodules or regenerating liver tissue in the presence of encircling bands of fibrous tissue and cell necrosis. The condition does not appear to develop in rats with the frequency that it does in humans with alcohol ingestion or following viral hepatitis. It can be produced in rats fed choline deficient diets or a diet of purified aminoacid (see review by Newberne, 1978). The clearly recognisable inflammatory process and the presence of the nodules within encircling, wide bands of fibrous tissue are the important features that distinguish these regenerating nodules from hyperplastic nodules.

Focal lesions of the liver, including neoplasia

Introduction

An understanding of the known aspects of neoplasia in the liver of rats is fundamental to the interpretation of carcinogenetic studies (Newberne and Butler, 1978). Much of the experimental work in carcinogenesis has been performed with the rat hepatocarcinoma as the model and this tumour has probably been more extensively studied than any other. Despite this, there is no general agreement on the histological criteria for evaluating the neoplasms or the lesions which precede it. There is agreement that nodules occur in the livers of both carcinogen-treated and untreated rats and that these nodules are histologically identical. At this point, opinions begin to differ.

There is not even agreement on what to call them. A group of pathologists taking part in a workshop organized by the National Cancer Institute in 1974 decided to call them neoplastic nodules (Squire and Levitt, 1975). This terminology was also preferred by Stewart et al. (1980) in their typing of rat liver tumours (see below). Newberne and Butler (1978), in contrast, preferred the term hyperplastic nodules which is becoming generally preferred. The name neoplastic nodule is misleading: most of these nodules regress or remodel and thus are not neoplastic in nature (Vesselinovitch, 1982). Frequently, authors choose not to commit themselves to anything more precise than simply liver nodules.

A well recognised sequence of events occurs in rat liver following carcinogen administration (Bannasch, 1978). Initially, there is centrilobular loss of glycogen, then foci of altered basophilic cells occur that are different in certain enzymes (e.g. glucose-6-phosphatase) and rich in glycogen. These are usually visible as enlarged clear cells in haematoxylin and eosin sections and eventually become large enough to be visible to the naked eye. The fact that the cells are increased in size and the nodules enlarge at the expense of the surrounding, compressed parenchyma, together with the fact that they may develop adjacent to foci of degenerating cells, suggests that they are a form of reactive hyperplasia, and this supports the use of the term hyperplastic nodule. These nodules can enlarge to several centimetres across and despite their size they may even regress (Grasso and Gray, 1977). The criteria for deciding that a nodule has developed into a hepatocellular carcinoma, therefore, should not be influenced by considerations of size. Instead, two essential histological findings should be present, true invasion and/or the presence of metastases, usually in the lungs.

A valuable point of differentiation of the first instance is the characteristic mode of spread of the hyperplastic nodule by expansion and compression of the surrounding parenchyma and not by invasion. In the second instance – the presence of metastasis – it cannot be emphasised too strongly that this is the hallmark of malignancy. The cells of metastatic deposits are a special population with different properties from those of the primary growth – a fact realised by Koch over half a century ago (Poste and Fidler, 1980). The spread of cancer cells is not a mere accident depending on anatomical considerations; experimental removal of metastatic deposits from the lung with subsequent dispersal of the cells and passage into a new host will result in the tumour cells re-establishing themselves as multiple pulmonary metastases, irrespective of the route of administration (Foulds, 1958). The preferred site for secondary growth has, therefore, become a heritable property of the tumour cells – just part of a considerable body of evidence that malignancy is a multistage process. These metastatic cancer cells are thus fundamentally different from hyperplastic cells even though the two may have similar cytological characteristics. The pathologist must be careful, therefore, to resist the temptation of deducing the biological behaviour of a tumour from cytological criteria only.

Hyperplastic nodules are produced by hepatocarcinogens, but they are also found in untreated rats, albeit usually in low incidence, although a high percentage has been reported in untreated, aged, germ-free Wistar rats (Pollard and Luckert, 1979). Furthermore, they can be induced by the simple surgical procedure of portacaval anastomosis (Weinbren and Washington, 1976), and all attempts so far to establish hyperplastic nodules as autonomous tumours after transplantation have failed (Farber,

1982). A significant contribution to the understanding of these nodules has been made by the work of Grasso and Gray (1977) and Teebor and Becker (1971), who found that if the stimulus inducing the nodules is withdrawn, they regress. This phenomenon is critically governed by time and is best illustrated by Teebor and Becker's (1971) work with N-2-fluorenylacetamide (2-FAA). They found that, by serially sampling rats who had been fed 0.06% of this potent carcinogen in their diet continuously for 3 months, the animals developed hepatic nodules which eventually changed into metastatizing hepatocarcinomas. If, however, the rats were given the same carcinogenic regimen as a cycle of 3 weekly periods interspersed with a week on normal diet between each period of 2-FAA administration, the rats also developed nodules but these regressed; the exact percentages were as follows: 90% had nodules after 3 months, 45% at 5 months, 8% at 9 months, and only 1 out of 25 (4%) had a hepatocellular carcinoma after 14 months. By way of illustrating how critical the dose is, however, if the rats were given a fourth week of 2-FAA diet, after 10 months 70% still had nodules, and after 14 months 14/23 (61%) had hepatocellular carcinomas.

More recently accumulated evidence suggests that as many as 98% of nodules undergo a complex process of remodelling to normal-looking liver and only a small minority persist to become, according to Farber (1982) 'sites for further steps in the evolution of cancer'.

The mere presence of hyperplastic nodules in treated rats in a carcinogenicity study, therefore, does not imply that the test substance is a carcinogen. The evaluation of such a situation depends on a detailed analysis of the liver of all animals carefully recording the incidence of clear cell and basophilic foci as well as nodules, and especially the time of onset of the nodules. The finding of a few nodules in treated rats, incidentally, at the termination of a study obviously has less significance than nodules appearing earlier in the animals' life. A knowledge of the biochemical properties of the test substance, for example whether it is an enzyme inducer, is obviously of paramount importance.

Foci of cellular alteration

Since the publication of the document on the typing of rat liver tumours by Stewart et al. (1980), any review of rat liver nodules should take it into account. In keeping with this classification, foci of hepatocytes showing alterations in cytology but neither evidence of compression of surrounding parenchyma nor alteration in architectural pattern, are grouped as foci of cellular alteration and described according to their principal cytological features:

Vacuolated focus (focal fatty change, fatty focus) (Fig. 72)

Focal cystic degeneration (focal cystic change, cystic focus) (Fig. 73)

Clear cell focus

Basophilic focus

Eosinophilic focus (eosinophilic change focal, acidophilic focus, ground glass focus) (Fig. 74)

Mixed cell focus (if more than one predominant cell type is present)

The presence of all the types of focal cellular change listed above should be carefully documented in both treated and control animals, and their incidence analysed in any evaluation of the potential toxicity and/or carcinogenicity of a test compound.

If evidence of compression of the surrounding liver parenchyma is found, then such groups of cells are referred to as hyperplastic or neoplastic nodules (see below).

Note:

Vacuolated foci (focal fatty change) have also been described in man where they may be mistaken for neoplastic lesions. It appears that focal ischaemia is an important factor in the development of these lesions in man (Brawer et al., 1980).

Focal cystic degeneration (spongiosis hepatis, cystic focus, focal cystic change)

Foci of small multilocular cyst-like formations thought to arise from degenerating hepatic cells. They sometimes contain eosinophilic material and red blood cells. This lesion occurs spontaneously in our aged Sprague-Dawley rats (Fig. 73). It may be a sequel to focal hepatic necrosis. Cystic degeneration may also be observed within other foci of cellular alteration or hyperplastic nodules. Bannasch et al. (1981) have suggested the name spongiosis hepatis for this condition which they found in rats treated with *N*-nitrosomorpholine.

Hyperplastic nodule (neoplastic nodule)

These are focal collections of usually enlarged liver cells that are discernable microscopically from the surrounding hepatic parenchyma. They vary in size from less than a millimetre to several centimetres. With increase in size the nodules lead to compression of the surrounding parenchyma. The cells are often vacuolated and may appear atypical, but tend to resemble those of the normal liver cell cords. Although the lesion reproduces the normal pattern of the hepatic lobule, portal tracts, bile ducts and central vessels are generally absent.

Hyperplastic nodules are found in untreated rats from the colonies used at Amboise and Lyon. They tend to make their appearance along with foci of cellular alteration (see above) at around one year of age (Figs 75, 76 and 77).

Neoplasia

Hepatocellular carcinoma

This is a tumour of hepatic parenchymal cells which retains sufficient cytological characteristics to make its origin from liver discernable. In well-differentiated tumours, the cellular architecture may in part even resemble that of normal liver. These tumours often display certain histological features that are known to be associated with metastatizing liver tumours – trabecular or adenoid structures – however, these are not enough in themselves to establish the diagnosis of hepatocellular carcinoma. This conclusively is associated with the presence of metastasis usually in the lungs. However, in some circumstances, even though evidence of metastases is lacking, the presence of numerous mitotic figures, a trabecular or adenoid pattern together with evidence of infiltration of the surrounding parenchyma, rather than compression, suggest that the tumour is malignant. In our experience, small numbers of these tumours are observed in untreated Sprague-Dawley rats and they have also been described in the F344 rat (Ward, 1981).

Haemangioma

Simple (cavernous) haemangiomas are seen occasionally within the liver parenchyma in untreated aged rat, although benign vascular tumours can also be induced in the rat liver by the administration of carcinogens (Schauer and Kunze, 1976). At other sites (see Skin/Subcutaneous tissue in Chapter I), these lesions are usually composed of endothelial-lined channels supported by a fibrous stroma.

Haemangiosarcoma

These tumours occur occasionally in the rat liver. They are histologically similar to those in other organs, being composed of malignant vascular endothelium and solid sarcomatous areas. Marked mitotic activity, inflammation, necrosis, and haemorrhage may be seen. However in the liver, growth characteristically occurs along the sinusoids and around surviving liver cell plates. Cytological appearances suggest origin from endothelial or Kupffer cells.

Other sarcomas

Rarely other mesenchymal sarcomas are found in the liver. The majority arising 'spontaneously' are associated with *Cysticercus fasciolaris*. These tumours are generally labelled fibrosarcomas but polymorphic tumours, liposarcomas, osteosarcomas and angiosarcomas have been described (see review by Schauer and Kunze, 1976). In our experience, the malignant histiocytoma (histiocytic sarcoma) may involve principally the liver and, in some cases, the liver must be regarded as the primary site.

Secondary tumours of the liver

A large variety of malignant tumours in the rat may metastatize to the liver but in general, diagnostic problems are not great (Stewart et al., 1980).

Leukaemia and lymphoma are only seldom confined to the liver but these must be distinguished from inflammatory change and extramedullary haemopoiesis (see Haemopoietic and Lymphatic Systems, Chapter II). Leukaemia commonly diffusely infiltrates hepatic sinusoids. Lymphomas frequently infiltrate the portal tract areas, often as a well-defined monomorphic infiltrate (Fig. 78). Correct diagnosis of such infiltrates may be difficult. A liver markedly infiltrated by metastatic neoplasia may also show degenerative changes such as necrosis, congestion, fatty change and pigmentation.

BILE DUCTS, BILIARY SYSTEM

Non-neoplastic lesions

A wide range of cystic and proliferative lesions of the biliary epithelium may be seen in the rat liver following various forms of liver injury and after treatment with carcinogens (Jones and Butler, 1978; Stewart et al., 1980). Chemical agents causing primary damage to the biliary system may also produce cholangioproliferative lesions (Rouiller, 1964).

The agent alpha-naphthylisothiocyanate may produce a striking bile duct proliferation in rats (see review by Zimmerman, 1978). Bile duct ligation not only produces cholestasis and cholangitis but bile duct proliferation also may result (Vital et al., 1982). Such proliferative changes may be reversible (Cameron et al., 1960; Cameron and Prasad, 1960). In man at least, proliferation of small bile ductules is a common response to liver injury of any kind (Scheuer, 1980).

Single cysts (cyst) or multiple cysts (cystic change) lined by flattened biliary epithelium do, however, occur in aged untreated rats, quite commonly in our experience, and in some colonies they are very common in rats over three years of age (Boorman and Hollander, 1973) (Fig. 79).

Sclerosed portal tracts (focal fibrosis) which commonly contain small cystic bile ducts lined by atrophic epithelium are also frequent changes in our 2-year-old Sprague-Dawley rats (Figs 80 and 81).

Less common, but certainly spontaneous lesions are proliferative bile duct changes. These lesions have been variously termed as bile duct proliferation, adenofibrosis, bile duct adenomatosis and fibroadenoma (Stewart et al., 1980). Simple non-neoplastic bile duct proliferation we prefer to indicate as bile duct hyperplasia. When the hyperplasia is cystic in character, the term cystic hyperplasia is used.

All these bile duct lesions occurring spontaneously in aged rats appear to be nutritionally modulated for their incidence is reduced in food-restricted rats (Yu et al., 1982).

Inflammation

Spontaneous intra-abdominal inflammatory disease may involve the biliary tree, giving rise to biliary inflammation (cholangitis) with or without cholestasis. This is seen occasionally in aged rats.

Inflammation of the portal areas accompanied by cholestasis may also be induced in the rat by administration of a number of chemical agents, including alpha-naphthylisothiocyanate. Simple ligation of the bile duct is also a well-known method of inducing biliary inflammation and cholestasis (Cameron and Prasad, 1960).

Neoplasia

Tumours of bile duct origin are uncommon in the rat liver. Cholangiocarcinomas have been described in rats treated with carcinogens (Jones and Butler, 1978). Particular care must be taken to make the distinction between a true cholangiocarcinoma and adenocarcinomatous differentiation occurring in otherwise unremarkable hepatocellular carcinomas. In fact, some authors have proposed the use of the non-committal term adenocarcinoma for hepatic tumours showing any glandular differentiation in view of the difficulty of making the distinction between a glandular hepatocellular carcinoma and a true cholangiocarcinoma (Stewart et al., 1980).

We have not yet observed a convincing cholangiocarcinoma in our rat populations.

PANCREAS

Introduction

The pancreas, embryologically derived from the dorsal and ventral pancreatic buds of the entodermal epithelium, is both an exocrine and endocrine gland. The bulk of its cells are concerned with producing exocrine secretions. The islets of Langerhans, producing several different polypeptides, including insulin, glucagon, somatostatin and pancreatic polypeptide, are equally important.

In the following section, the exocrine pancreas and the islets are considered separately, but it always must be remembered that the exocrine and endocrine functions of the pancreas are interrelated. All four major islet hormones do affect exocrine function (Saito et al., 1980; Söling and Ungar, 1972; Raptis et al., 1978). In addition, the pancreatic hormones have an effect on gastrointestinal function and gastrin, a gastrointestinal hormone, not only exerts a trophic effect on oxyntic cells of the stomach and on the duodenal mucosa but also on the pancreas (Johnson, 1976). Finally, it should also be remembered that embryologically it is not certain whether islet cells are of neural crest origin (APUD cells) or whether they develop from entoderm as does exocrine pancreatic tissue (Gould, 1978; Stevens and Moore, 1983).

Exocrine pancreas

Ectopic tissue

Small nodules of ectopic (heterotopic tissue, accessory pancreas) pancreatic tissue may be found within the abdominal cavity, usually related to the duodenum, jejunum, stomach, gall bladder or mesentery.

Acute inflammation (acute pancreatitis, necrosis)

Several methods exist for inducing acute pancreatitis in the rat including the injection of blood, bacteria, bile, detergents, enzymes or combinations of these agents into the pancreatic duct. Although certain differences exist between various systems and agents, it appears that acinar cell necrosis, possibly due to the activation of phospholipase, precedes frank inflammation (Aho and Nevalainen, 1982). Evidence from the duodenal ligation model of acute pancreatitis has suggested that necrosis may also be the result of decreased vascular perfusion (Rao et al., 1981). Intravenous injection of 4-hydroxyaminoquinoline-1-oxide has also been shown to produce pancreatic acinar cell necrosis in rats (Hayashi et al., 1972).

Recent observations in man have suggested that two different types of pancreatitis can be distinguished on histopathological grounds. Perilobular necrosis and inflammation appear to be principally the result of ischaemia affecting the microcirculatory periphery of the pancreatic lobule. The presence of inflammation in the pancreatic duct or ductules suggests primary duct disease or duct-borne inflammation (Foulis, 1980).

Acute inflammation (acute pancreatitis) is observed to arise spontaneously in rats, but far less frequently than chronic inflammatory change (see below). In our experience, this spontaneous condition is characterized by the presence of acute inflammatory cells in the ducts and ductules, focal acute inflammation involving acinar cells and striking interstitial oedema. Duct epithelium can be quite hyperplastic (focal hyperplasia) and contain numerous mitoses. The oedematous connective tissue includes a scattering of acute inflammatory cells, macrophages, as well as a few fibroblasts (Fig. 82). Blood vessels are usually dilated, although frank vasculitis (arteritis) is not striking. Fat necrosis may be evident. Islets remain relatively unaffected.

In the few spontaneous cases we have observed in the rat, the overall histological appearances are most in keeping with primary duct disease, particularly as an ascending cholangitis can be associated with the pancreatitis and abnormally dilated pancreatic ducts may be also seen (see below).

Chronic inflammation (chronic pancreatitis, chronic relapsing pancreatitis)

The pancreas in certain strains of rats commonly shows non-specific chronic inflammation usually associated with lobular atrophy (see also Atrophy, below). These features were well described by Kendry and Roe (1969) in 3 inbred strains of rats and called by them chronic relapsing pancreatitis.

Early changes are indicated histologically by infiltration of the intralobular connective tissue by mononuclear cells (focal chronic inflammation). In severe or advanced cases, there is decreased basophilia and actual loss of acinar cells. Acini often degenerate completely to be replaced by flattened epithelium giving rise to cystic change (microcystic change) (Figs 83, 84 and 88). Ducts and ductules become dilated (dilatation, ectasia). Fibrosis of the interstitium may become prominent. Increased numbers of fat cells are seen and in some aged rats a complete lobule or even the entire gland becomes replaced by adipose tissue (atrophy, fatty atrophy) (Fig. 85). However, in diffusely involved glands, the head of the pancreas often remains surprisingly unaffected. Kendry and Roe (1969) originally reported prominent vascular changes (arteritis, polyarteritis, thrombosis) in their affected rats. Vascular disease is not generally common in the rat population we observe and, although arteritis is occasionally seen in the rat pancreas (Fig. 86), its occurrence does not appear to have a particular association with chronic inflammation of the pancreatic parenchyma (see under Cardiovascular System, Chapter V).

The islets of Langerhans remain unaffected by this condition until advanced disruption and fibrosis of the pancreas occurs. However, proliferative changes may occur in the endocrine tissue if fibrosis is marked, and care should be taken to distinguish florid proliferation from neoplasia.

The cause of this condition in rats is uncertain. Both duct obstruction and infective agents including viruses have been suggested as possible causes (Kendry and Roe, 1969; Roe and Roberts, 1973). The anatomy of the pancreas in the rat, in particular the numerous ducts entering directly into the common bile duct (Doerr and Becker, 1958), could possibly predispose to obstructive damage affecting individual pancreatic lobules. Indeed, pancreatic duct ligation in the rat seems also to produce similar histological changes (Pound and Walker, 1981). These authors have shown that following duct ligation, acinar cells are completely lost by cell death and they are replaced by proliferating small duct cells (Walker and Pound, 1983). Strain differences are undoubtedly important. In a study conducted to compare the pathology of Sprague-Dawley and Long-Evans rats under identical conditions, chronic relapsing pancreatitis occurred infrequently among Sprague-Dawley rats but 40% of Long-Evans rats were affected (Greaves and Rabemampianina, 1982).

Atrophy

Although atrophy of the pancreas in the rat occurs most commonly in association with spontaneous inflammatory disease (see above), diffuse non-inflammatory atrophy results from a variety of other disturbances. These include starvation, malnutrition, protein deprivation, treatment with protein inhibitors and non-metabolisable amino-acid analogues such as ethionine (De Almeida and Grossman, 1952; Doerr and Becker, 1958; Platt et al., 1964). Zinc deficiency also causes some degree of acinar cell degeneration (Koo and Turk, 1977). Recent study has also confirmed the observations of Müller (1970) that dietary copper deficiency or dietary copper deficiency enhanced by treatment with copper chelating agents can lead to simple atrophy of pancreatic acinar tissue (Smith et al., 1982; Fell et al., 1982). Pancreatic duct ligation may also lead to non-inflammatory pancreatic exocrine involution (Pound and Walker, 1981). The absence of inflammation in such cases of induced atrophy suggests that disturbances in protein synthesis may be responsible (Smith et al., 1982). However, studies on intravenously alimented rats have shown that some of the decreases in pancreatic weight in starvation may be due to the reduced secretion of gastrin by the unstimulated gastrointestinal tract rather than the metabolic changes associated with starvation, for gastrin normally exerts a trophic effect on the pancreas (Johnson, 1976).

Histologically, non-inflammatory atrophy is characterized by diffuse loss of exocrine tissue and a general absence of inflammation, the end result being a gland diffusely replaced by intra- and perilobular fat (fatty atrophy). Pancreatic ducts and islets remain generally well preserved (Smith et al., 1982).

Oedema

Interstitial oedema of the pancreas accompanies acute pancreatitis (Fig. 82). Oedema of the pancreas may, however, be seen as an agonal change or a change related to mode of death, e.g. cardiac failure.

Fatty change

Prolonged ethanol administration to rats may produce accumulation of lipid droplets in acinar and ductal cells (fatty change) (Singh et al., 1982). Other toxins may produce similar changes (Hayashi et al., 1972).

Eosinophilic change, focal

Small irregular non-neoplastic foci of pancreatic acinar cells exhibiting increased cytoplasmic eosinophilia (or decreased peripheral cytoplasmic basophilia) may be seen in the rat pancreas. These lesions are usually confined to parts of single lobules but may occasionally affect several lobules (Kendry and Roe, 1969). Their pathogenesis is uncertain but they presumably represent mild zonal functional differences.

Dilatation of the pancreatic duct (cyst)

This is occasionally seen in an otherwise normal pancreas, but in association with dilated biliary ducts. The dilatation may be quite marked and cystic (pancreatic duct cyst), and occasionally associated with acute pancreatitis.

Pigmentation

Chronic inflammation in the pancreas may be associated with the deposition of pigment (generally iron). Spontaneous deposition of pigment (haemosiderin) may also occur in and around the islets of aging Sprague-Dawley rats (Reavon and Rea von, 1981).

Arteritis (periarteritis, polyarteritis, perivasculitis)
   Arteritis is occasionally observed in the pancreas of an aged rat (Fig. 86) (see also Cardiovascular System, Chapter V). This condition shows no particular association with chronic pancreatitis or atrophy in our material (see above).
   Peritonitis or diffuse peritoneal involvement by malignant neoplasia may produce thrombosis of the pancreatic and splenic blood vessels.

Hypertrophy
   In certain strains of rats, the pancreas shows an increase in weight with increasing age when fed on standard laboratory diet and certain dietary constituents may produce an even greater increase in pancreatic weight (McGuinness et al., 1980). Gastrin, pentagastrin and cholecystokinin also exert trophic effects on the pancreas (Mayston and Barrowman, 1971; Barrowman and Mayston, 1974; Johnson, 1976). Although it is not clear in all cases whether increases in pancreatic weight are the result of increase in cell size (hypertrophy) or increase in cell number (hyperplasia), it has been shown that gastrin or pentagastrin administered to normal rats does induce an increase in acinar cell size, i.e. true hypertrophy (Mayston and Barrowman, 1971).

Hyperplasia, diffuse
   Although increases in pancreatic weight may simply be due to increase in acinar cell size (see above), under certain experimental conditions a true diffuse hyperplasia occurs. Administration of pentagastrin does not induce pancreatic hyperplasia in intact rats (see above), but acinar cell hyperplasia has been reported to occur when pentagastrin is administered to hypophysectomized rats (Mayston and Barrowman, 1973).

Note:
   Careful morphimetric examination may be necessary to make a distinction between diffuse hyperplasia and hypertrophy.

Focal lesions of the exocrine pancreas, including neoplasia

Introduction
   The pancreas of the aged, untreated rat, or the pancreas from rats treated with carcinogens may contain a variety of focal lesions and the pathologist is faced with a situation which parallels that in the rat liver, particularly as regards the relationship of such focal lesions to pancreatic neoplasia (see below). These difficulties have been previously commented on by Rowlatt (1967).

Foci of cellular alteration (basophilic foci, focal dysplasia)
   Small foci of atypical acinar cells or acinar cells which are different cytologically from the surrounding normal exocrine tissue have been described in the pancreas of the rat treated with carcinogens (Hayashi et al., 1972; Longnecker and Curphey,

1975). Similar lesions have also been described in the pancreas in man (focal acinar cell dysplasia) and their incidence increases with age and tends to be more prevalent in people with a history of heavy cigarette smoking or alcohol consumption (Longnecker et al., 1980a, b). Their significance is unknown although they may be related to the process of carcinogenesis. Histologically, these lesions are characterized by focal alteration in acinar cell cytology (generally increased basophilia), but with *no* compression of the surrounding tissues.

Focal hyperplasia, hyperplastic nodules and adenomas

Nodular lesions of the rat pancreas are seen in the untreated animal in small numbers and it may be difficult or impossible to make a valid distinction between a focus of hyperplasia (hyperplastic nodule) or true neoplasm (Rowlatt, 1967). As in other glandular organs, no sharp separation of hyperplasia, benign tumours and malignant tumours may be possible.

Although some authors have avoided using the term adenoma altogether and have employed terms such as focal hyperplasia and focal adenomatous hyperplasia to indicate progression towards invasive cancer (McGuinness et al., 1980; Shinozuka et al., 1976), it is usual to try and distinguish an adenoma from adenoma-like nodules in the rat exocrine pancreas (see below).

Adenomas, therefore, may be characterized by the fact that they are usually (but not always) single, are well-encapsulated, possess a uniform structure of zymogen containing acini, which are however different from the surrounding exocrine gland and, in addition, compress the surrounding tissue. Size of a lesion is not an absolute criterion, but of course, the larger mass the more likely it is to have compressed adjacent tissue and the more likely it is to be an autonomous growth (Rowlatt, 1967).

Focal hyperplasia (hyperplastic nodules) are also nodular and may compress surrounding tissue but tend to be multiple and less distinct cytologically from the surrounding gland and possess no capsule (Fig. 87).

In our experience, both focal hyperplasias and adenomas are found in untreated rats and this is also the experience of other authors (Rowlatt and Roe, 1967; Rowlatt, 1967; Roe and Roberts, 1973; Love et al., 1977; Goodman et al., 1979; Kroes et al., 1981). They may also be observed in increased numbers after treatment with carcinogens and certain food substances (Hayashi et al., 1972; Shinozuka and Konishi, 1974; McGuinness et al., 1980).

Carcinoma of the exocrine pancreas

These vary from being well to poorly differentiated adenocarcinomas and are characterized by neoplastic glandular tissue showing unequivocal local tissue invasion, extension into the mesentery or metastatic spread (Roe and Roberts, 1973). They are seen occasionally in aged untreated rats (Rowlatt and Roe, 1967; Rowlatt, 1967; MacKenzie and Garner, 1973; Naumann and Kunstyr, 1982).

Although focal hyperplasia of the pancreatic duct is occasionally observed in the untreated rat (Goodman et al., 1979), true ductular neoplasia (cystadenoma or cystadenocarcinoma) similar to that which occurs in man is rare in the rat (Rowlatt and Roe, 1967).

Islets of Langerhans

Classical histological and histochemical staining techniques as well as electron microscopic study have shown that several different cell types are present in the islets of Langerhans. These include the alpha cell (A cell), the beta cell (B cell), the delta cell (D cell) and the chromophobic cell (C cell). In the rat, alpha cells can be characterized by positive staining with the Grimelius techniques (Grimelius, 1968). The beta cells stain with the Gomori aldehyde fuchsin technique (Gomori, 1950; Seemayer et al., 1982). Other classic stains have been used (Doerr and Becker, 1958).

Electron microscopic examination allows separation of the various cell types by virtue of the type of secretory granules present (Rhodin, 1974; Ghadially, 1982).

More recently, the use of immunocytochemical techniques has permitted more accurate localization of the principal pancreatic hormones and their precursors within the islet cells of the rat. Insulin containing (beta) cells represent 80-85% of islet cells and are situated in the core of rat islets. Glucagon containing (alpha) cells comprise only about 10% of normal rat islet cells and are located as a narrow peripheral rim of cells in the islet. Somatostatin secretory cells are also present in the rat islet cell periphery but in very small numbers (delta cells) (Pelletier et al., 1975; Orci et al., 1976; Falkmer and Ostberg, 1977; Falkmer, 1979; Seemayer et al., 1982). Pancreatic peptide containing cells (PP cells, probably also delta cells) are somewhat different in that in the rat (as well as other higher vertebrates) they are present only in islet cells located in the lower dorsal part of the head of the pancreas (Orci et al., 1976; Falkmer, 1979). Their localization, close to the gastrointestinal tract gives support to the general hypothesis that pancreatic polypeptide is involved in the regulatory process for food intake and digestion (Falkmer, 1979).

Functional differences between ventral and dorsally located islets may also exist with regard to glucagon content and insulin biosynthesis in the rat (Trimble et al., 1982). In addition, individual islet cell populations may not be functionally homogeneous (Gold et al., 1982). Other active peptides are present in islet cells (Erlandsen, 1980; Graf, 1981). The microvasculature of the rat islet of Langerhans in relation to the islet cell populations has recently been studied (Bonner-Weir and Orchi, 1982).

Inflammation

Spontaneous inflammatory disease of the pancreas usually spares the islets, although mononuclear inflammatory cells (focal chronic inflammation) may be seen occasionally in individual islets in aged rats.

The need for an animal model of insulin-dependent diabetes has, however, promoted the development of rat models of diabetes, and these include the rat treated with streptozotocin and other beta islet-cell toxins and the spontaneously diabetic rat (BB rat from Bio Breeding Laboratories, see Nakhooda et al., 1976).

Both these models share certain pathological features which, in the early phases, are characterized by beta cell damage. Oedema, cytoplasmic swelling, vacuolization (vacuolar change), nuclear pyknosis and islet cell necrosis. In fully developed cases, islets are infiltrated by mononuclear cells including lymphocytes and debris laden macrophages (i.e. chronic inflammation) (Seemayer et al., 1980).

In the spontaneous diabetic (BB) rat, these inflammatory changes are probably mediated by an autoimmune reaction (Naji et al., 1981; Seemayer et al., 1980).

Atrophy

The size of the islets in the rat pancreas varies considerably in any given section and this is particularly true in the aged animal (see below). The plane of sectioning may also give a false impression of variability in islet size. In very advanced cases of chronic relapsing pancreatitis with atrophy and fibrosis of the exocrine tissue, islets do become disrupted and atrophied. However, in our experience, although islets may appear totally absent in haematoxylin and eosin-stained sections, immunoperoxidase staining reveals considerable numbers of islet cells containing immune-reactive insulin, glucagon and somatostatin scattered diffusely throughout the atrophied gland.

Atrophy of the islet (beta) cells occurs as a final result in the streptozotocin-induced or spontaneously diabetic rat (Rossi and Heldstab, 1981).

Islet cell hyperplasia

Aging rats commonly develop large islets of Langerhans and this may be particularly marked in obese strains or after repeated breeding (Wexler, 1970; Wexler et al., 1980). In our experience, the usual laboratory rat strains develop large hyperplastic islets with increasing age when housed under the usual laboratory conditions including ad libitum feeding. In an important recent study, it was shown that islet cell hyperplasia in the rat can be prevented by increased physical activity and/or weight control (Reavon and Reavon, 1981). Furthermore, these authors showed that islet cell function does decline with increasing age even in the non-obese rat. It was, therefore, postulated that overnutrition in the rat not only increases fat accumulation but increases insulin demand or insulin resistance. In the face of declining function, some beta cells cannot keep up the increased production but degenerate or die. In order to compensate new cells are formed, resulting in enlarged multilobulate, hyperplastic (giant) islets.

Islet cell hyperplasia is characterized histologically by the presence of several or even many pleomorphic and enlarged islets. A helpful diagnostic feature is their irregularity, as they often appear multilobulated or multinodular. Connective tissue may be increased both within and around such islets. Occasionally, chronic inflammatory cells and pigment-laden (iron) macrophages are present in or around the islets.

Immunoperoxidase staining of hyperplastic islets in our laboratory has shown that the insulin-containing (beta) cells are those principally affected and that in large or hyperplastic islets a narrow, normal-looking rim of glucagon and somatostatin-containing cells is retained (Fig. 87). Pronounced morphological change, particularly hyperplasia of D cells, appears to occur in the rat pancreas after portacaval shunt (Sacchi et al., 1982).

Islet cell adenoma

As in the exocrine pancreas, it may be difficult to distinguish islet cell adenomas from hyperplastic or giant islets (Rowlatt, 1967). However, the same basic criteria used for other endocrine glands can be applied in a pragmatic fashion to islet pathology. Adenomas tend to be single and usually possess rounded contours, in contrast to hyperplastic islets. They may compress surrounding exocrine tissue, and a fibrous capsule can be quite prominent. Size too may be a helpful criterion as well as the ribbon-like arrangement of cells along thin walled sinusoids (Roe and Roberts, 1973) (Figs 89 and 90). Capsular invasion or pseudoinvasion of pancreatic exocrine tissue is quite common in these tumours and these findings should be evaluated with caution and not simply regarded as indicative of malignant change (Rowlatt, 1967).

Islet cell tumours occur spontaneously in a variety of rat strains in varying frequencies (Rowlatt, 1967; MacKenzie and Garner, 1973; Coleman et al., 1977; Goodman et al., 1980; Kroes et al., 1981; Anver et al., 1982), and they may be induced by treatment with chemical agents (Hayashi et al., 1972).

Islet cell adenomas are thought generally to be of beta cell origin in the rat (Roe and Roberts, 1973). Recent immunocytochemical study of islet cell tumours in Fischer 344 rats has demonstrated the presence of insulin in 90% of cases (Stromberg et al., 1983). However, immunoperoxidase staining of islet cell tumours occurring in Sprague-Dawley and Long-Evans rats in our laboratory has shown that immune-reactive glucagon and somatostatin also occur and hormones of more than one type may be present in these tumours. This is in accord with findings in similar tumours in man and this fact has led to the suggestion that so-called islet cell adenomas are not primarily neoplastic but rather of hyperplastic origin (Heitz et al., 1979). However, true islet cell tumours in man can secrete more than one hormone (Aabo et al., 1983).

Islet cell carcinomas

Distant spread of islet cell tumours is generally accepted as the only reliable criterion for diagnosis of malignancy in islet cell tumours in rats (Rowlatt, 1967; Rowlatt and Roe, 1967). In a recent review, Lewis and his colleagues (1982) found no convincing previous report of a metastasizing islet cell tumour in the rat. They did, however, describe 9 cases of islet cell carcinoma probably representing less than 1% of all islet tumours found in a very large number of animals. Evidence from this study suggested that this is one of the few instances in which apparent capsular infiltration and penetration of tumour into blood vessels is not of diagnostic value when assessing malignancy and it confirmed the view that search for metastatic spread is of prime importance. We have observed an occasional case of metastasizing islet cell tumour in our laboratory rat populations.

Histologically, these tumours are characterized by well-differentiated cells of beta type showing little cellular pleomorphism and mitotic activity. Lewis and his colleagues (1982) found metastatic deposits mainly in the liver but in one case a local lymph node deposit was found.

OESOPHAGUS

The oesophagus, a 7-8 cm long tube, is lined by keratinized squamous epithelium similar to that lining the forestomach. The pathology of the oesophagus is indeed also similar to that occurring in the forestomach (see below). Oesophageal impaction has been described as a spontaneous lesion in certain rat colonies, although it is seldom observed in the Sprague-Dawley rat. It is characterized by an oesophagus distended with food and debris. Histologically, atrophy and degeneration of oesophageal smooth muscle fibres are seen (Ruben et al., 1983).

FORESTOMACH

Like the oesophagus, the forestomach is lined by squamous epithelium (see above).

Non-neoplastic lesions

Inflammation, ulceration, perforation

Ulceration and accompanying inflammation of the squamous mucosa of the fore-stomach is one of the most common spontaneous lesions of the gastrointestinal tract (Burek, 1978). These lesions vary in severity from focal acute or chronic inflamma-tion in the non-glandular epithelium to frank ulceration of the mucosa and penetra-tion of the inflammatory process into the stomach wall (Fig. 91). Severe ulceration is accompanied by marked acute and chronic inflammation, oedema, endarteritis (in-timal proliferation, arteritis), and fibrosis in the stomach wall. Haemorrhage may fol-low erosion or rupture of blood vessels. Complete penetration (perforation, inflam-matory perforation) of the stomach wall with inflammatory peritoneal involvement (peritonitis) may also occur.

Hyperplasia (acanthosis, hyperkeratosis, parakeratosis, papillomatosis)

Reactive proliferative or hyperplastic changes occur in the squamous mucosa of the forestomach mainly in association with foci of gastric inflammation. Occasional-ly, the entire forestomach may be involved in the absence of ulceration. Focal hyper-plasia of the squamous mucosa is also observed at the junction with the glandular stomach. Histologically, hyperplasia is characterized by acanthosis, hyperkeratosis, and parakeratosis of the epithelium (Fig. 92). The hyperplastic mucosa may become oedematous and papillomatous, and at times it is difficult to make a clear distinction between florid but reactive hyperplasia and a true benign neoplasm (squamous papil-loma). Indeed, in some cases, the acanthosis and mitotic activity may be associated with down-growing buds of squamous epithelium suggesting the diagnosis of squa-mous carcinoma. However, usually unequivocal invasion is not seen nor is there suf-ficient dysplasia or lack of maturation to make the diagnosis of carcinoma. Indeed in the few doubtful cases observed, it may be advisable just to record the degree of dysplasia present (minimal, moderate, or marked dysplasia) rather than inappropri-ately grouping a borderline lesion with true invasive cancer.

Neoplasia

Although neoplasms of the stomach are rare in untreated rats, they are occasional-ly found in the squamous mucosa of the forestomach and they can be induced by some carcinogens (Nagayo, 1973).

Squamous papilloma

True squamous papillomas occasionally occur in the forestomach of the untreated rat (Squire et al., 1978). These lesions are characterized by marked acanthosis and infolding proliferation of the squamous epithelium. Hyperkeratosis may be marked and chronic inflammation is usually present in the underlying submucosa. They show no evidence of true invasion of the submucosa and, therefore, can be regarded as benign neoplasms (see also under Hyperplasia (of the forestomach), above).

Squamous carcinoma

Squamous carcinoma only infrequently arises as a spontaneous tumour in the laboratory rat. However, a frankly invasive keratinizing squamous carcinoma is, in our experience, occasionally observed in untreated aged rats, and similar occasional cases have been reported by others in aging rat populations (Goodman et al., 1979, 1980).

Mesenchymal tumours

Soft tissue tumours or sarcomas may arise from the mesenchymal elements of the gastric wall as well as other parts of the gastrointestinal tract. Leiomyomas and leiomyosarcomas are some of the most commonly reported (see below and under Skin/ Subcutaneous tissue in Chapter I).

STOMACH (GLANDULAR)

Non-neoplastic lesions

Gastric ulceration – Introduction

Damage to the gastric glandular mucosa occurs under a wide variety of circumstances in both man and laboratory animals. In the rat, ulceration of the glandular mucosa may follow both cold and restraint stress (Brodie and Valitski, 1963; Senay and Levine, 1967), ischaemia following vascular occlusion or shock (Mersereau and Hinchey, 1973), pyloric ligation (Brodie, 1966), as well as after the administration of a wide variety of different chemical and biological agents. Chemical compounds include acid, alkali, and ethanol (Robert et al., 1979; Lacy and Ito, 1982), hyperosmolar solutions (Robert et al., 1979; Puurunen et al., 1980), detergents, bile salts (Whittle, 1977), histamine and reserpine (Okabe et al., 1977; Djahanguiri et al., 1978), as well as aspirin and the non-steroidal anti-inflammatory drugs (Rainsford, 1977; Rainsford et al., 1982). In the early stages after administration of gastric carcinogens, erosion and ulcers may be also seen (Uchida et al., 1976). Synergism between different agents is also a well-described phenomenon.

Often the precise mechanisms involved are still a subject of discussion, although the importance of acid-peptic activity in the genesis of gastric ulceration is generally accepted. However, gastric secretion is itself a complex process (Ackerman, 1982). Damage to the mucosa is probably triggered by breakdown of the gastric mucosal barrier (Mersereau and Hinchey, 1978). It has been suggested that inhibition of prostaglandin synthesis is a factor accounting for gastric mucosal damage induced by non-steroidal anti-inflammatory agents (Vane, 1971; Rainsford et al., 1982) and also that prostaglandins are cytoprotective in the rat stomach (Robert et al., 1979; Lacy and Ito, 1982). In contrast, a number of investigators have suggested the converse, that prostaglandins under some circumstances are injurious to the gastrointestinal mucosa (see review by Northway and Castell, 1981).

Experimentally induced ulceration generally occurs in the glandular mucosa of the body of the rat stomach, and it has been recently shown that distribution of ulceration may depend on the feeding schedule (Satoh et al., 1981).

Finally, it should be noted that in most toxicity and carcinogenicity studies, ulceration of the gastric glandular mucosa is a sporadic phenomenon for which often no clear cause is demonstrable.

Erosion (focal necrosis)

Early or mild damage to the gastric glandular epithelium is characterized by small, superficial, or shallow foci of necrosis, not involving the full thickness of the mucous membrane (erosions). They may be accompanied by acute inflammation (acute necrotizing inflammation).

Ulceration

Damage to the glandular mucosa which involves the full thickness of the mucous membrane is termed an ulcer (ulceration). In an acute ulcer, the amount of fibrous reaction is minimal, and this differentiates them from chronic ulcers in which fibrosis and fibroblastic reaction is marked. Cellular debris, fibrin and inflammatory cells are usually present in the larger ulcer craters and the surrounding intact mucosa may show inflammation and reactive hyperplasia. Necrosis can be marked (necrotizing inflammation).

Bleeding (haemorrhage) or perforation (inflammatory perforation) with ensuing peritonitis may result from gastric ulceration in the rat.

Inflammation (gastritis)

Gastric erosions and ulcers are often accompanied by active (acute) inflammation of the surrounding mucosa. However, inflammation of the mucosa may occur in the absence of frank ulceration or necrosis of the mucosa. The mucosa may contain a scattering of acute inflammatory cells (acute inflammation, acute gastritis) or occasional crypts are found containing acute inflammatory cells (crypt abscess). Mild non-specific chronic inflammation is occasionally observed in the submucosa, sometimes accompanied by prominent lymphoid tissue (lymphoid hyperplasia). Such inflammatory lesions are seen sporadically in untreated rats (Burek, 1978; Anver et al., 1982).

Mineralization (calcification)

Focal aggregates of calcium are found in the gastric glandular epithelium, and the basal part of affected glands may also show cystic dilatation. The cause of calcium deposition is not clear, although rats often suffer from renal disease and there may be some disturbance in calcium metabolism leading to deposition at sites of maximum ion exchange (i.e. kidney, gastric glandular epithelium). Metastatic calcification has been described in rats in association with severe renal disease and parathyroid hyperplasia (Snell, 1967). Focal calcification is also seen in the muscularis of the stomach (Fig. 93). This may be seen elsewhere in the gastrointestinal tract and is probably inflammatory (dystrophic) in origin.

Congestion

The gastric mucosa becomes congested with blood commonly as an agonal change, as well as in association with inflammatory disease.

Atrophy

Focal atrophy of the glandular mucosa, often accompanied by increase in collagen or fibrosis of the lamina propria and dilatation of gastric glands, is occasionally observed in untreated rats, a possible result of previous gastric inflammation or ulceration. In aged Sprague-Dawley rats of some colonies these lesions may be very common (Anver et al., 1982).

Diffuse gastric mucosal atrophy occurs after antrectomy in the rat (Martin et al., 1970) and atrophy of the stomach mucosa (atrophic gastritis) occurs after a similar procedure in man (Gjurldsen et al., 1968; Neilsen et al., 1972). This may be a result of the reflux of duodenal contents and bile into the stomach or more probably the reduction of trophic peptide (gastrin) production after surgical removal of gastrin producing cells located in the antrum.

Gastric hyperplasia, hypertrophy, adenomatous hyperplasia, hypertrophic gastritis

Gastric mucosal hypertrophy associated with glandular proliferation, cystic change and chronic inflammation characterizes a number of conditions in the stomach of both man and animals. Cystic change with chronic inflammation and foveolar hyperplasia is seen in the mucosa from the edges of gastric ulcers in man (Franzin and Novelli, 1981). Ménétrier's disease in man is characterized by hypertrophy and hyperplasia of mucous glands as well as marked cystic glandular change (Berenson et al., 1976).

Hypertrophic gastritis has been observed in several animal species with nematode parasites in the gastric lumen (Jubb and Kennedy, 1963). Similar changes have been reported in rats as a response to heavy experimental hepatic infestation with the cestode *Taenia taeniaformis* and this effect seems to be humorally mediated (Cook and Williams, 1981; Cook et al., 1981). In our experience, this condition is very occasionally seen in an aged rat, with no apparent association with parasitic infestation.

In the rat, this condition is characterized by hyperplasia of the foveolar and mucus secreting cells in the fundus and body mucosa, but with relative sparing of the antrum and pylorus (Fig. 94). Cystic glands are seen (cystic change) and these are usually lined by simple, mucous or flattened cells. The lamina propria, thickened by increased glandular tissue also contains prominent bundles of smooth muscle and there may be considerable focal chronic inflammation (Fig. 95). Submucosal blood vessels are usually prominent and dilated.

Various names have been used for this type of change including hypertrophic gastritis, giant hypertrophic gastritis, hyperplastic gastropathy, gastric mucous cell hyperplasia, adenomatous hyperplasia or even adenomatous polyp and adenoma. In the rat at least, these spontaneously arising changes do not appear to be truly neoplastic (see below).

Note:

Particular care should always be taken to define the histological nature of these changes for hyperplasia and hypertrophy of the gastric mucosa can occur under different circumstances. Under certain physiological conditions such as lactation there may be thickening of the gastric mucosa, but the mucosa remains essentially normal, except for increase in the parietal cell mass (Fell et al., 1963). Administration of gastrin or synthetic analogues of gastrin may produce similar thickening of the mucosa

(Crean et al., 1969). Scattered hyperplastic glands (focal hyperplasia) comprising hyperactive chief cells have been described in the rat after administration of sulphite salts (Beems et al., 1982). Glandular hyperplasia occurs in the early stages after administration of gastric carcinogens to the rat (Uchida et al., 1976).

Neoplasia

Carcinoma of the stomach is one of the rarest spontaneous cancers in animals. However, it occasionally arises spontaneously and several reliable methods now exist for the induction of malignant tumours of the forestomach (see above) and the glandular stomach of the rat (see review by Bralow, 1972).

The histopathological criteria for the diagnosis of experimental gastric malignancy in the glandular stomach are not uniform between different workers. Stewart and his co-workers (1961) arbitrarily defined experimental invasive carcinoma as neoplastic lesions that had penetrated to the serosa. Invasive cancer in man is defined by its relationship to the muscularis mucosae, those having invaded through it being regarded as invasive neoplasms, and this definition is applied by some workers to the experimental situation (Tsiftsis et al., 1980). The pathologist must be aware of these differences in interpretation and he must strictly define his terms.

It is our belief that a tumour showing *true* invasion of glandular epithelial tissue into the submucosa should be regarded as potentially malignant. True invasion has, however, to be distinguished from pseudo-invasion, such as is seen in hyperplastic conditions when non-neoplastic glands may penetrate the muscle layers, but always in continuity with more superficial glands. Assessment of the overall cellular and structural abnormalities are particularly important in making these diagnoses (Nagayo, 1973).

SMALL INTESTINE (DUODENUM, JEJUNUM, ILEUM)

Non-neoplastic lesions

Inflammation, ulceration (duodenitis, jejunitis, ileitis)
The small intestine, particularly the duodenum and jejunum, is damaged by a variety of chemical and biological agents in a rather similar way to the glandular mucosa of the stomach. Such agents include stress, gastric secretagogues (Carr et al., 1979), a variety of microbiological toxins, dietary lectins (King et al., 1982), various drugs and carcinogens (Murgatroyd, 1980; Sunter et al., 1981), as well as some of the nonsteroidal anti-inflammatory agents (Shriver et al., 1975). The actual site of ulceration induced by anti-inflammatory agents may be dependent on factors such as whether the rat is starved or not when compound is administered (Satoh et al., 1981).

Certain bacterial infections are particularly liable to produce inflammatory disease of the small bowel in the rat, notably *Bacillus piliformis* (Tyzzer's disease) and Salmonella species (Weisbroth, 1979). Intestinal parasites such as *Giardia muris* also produce intestinal inflammation if present in large numbers (Hsu, 1979). However, in most routine experiments, inflammation and ulceration of the intestine is only occasionally observed and usually without obvious cause.

Histologically, changes include focal necrosis or ulceration of the epithelium, usually associated with accumulation of cellular debris, fibrin and acute inflammatory cells (acute inflammation, acute necrotizing inflammation). A variable amount of chronic inflammation, fibrosis and reactive lymphoid hyperplasia may also be seen dependent on the cause and chronicity of the inflammatory process. Oedema and haemorrhage can also be quite marked. The surrounding intact epithelium may show marked reactive hyperplasia (see below). In severe cases, associated inflammatory changes are observed in Peyer's patches and mesenteric lymph nodes, and occasionally perforation (inflammatory perforation) results with ensuing peritonitis.

Lymphoid hyperplasia

The normal gastrointestinal tract contains abundant lymphoid tissue (gut-associated lymphoid tissue, GALT). The most prominent are aggregates of lymphoid follicles (Peyer's patches) which are most numerous in the distal ileum. It has been shown in the rat that precursor cells from the Peyer's patches migrate to the mesenteric lymph nodes where they mature to IgA producing cells, capable of seeding to the lamina propria of the gut (Roux et al., 1981). It would appear that IgA secreting cells do not generally mature in the Peyer's patches although IgM and IgG cells may do so (Sminia and Plesch, 1982). T cells are localized in the interfollicular zones and within the intestinal epithelium in man and rat (Carter and Bazin, 1980; Selby et al., 1981).

Lymphoid follicles in the gastrointestinal tract normally have a conspicuous germinal centre in the conventionally housed rat and, therefore, the presence of an active germinal centre is not generally of pathological significance. The term lymphoid hyperplasia is, therefore, reserved for particularly marked increases in lymphoid tissue, especially when this is present in parts of the intestine where it is not usually prominent.

Congestion

As in other parts of the gastrointestinal tract, the mucosa becomes congested as an agonal change. Blood vessels also become congested secondary to any inflammatory change.

Dilatation

The small (and large) bowel may become dilated under a variety of circumstances, including simple inflammatory disease. Post-mortem change is one of the most common causes.

Atrophy

Loss, shortening, stunting, or atrophy of the small intestinal villi can occur as a result of any direct injury. Atrophy (and hyperplasia, hypertrophy) also results from hormonal factors (see review by Johnson, 1976). Mucosal atrophy follows hypophysectomy in the rat, propably because the maintenance of normal villous architecture is dependent on hypophyseal hormones (Bastie et al., 1982). Such influences may be mediated at a local level by gastrin or other gastrointestinal peptides (Johnson, 1976). It has been known for a long time that reduced food intake or starvation causes a reduction in villous height and crypt length (Altman, 1972).

111

Histologically, mucosal atrophy is characterized by reduction in the height and size of the villi (villous stunting) and in severe cases there may be total loss of villi and flattening of the mucosa. Columnar epithelial cells may appear degenerate depending on the type of injury, and a chronic inflammatory infiltrate may be seen. Enzyme histochemistry may be useful in characterizing drug-induced changes (Murgatroyd, 1980). Morphimetric analysis appears necessary to detect minor changes in the mucosa (Bastie et al., 1982).

Hypertrophy, hyperplasia

Focal reactive hyperplasia or hypertrophy of the intestinal epithelium of the intestinal mucosa may occur around areas of inflammation or ulceration, or in association with heavy parasitic infestation (Cook and Williams, 1981). Intestinal mucosa is often thickened and hyperplastic near intestinal neoplasms (Fig. 96). Hypertrophy of all layers of the small intestinal wall (mucosa and muscle coats) and hyperplasia of the epithelium has been reported in the normal lactating rat (Fell et al., 1963). Increased numbers of mucous cells (mucous cell hyperplasia) have been described in the small bowel mucosa in rats given increased amounts of dietary bran (Schneeman et al., 1982).

Note:

Although there is no apparent increase in villous size with increasing age, recent morphimetric analysis has suggested that the *number* of villi *increase* with age in the rat, indicating continuing mucosal growth into old age (Ecknauer et al., 1982).

Parasites

Although generally not of great importance in most colonies, certain parasites do occur in the lumen of the small intestine, particularly *Giardia muris*, *Hexamitis (spironucleus) muris* and Trichomonas species (Hsu, 1979). They may be visualized in histological sections and smear preparations.

Lipoidosis, fatty change

Derangement of lipid metabolism, particularly by some drugs and chemicals, may induce the deposition of lipid droplets in the intestinal villi (Visscher et al., 1980). Lipid droplets can be observed in intestinal epithelial cells or in the lamina propria within macrophages (Gray et al., 1974; Visscher et al., 1980).

Neoplasia

Spontaneous epithelial tumours in the intestines are rare in rats and most reported cases appear to have developed in the colon (see below and Wells, 1971). However, they do arise spontaneously in the small bowel and we have observed several at Amboise. Most appear to be frankly invasive adenocarcinomas, infiltrating all layers of the bowel wall and metastatizing to adjacent lymph nodes and peritoneum (Figs 97 and 98). As in the large intestine, tumours can be induced by a wide variety of chemical compounds. Neoplasms are best classified in the same way as large bowel tumours (see under Large intestine, below).

As in all parts of the gastrointestinal tract, mesenchymal tumours may be found, particularly those of smooth muscle origin (see Skin/Subcutaneous tissue in Chapter I).

Although not particularly common in the rat, malignant lymphoma may occasionally be seen apparently arising from gastrointestinal lymphoid tissue (Peyer's patches) (see Haemopoietic and Lymphatic Systems, Chapter II).

LARGE INTESTINE (CAECUM, COLON, RECTUM)

Non-neoplastic lesions

The normal anatomy, light and electron microscopic and mucin histochemical characteristics of the normal rat caecum and colon have been recently reviewed (Snipes, 1981; Shamsuddin and Trump, 1981a), although not all questions have been resolved (see correspondence, Chang et al., 1981). It is influenced by a similar range of hormonal, chemical and biological agents as the small intestine (see above).

Inflammation (colitis)
Mild, non-specific inflammation is described in the colon of the aging rat (Burek, 1978). As a slight increase in the inflammatory cell content of the lamina propria is of doubtful significance, inflammation is described only when there is definite evidence of active inflammation or inflammatory change. This may occur in the glandular epithelium or extend into the other parts of the colon wall. Acute inflammation, ulceration and necrosis of the colon (necrotizing inflammation) also occur in Tyzzers' disease and salmonellosis and other gastrointestinal infections (Weisbroth, 1979). Degraded carrageenan may also produce colonic ulceration in the rat (Marcus and Watt, 1971).

Mineralization (calcification)
Round foci of inflammation with necrosis and calcification may be found in the muscularis externa of the gastrointestinal tract, including the colon (see also Stomach, above) (Fig. 93). The cause of these lesions remains obscure, but they probably result from inflammation and necrosis due to subclinical infection.

Atrophy
Focal atrophy of the large intestinal mucosa may be occasionally observed in the rodent colon in the absence of any clear associated pathology. It may be the result of previous inflammatory damage. Mucosal fibrosis is also occasionally observed in the colon.

Parasites: nematode Syphacia (pin worm)
Oxyurid nematodes of the genus Syphacia are commonly found in the caecum of albino rats and mice, *Syphacia muris* being the usual Syphacia of rats (Hussey, 1957). They may be partially characterized in tissue sections (Chitwood and Lichtenfels, 1972). They appear not to be associated with pathological changes in the colon (Fig. 99).

Transmission studies have shown, however, that the rat is also susceptible to *Syphacia obvelata*, the usual pin worm of the mouse (Kellogg and Wagner, 1982).

Hypertrophy and hyperplasia

As in other parts of the gastrointestinal tract, mucosal hypertrophy and hyperplasia may be observed in the large intestine. In general such changes are observed as reactive phenomena, usually when there is evidence of inflammation or frank ulceration. Mucous cell hyperplasia has been also described in rats given increased amounts of dietary bran (Schneeman et al., 1982) and colonic mucosal hypertrophy occurs under certain physiological conditions such as lactation (Fell et al., 1963).

Hyperplasia may also be observed in the mucosa surrounding colon carcinomas and in early stages after administration of colonic carcinogens to the rat, before the appearance of tumours (Shamsuddin and Trump, 1981b).

These areas of hyperplasia are associated with changes in mucin secretion, particularly in the descending colon where the normal sulphomucin secretion is replaced by non-sulphated sialomucin. These changes are best demonstrated by the high iron diamine-alcian blue stain (Spicer, 1965). These changes parallel remarkably well those occurring in association with colon cancer in man (Filipe and Branfoot, 1974; Greaves et al., 1980).

Squamous metaplasia

Squamous metaplasia of the colo-rectal mucosa may occur in the rat colon. It has been reported following the oral administration of degraded carrageenan and dextran sulphate sodium (Fabian et al., 1973; Hirono et al., 1981; Oohashi et al., 1981).

Neoplasia

Although adenocarcinomas of the colon and rectum are among the most prevalent human cancers in the United States and some European countries, similar tumours are relatively rare in the rat. However, spontaneous intestinal carcinomas have been reported in rats and most of these reports are of carcinomas of the large intestine (Wells, 1971). Adenomas and adenocarcinomas, however, develop in the rat gastrointestinal tract after the administration of a wide variety of synthetic and natural chemical substances (Lingeman and Garner, 1972; Pozharisski, 1973). In general these induced large intestinal tumours morphologically resemble those occurring in man (Spjut and Spratt, 1965; Spjut and Smith, 1967) and this also appears to be true of the spontaneous type (Burn et al., 1966). However, some carcinogens do not seem to produce a true benign adenomatous polyp in the rat (Shamsuddin and Trump, 1981b). More recently, colonic and caecal adenomas and adenocarcinomas have been induced by substances such as degraded carrageenan and dextran sulphate sodium, a synthetic sulphated polysaccharide (Oohashi et al., 1981; Hirono et al., 1981). As neither of these agents are mutagenic, it has been suggested that they may act as promotors in the rat colon (Oohashi et al., 1981), a suggestion of potential importance in toxicology.

As these tumours do appear to develop in a similar way to those in man, it is appropriate to use the same classification. This was the approach also used by Lingeman and Garner (1972) for animal gastrointestinal tract carcinomas.

Adenoma (polypoid adenoma, adenomatous polyp, villous adenoma)
These are benign neoplasms, comprising proliferating tubular glandular epithelium showing varying degrees of nuclear hyperchromatism and cellular pleomorphism. They may be sessile and supported by a stalk or stroma. The diagnosis of invasive carcinoma is only made if there is evidence of invasion of tumour cells into the stalk or bowel wall (Lingeman and Garner, 1972).

Villous adenomas are somewhat similar tumours with a villous rather than a tubular glandular pattern.

Carcinoma
These are malignant and usually glandular neoplasms (adenocarcinoma) which penetrate into the intestinal wall. They often infiltrate pericolic tissue and metastatize to local lymph nodes. The degree of differentiation is variable and mucin production may be marked.

Squamous carcinoma has been described in the rat colon following administration of carrageenan or dextran sulphate (Oohashi et al., 1981; Hirono et al., 1981).

PERITONEUM

The peritoneum responds to injuring in a similar way to the pericardial and pleural mesothelium. Perforation of the gastrointestinal tract or inflammation in an abdominal organ gives rise to inflammation within the peritoneal cavity (acute, chronic inflammation, granulomatous inflammation, fibrosis, fat necrosis). Reactive hyperplasia of the mesothelium may be quite marked and must be distinguished from neoplasia. Haemorrhage occurs as a result of rupture of an intra-abdominal blood vessel (haemoperitoneum). Metastatic neoplasia is particularly liable to spread throughout the peritoneal cavity. The malignant histiocytoma (histiocytic sarcoma) is particularly liable to do this, although lymphomas and other infiltrating neoplasms may also spread in this way.

REFERENCES

AABO, K., ROMOND, E., DIMITROV, N.V., DENNY, T.N. and SUHR, L.G. (1983): Pancreatic islet cell carcinoma associated with multiple hormone secretion and pancytopenia. *Cancer, 51*, 1691-1696.
ACKERMAN, S.A. (1982): Ontogeny of gastric acid secretion in the rat: Evidence for multiple response system. *Science, 217*, 75-77.
AHO, H.J. and NEVALAINEN, T.J. (1982): Experimental pancreatitis in the rat. Light and electron microscopical observations in early pancreatic lesions induced by intraductal injection of trypsin, phospholipase A2, lysolecithin a non-ionic detergent. *Virchows Arch.Cell Pathol., 40*, 347-356.
ALTMAN, G.G. (1972): Influence of starvation and refeeding on mucosal size and epithelial renewal in the rat small intestine. *Am.J.Anat., 133*, 391-400.
ALTMAN, N.H. and GOODMAN, D.G. (1979): Neoplastic diseases. In: H.J. Baker, J.R. Lindsey and S.H. Weisbroth (Eds), *The Laboratory Rat, Vol. 1*, Chap. 13, pp. 333-376. Academic Press, New York.

ANVER, M.R., COHEN, B.J., LATTUADA, C.P. and FOSTER, S.J. (1982): Age-associated lesions in barrier-reared male Sprague-Dawley rats: A comparison between Hap:(SD) and Crl:COBS-CD(SD) stocks. *Exp.Aging Res., 8*, 3-24.

BANNASCH, P. (1978): Sequential cellular alterations during hepatocarcinogenesis. In: W.H. Butler and P.M. Newberne (Eds), *Rat Hepatic Neoplasia*, Chap. 4, pp. 58-93. MIT Press, Cambridge, MA.

BANNASCH, P., BLOCH, M. and ZERBAN, H. (1981): Spongiosis hepatis. *Lab.Invest., 44*, 252-264.

BARROWMAN, J.A. and MAYSTON, P.D. (1974): The trophic influence of cholecystokinin on the rat pancreas. *J.Physiol., 238*, 73P-75P.

BASTIE, M.J., BALAS, D., LAVAL, J., SENEGAS-BALAS, F., BERTRAND, C., FREX-INOS, J. and RIBET, A. (1982): Histological variations of jejunal and ileal mucosa on days 8 and 15 after hypophysectomy in rat: Morphimetric analysis in light and electron microscopy. *Acta Anat., 112*, 321-337.

BEACONSFIELD, P. (1974): Liver tumours and steroid hormones. *Lancet, 1*, 516-517.

BEEMS, R.B., SPIT, B.J., KOËTER, H.B.W.M. and FERON, V.J. (1982): Nature and histogenesis of sulphite-induced gastric lesions in rats. *Exp.Mol.Pathol., 36*, 316-325.

BERENSON, M.M., SANNELLA, J. and FRESTON, J.W. (1976): Ménétrier's disease. Serial morphological, secretory and serological observations. *Gastroenterology, 70*, 257-263.

BHATT, M.N., PERCY, D.H. and JONAS, A.M. (1972): Characterization of the virus of sialodacryoadenitis of rats. A member of the coronavirus group *J.Infect.Dis., 126*, 123-130.

BONNER-WEIR, S. and ORCHI, L. (1982): New perspectives on the microvasculature of the islets of Langerhans in the rat. *Diabetes, 31*, 883-889.

BOORMAN, G.A. and HOLLANDER, C.F. (1973): Spontaneous lesions in the female WAG/Rij(Wistar) rat. *J.Gerontol., 28*, 152-159.

BRALOW, S.P. (1972): Experimental gastric carcinogenesis. *Digestion, 5*, 290-310.

BRAWER, M.K., AUSTIN, G.E. and LEWIN, K.J. (1980): Focal fatty change of the liver, a hitherto poorly recognized entity. *Gastroenterology, 78*, 247-252.

BRODIE, D.A. (1966): The mechanism of gastric hyperacidity produced by pylorus ligation in the rat. *Am.J.Dig.Dis., 11*, 231-241.

BRODIE, D.A. and VALITSKI, L.S. (1973): Production of gastric haemorrhage in rats by multiple stresses. *Proc.Soc.Exp.Biol.Med., 133*, 998-1001.

BUREK, J.D. (1978): Age-associated pathology. In: *Pathology of Aging Rats*. Chap. 4, pp. 29-167. CRC Press, West Palm Beach, FL.

BURN, J.I., SELLWOOD, R.A. and BISHOP, M. (1966): Spontaneous carcinoma of the colon of the rat. *J.Pathol.Bacteriol., 91*, 253-254.

CAMERON, G.R. and PRASAD, L.B.M. (1960): Recovery from biliary obstruction after the spontaneous restoration of the obstructed common bile duct. *J.Pathol.Bacteriol., 80*, 127-136.

CAMERON, G.R., McLEAN, M.R. and PRASAD, L.B.M. (1960): Recovery from the bile duct hyperplasia induced by feeding alpha-naphthylisothiocyanate to rats. *J. Pathol. Bacteriol., 80*, 137-141.

CARR, K.E., JOFFE, S.N., TONER, P.G. and WATT, C. (1979): A preliminary study of scanning electron microscopic changes of the duodenum during healing of duodenal ulcers. *Scand.J.Gastroenterol., Suppl. 14*, 78-83.

CARTER, P.B. and BAZIN, H. (1980): Immunology. In: H.J. Baker, J.R. Lindsey and S.H. Weisbroth (Eds), *The Laboratory Rat, Vol. 2*, Chap. 9, pp. 181-212. Academic Press, New York.

CARTHEW, P. and SLINGER, R.P. (1981): Diagnosis of sialodacryoadenitis virus infection of rats in a virulent enzootic outbreak. *Lab.Anim., 15*, 339-342.

CHANG, W.W.L., SHAMSUDDIN, A.K.M. and TRUMP, B.F. (1981): Two types of mucous cells in the colon crypt? *J.Natl Cancer Inst., 64*, 746-747.

CHITWOOD, M. and LICHTENFELS, J.R. (1972): Parasitological review. Identification of parasitic metazoa in tissue sections. *Exp.Parasitol., 32,* 407-519.

CLARK, D.G., TOPPING, D.L., ILLMAN, R.J., TRIMBLE, R.P. and MALTHUS, R.S. (1980): A glycogen storage disease (gsd/gsd) rat: Studies on lipid metabolism, lipogenesis, plasma metabolites and bile acid secretion. *Metabolism, 29,* 415-420.

COHEN, A.J. and GRASSO, P. (1981): Review of the hepatic response to hypolipidaemic drugs in rodents and assessment of its toxicological significance to man. *Food Cosmet.Toxicol., 19,* 585-605.

COLEMAN, G.L., BARTHOLD, S.W., OSBALDISTON, G.W., FOSTER, S.J. and JONAS, A.M. (1977): Pathological changes during aging in barrier-reared Fischer 344 male rats. *J.Gerontol., 32,* 258-278.

COOK, R.W. and WILLIAMS, J.F. (1981): Pathology of *Taenia taeniaeformis* infection in the rat: Gastrointestinal changes. *J.Comp.Pathol., 91,* 205-217.

COOK, R.W., WILLIAMS, J.F. and LICHTENBERGER, L.M. (1981): Hyperplastic gastropathy in the rat due to *Taenia taeniaeformis* infection. Parabiotic transfer and hypergastrinemia. *Gastroenterology, 80,* 728-734.

CRAMPTON, R.F., GRAY, T.J.B., GRASSO, P. and PARKE, D.V. (1977a): Long term studies on chemically induced liver enlargement in the rat. I. Sustained induction of microsomal enzymes with absence of liver damage on feeding phenobarbitone or butylated hydroxytoluene. *Toxicology 7,* 289-306.

CRAMPTON, R.F., GRAY, T.J.B., GRASSO, P. and PARKE, D.V. (1977b): Long term studies on chemically induced liver enlargement in the rat. II. Transient induction of microsomal enzymes leading to liver damage and nodular hyperplasia produced by Safrole and Ponceau MX. *Toxicology, 7,* 307-326.

CREAN, G.P., MARSHALL, M.W. and RUMSEY, R.D.E. (1969): Parietal cell hyperplasia induced by the administration of pentegastrin (ICI 50,123) to rats. *Gastroenterology, 57,* 147-155.

DAVID, H. (1978): Cellular pathobiology. In: J.V. Johannessen (Ed.), *Electron Microscopy in Human Medicine, Vol. 2, Part 1,* Chap. 3, pp. 102-124. McGraw-Hill, New York.

DE ALMEIDA, A.L. and GROSSMAN, M.I. (1952): Experimental production of pancreatitis with ethionine. *Gastroenterology, 20,* 554-577.

DENK, H., FRANKE, W.W., KERJASCHKI, D. and ECKERSTORFER, R. (1979): Mallory bodies in experimental animals and man. *Int.Rev.Exp.Pathol., 20,* 77-121.

DJAHANGUIRI, B., ZARRINDAST, M.R. and GERAYESH-NEJAD, S. (1978): Effects of cold or restraint on incidence of gastric ulceration induced in rats by ulcerogenic drugs. *Eur.J. Pharmacol., 51,* 77-79.

DOERR, W. and BECKER, V. (1958): Bauchspeicheldrüse. In: P. Cohrs, R. Jaffé and H. Meesen (Eds), *Pathologie der Laboratoriumstiere, Vol. 1,* pp. 130-155. Springer-Verlag, Berlin

ECKNAUER, R., VADAKEL, T. and WEPLER, R. (1982): Intestinal morphology and cell production in aging rats. *J.Gerontol., 37,* 151-155.

ERLANDSEN, S.L. (1980): Types of pancreatic islet cells and their immunocytochemical identification. In: P.J. Fitzgerald and A.B. Morrison (Eds), *Pancreas,* pp. 140-155. Williams and Wilkins, Baltimore.

FABIAN, R.J., ABRAHAM, R., COULSON, F. and GOLDBERG, L. (1973): Carrageenan-induced squamous metaplasia of the rectal mucosa in the rat. *Gastroenterology, 65,* 265-276.

FALKMER, S. (1979): Immunocytochemical studies of the evolution of islet hormones. *J. Histochem.Cytochem., 27,* 1281-1282.

FALKMER, S. and OSTBERG, Y. (1977): Comparative morphology of pancreatic islets in animals. In: B.W. Volk and K.F. Wellman (Eds), *The Diabetic Pancreas.* Plenum, New York.

FARBER, E. (1982): Chemicals, evolution and cancer development. *Am.J.Pathol., 108,* 270-275.

FELL, B.F., SMITH, K.A. and CAMPBELL, R.M. (1963): Hypertrophic and hyperplastic changes in the alimentary canal of the lactating rat. *J.Pathol. Bacteriol., 85,* 179-188.

FELL, B.F., KING, T.P. and DAVIES, N.T. (1982): Pancreatic atrophy in copper-deficient rats: Histochemical and ultrastructural evidence of a selective effect on acinar cells. *Histochem.J., 14,* 665-680.

FILIPE, M.I. and BRANFOOT, A.C. (1974): Abnormal patterns of mucous secretion in apparently normal mucosa of large intestine with carcinoma. *Cancer, 34,* 282-290.

FOULDS, L. (1958): The natural history of cancer. *J.Chronic Dis., 8,* 2-37.

FOULIS, A.K. (1980): Histological evidence of initiating factors in acute pancreatitis in man. *J.Clin.Pathol., 33,* 1125-1131.

FRANZIN, G. and NOVELLI, P. (1981): Gastritis cystica profunda. *Histopathology, 5,* 535-547.

FURTH, J. and BOON, M.C. (1945): Liver changes associated with transplantable granulosa cell carcinoma in mice. *Proc.Soc.Exp.Biol.Med., 58,* 112-114.

GHADIALLY, F.N. (1982): Golgi complex and secretory granules In: *Ultrastructural Pathology of the Cell and Matrix, 2nd Ed.,* Chap. 4, pp. 265-313. Butterworths, London.

GJURLDSEN, S.T., MYREN, J. and FRETHEIM, B. (1968): Alterations of gastric mucosa following a graded partial gastrectomy. *Scand.J.Gastroenterol., 3,* 465-470.

GLUCKSMAN, A. and CHERRY, C.P. (1973): Tumours of the salivary glands. In: V.S. Turusov (Ed.), *Pathology of Tumours in Laboratory Animals, Vol. 1, Part 1,* pp. 75-86. IARC Scientific Publ. No. 5, Lyon.

GOLD, G., LANDAHL, H.D., GISHIZKY, M.L. and GRODSKY, G.M. (1982): Heterogeneity and compartmental properties of insulin storage and secretion in rat islets. *J.Clin.Invest., 69,* 554-563.

GOMORI, G. (1950): Aldehyde-fuchsin: New stain for elastic tissue. *Am.J. Clin.Pathol., 20,* 665-666.

GOODMAN, D.G., WARD, J.M., SQUIRE, R.A., CHU, K.C. and LINHART, M.S. (1979): Neoplastic and non-neoplastic lesions in aging F344 rats. *Toxicol.Appl. Pharmacol., 48,* 237-248.

GOODMAN, D.G., WARD, J.M., SQUIRE, R.A., PAXTON, M.B., REICHARDT, W.D., CHU, K.C. and LINHART, M.S. (1980): Neoplastic and non-neoplastic lesions in aging Osborne-Mendel rats. *Toxicol.Appl.Pharmacol., 55,* 433-447.

GOULD, R.P. (1978): The APUD cell system. In: P.P. Anthony and N. Woof (Eds), *Recent Advances in Histopathology, Vol. 10,* Chap. 1, pp. 1-22. Churchill Livingstone, Edinburgh.

GRAF, R. (1981): Immunocytochemical detection of anti-ACTH reactivity in pancreatic islet cells of normal and steroid diabetic rats. *Histochemistry, 73,* 233-238.

GRASSO, P. and GRAY, T.J.B. (1977): Long-term studies on chemically induced liver enlargement in the rat. III. Structure and behaviour of the hepatic nodular lesions induced by Ponceau MX. *Toxicology, 7,* 327-347.

GRAY, J.E., WEAVER, R.N., SINKULA, A.A., SCHURR, P.E. and MORAN, J. (1974): Drug-induced enteropathy characterized by lipid in macrophages. *Toxicol. Appl.Pharmacol., 27,* 145-157.

GREAVES, P., FILIPE, M.I. and BRANFOOT, A.C. (1980): Transitional mucosa and survival in human colorectal cancer. *Cancer, 46,* 764-770.

GREAVES, P. and RABEMAMPIANINA, Y. (1982): Choice of rat strain: A comparison of the general pathology and the tumour incidence in 2-year old Sprague-Dawley and Long-Evans rats. In: New Toxicology for Old. *Arch.Toxicol., Suppl. 5,* 298-303.

GRIMELIUS, L. (1968): A silver nitrate stain for alpha 2-cells in human pancreatic islets. *Acta Soc.Med.Ups., 73,* 243-270.

HAYASHI, Y., FURUKAWA, H. and HASEGAWA, T. (1972): Pancreatic tumors in rats incuded by 4-nitroquinoline 1-oxide derivatives. In: W. Nakayara, S. Takayama, T. Sugimura and S. Odashima (Eds), *Topics in Chemical Carcinogenesis*, pp. 53-61. University Park Press, Baltimore, MD.

HAYNES, D., HALL, P. and CLARK, D. (1983): A glycogen storage disease in rats. Morphological and biochemical investigations. *Virchows Arch.Cell.Pathol., 42*, 289-301.

HEITZ, P.U., KASPER, M., POLAK, J.M. and KLÖPPEL, G. (1979): Pathology of the endocrine pancreas. *J.Histochem.Cytochem., 27*, 1401-1402.

HIRONO, I., KUHARA, K., HOSAKA, S., TOMAIZAWA, S. and GOLDBERG, L. (1981): Induction of intestinal tumors in rats by dextran sulphate sodium. *J.Natl Cancer Inst., 66*, 579-583.

HSU, C.K. (1979): Parasitic diseases. In: M.J. Baker, J.R. Lindsey and S.H. Weisbroth (Eds), *The Laboratory Rat, Vol. I, Biology and Diseases*, Chap. 12, pp. 307-330. Academic Press, New York.

HUSSEY, K.L. (1957): *Syphacia muris* vs. *S. obvelata* in laboratory rats and mice. *J.Parasitol., 43*, 555-559.

INNES, J.R.M. and STANTON, M.F. (1961): Acute diseases of the submaxillary and harderian glands (sialodacryoadenitis) of rats with cytomegaly and no inclusion bodies. *Am.J. Pathol., 38*, 455-468.

ISHAK, K.G. (1981): Hepatic lesions caused by anabolic and contraceptive steroids. *Semin. Liver Dis., 1*, 116-128.

JACOBY, R.O., BHATT, P.N. and JONAS, A.M. (1979): Viral diseases. In: H.J. Baker, J.R. Lindsey and S.H. Weisbroth (Eds), *The Laboratory Rat, Vol. 1, Biology and Diseases*, Chap. 11, pp. 271-306. Academic Press, New York.

JEZEQUEL, A.M. and ORLANDI, F. (1972): Fine morphology of the human liver as a tool in clinical pharmacology. In: F. Orlandi and A.M. Jezequel (Eds), *Liver and Drugs*, Chap. 6, pp. 176-178. Academic Press, New York.

JOHNSON, L.R. (1976): The trophic action of gastrointestinal hormones. *Gastroenterology, 70*, 278-288.

JONES, G. and BUTLER, W.H. (1978): Light microscopy of rat hepatic neoplasia. In: P.M. Newberne and W.H. Butler (Eds), *Rat Hepatic Neoplasia*, Chap. 6, pp. 114-138. MIT Press, Cambridge, MA.

JUBB, K.V.F. and KENNEDY, P.C. (1963): The lower alimentary system. In: *Pathology of Domestic Animals, Vol. 1, 1st Ed.*, Chap. 2, pp. 61-167. Academic Press, New York.

KELLOGG, H.S. and WAGNER, J.E. (1982): Experimental transmission of *Syphacia obvelata* among mice, rats, hamsters and gerbils. *Lab.Anim.Sci., 32*, 500-501.

KENDRY, G. and ROE, F.J.C. (1969): Histopathological changes in the pancreas of laboratory rats. *Lab.Anim., 3*, 207-220.

KING, T.P., PUSZTAI, A. and CLARKE, E.M.W. (1982): Kidney bean (*Phaseolus vulgaris*) lectin-induced lesions in rat small intestine. I. Light microscope studies. *J.Comp.Pathol., 90*, 585-595.

KLINGE, O. (1973): Cytologic and histological aspects of toxically induced liver reactions. *Curr.Top.Pathol., 58*, 91-116.

KOO, S.I. and TURK, D.E. (1977): Effect of zinc deficiency on the ultrastructure of the pancreatic acinar cell and intestinal epithelium in the rat. *J.Nutr., 107*, 896-908.

KROES, R., GARBIS-BERKVENS, J.M., DE VRIES, T. and VAN NESSELROOY, J.H.J. (1981): Histopathological profile of a Wistar rat stock including survey of the literature. *J.Gerontol., 36*, 259-279.

LACY, E.R. and ITO, S. (1982): Microscopic analysis of ethanol damage to rat gastric mucosa after treatment with a prostaglandin. *Gastroenterology, 83*, 619-625.

LEWIS, D.J., OFFER, J.M. and PRENTICE, D.E. (1982): Metastatizing pancreatic islet cell tumours in the rat. *J.Comp.Pathol., 92*, 139-147.

119

LINGEMAN, C.H. and GARNER, F.M. (1972): Comparative study of intestinal adenocarcinomas of animals and man. *J.Natl Cancer Inst., 48*, 325-346.

LONGNECKER, D.S. and CURPHEY, T.J. (1975): Adenocarcinoma of the pancreas in azaserine-treated rats. *Cancer Res., 35*, 2249-2257.

LONGNECKER, D.S., HASHIDA, Y. and SHINOZUKA, H. (1980a): Relationship of age to prevalence of focal acinar dysplasia in the human pancreas. *J.Natl Cancer Inst., 65*, 63-66.

LONGNECKER, D.S., SHINOZUKA, H. and DEKKER, A. (1980b): Focal acinar cell dysplasia in human pancreas. *Cancer, 45*, 534-540.

LOVE, L., PELFRENE, A. and GARCIA, H. (1977): Acinar adenomas of the pancreas in MRC-Wistar rats. *J.Comp.Pathol., 87*, 307-310.

MacKENZIE, W.F. and GARNER, F.M. (1973): Comparison of neoplasms in six sources of rats. *J.Natl Cancer Inst., 50*, 1243-1257.

MARCUS, R. and WATT, J. (1971): Colonic ulceration in young rats fed degraded carrageenan. *Lancet, 2*, 765-766.

MARTIN, F., MACLEOD, I.B. and SIRCUS, W. (1970): Effects of antrectomy on the fundic mucosa of the rat. *Gastroenterology, 59*, 437-444.

MAYSTON, P.D. and BARROWMAN, J.A. (1971): The influence of chronic administration of pentagastrin on the rat pancreas. *Q.J.Exp.Physiol., 56*, 113-122.

MAYSTON, P.D. and BARROWMAN, J.A. (1973): Influence of chronic administration of pentagastrin on the pancreas in hypophysectomized rats. *Gastroenterology, 64*, 391-399.

McGUINNESS, E.E., MORGAN, R.G.H., LEVISON, D.A., FRAPE, D.L., HOPWOOD, D. and WORMSLEY, K.G. (1980): The effects of long-term feeding of soya flour on the rat pancreas. *Scand.J.Gastroenterol., 15*, 497-502.

MERSEREAU, W.A. and HINCHEY, E.J. (1973): Effect of gastric acidity on gastric ulceration induced by hemorrhage in the rat utilizing a gastric chamber technique. *Gastroenterology, 64*, 1130-1135.

MERSEREAU, W.A. and HINCHEY, E.J. (1978): Interactions of gastric blood flow, barrier breaker, and hydrogen ion back diffusion during ulcer formation in the rat. *Surgery, 83*, 248-251.

MÜLLER, H.B., (1970): Der Einfluss kupferarmer Kost auf das Pankreas. Lichtmikroskopische Untersuchungen am exokrinen Teil der Bauchspeicheldrüsen weisser Ratten. *Virchows Arch.Path.Anat.Physiol., 350*, 353-367.

MURGATROYD, L.B. (1980): A morphological and histochemical study of a drug induced enteropathy in the Alderley Park rat. *Br.J.Exp.Pathol., 61*, 567-578.

NAGAYO, T. (1973): Tumours of the stomach. In: V.S. Turusov (Ed.), *Pathology of Tumours in Laboratory Animals, Vol. 1, Tumours of the Rat, Part 1*, pp. 101-118. IARC Scientific Publ. No. 5, Lyon.

NAJI, A., SILVERS, W.K., BELLGRAU, D. and BARKER, C.F. (1981): Spontaneous diabetes in rats: Destruction of islets is prevented by immunological tolerance. *Science, 213*, 1390-1392.

NAKHOODA, A.F., LIKE, A.A., CHAPPEL, C.I., MURRAY, F.T. and MARLISS, E.B. (1976): The spontaneous diabetic Wistar rat: Metabolic and morphological studies. *Diabetes, 26*, 100-112.

NAUMANN, S. and KUNSTYR, I. (1982): Adenocarcinom des exokrinen Pancreas bei einer Ratte. *Z.Versuchstierk., 24*, 181-183.

NEILSEN, J.A., HESS THAYSEN, E., OLESEN, H. and NIELSEN, R. (1972): Fundal gastritis after Billroth-II-type resection in patients with duodenal ulcer. *Scand.J.Gastroenterol., 7*, 337-343.

NEWBERNE, P.M. (1978): Nutritional and metabolic diseases. In: K. Benirschke, F.M. Garner and T.C. Jones (Eds), *Pathology of Laboratory Animals, Vol. 2*, Chap. 23, pp. 2065-2171. Springer-Verlag, New York.

NEWBERNE, P.M. and BUTLER, W.H. (1978): In: *Rat Hepatic Neoplasia*, pp. 1-6. MIT Press, Cambridge, MA.

NORTHWAY, M.G. and CASTELL, D.O. (1981): Do prostaglandins cause gastrointestinal mucosal injury? *Dig.Dis.Sci., 26*, 453-456.

OKABE, S., TAKEUCHI, K., URUSHIDANI, T. and TAKAGI, K. (1977): Effects of Cimetidine, a histamine H_2-receptor antagonist, on various experimental gastric and duodenal ulcers. *Dig.Dis., 22*, 677-684.

OOHASHI, Y., ISHIOKA, T., WAKABAYASHI, K. and KUWAGARA, N. (1981): A study on carcinogenesis induced by degraded carrageenan arising from squamous metaplasia of the rat colorectum. *Cancer Lett., 14*, 267-272.

ORCI, L., BAETENS, D., RAVAZZOLA, M., STEFAN, Y. and MALAISSE-LAGAË, F. (1976): Ilots à polypeptide pancréatique (PP) et îlots à glucagon: Distribution topographique distincte dans le pancréas de rat. *C.R.Acad. Sci., 283*, 1213-1216.

PELLETIER, G., LECLERC, R., ARIMURA, A. and SCHALLY, A.V. (1975): Immunohistochemical localization of somatostatin in the rat pancreas. *J.Histochem.Cytochem., 23*, 699-701.

PLATT, B.S., HEARD, C.R.C. and STEWART, R.J.C. (1964): Experimental protein-caloric deficiency. In: H.N. Munro and J.B. Allison (Eds), *Mammalian Protein Metabolism, Vol. 2*, Chap. 21, pp. 445-514. Academic Press, New York.

POLLARD, M. and LUCKERT, P.M. (1979): Spontaneous liver tumors in aged germ-free Wistar rats. *Lab.Anim.Sci., 29*, 74-77.

POSTE, G. and FIDLER, I.J. (1980): The pathogenesis of cancer metastasis. *Nature (London), 283*, 139-146.

POUND, A.W. and WALKER, N.I. (1981): Involution of the pancreas after ligation of the pancreatic ducts. 1. A histological study. *Br.J.Exp.Pathol., 62*, 547-558.

POZHARISSKI, K.M. (1973): Tumours of the intestine. In: V.S. Turusov (Ed.), *Pathology of Tumours in Laboratory Animals, Vol. 1, Tumours of the Rat, Part 1*, pp. 119-140. IARC Scientific Publ. No. 5, Lyon.

PUURUNEN, J., HUTTUNEN, P. and HIRVONEN, J. (1980): Is ethanol-induced damage of gastric mucosa a hyperosmotic effect? Comparative studies on the effects of ethanol, some other hyperosmotic secretions and acetylsalicylic acid on rat gastric mucosa. *Acta Pharmacol.Toxicol., 47*, 321-327.

RAINSFORD, K.D. (1977): Aspirin and gastric ulceration: Light and electron microscopic observations in a model of aspirin plus stress-induced ulcerogenesis. *Br.J.Exp.Pathol., 58*, 215-219.

RAINSFORD, K.D., WILLIS, C.M., WALKER, S.A. and ROBINS, P.G. (1982): Electron microscopic observations comparing the gastric mucosal damage induced in rats and pigs by benoxaprofen and aspirin, reflecting their differing actions as prostaglandin-synthesis-inhibitors. *Br.J.Exp.Pathol., 63*, 25-34.

RAO, S.S., WATT, I.A., DONALDSON, L.A., CROCKET, A. and JOFFE, S.N. (1981): A serial histologic study of the development and progression of acute pancreatitis in the rat. *Am.J.Pathol., 103*, 39-46.

RAPPAPORT, A.M. (1963): Acinar units and the pathophysiology of the liver. In: C.H. Rouiller (Ed.), *The Liver. Morphology, Biochemistry, Physiology, Vol. 1*, Chap. 6, pp. 265-320. Academic Press, London.

RAPTIS, S., SCHLEGEL, W., LEHMAN, E., DOLLINGER, H.C. and ZOUPAS, C. (1978): Effects of somatostatin on the exocrine pancreas and the release of duodenal hormones. *Metab. Clin.Exp., 27*, 1321-1328.

REAVON, E.P. and REAVON, G.M. (1981): Structure and function changes in the endocrine pancreas of aging rats with reference to the modulating effects of exercise and caloric restriction. *J.Clin.Invest., 68*, 75-84.

RHODIN, J.A.G. (1974): *Histology. A Text and Atlas*, Chap. 30, pp. 594-606. Oxford University Press, New York.

RICHTER, G.W. (1974): Effects of cyclic starvation-feeding and of splenectomy on the development of hemosiderosis in rat livers. *Am.J.Pathol., 74*, 481-506.

ROBERT, A., NEZAMIS, J.E., LANCASTER, C. and HANCHAR, A.J. (1979): Cytoprotection by prostaglandins in rats. Prevention of gastric necrosis produced by alcohol, HCl, NaOH, hypertonic NaCl and thermal injury. *Gastroenterology, 77*, 433-443.

ROE, F.J.C. and ROBERTS, J.D.B. (1973): Tumours of the pancreas. In: V.S. Turusov (Ed.), *Pathology of Tumours in Laboratory Animals, Vol. 1, Tumours of the Rat, Part 1*, pp. 141-150. IARC Scientific Publ. No. 5, Lyon.

ROSSI, G.L. and HELDSTAB, A. (1981): Morphimetric studies of pancreatic islets and retinal vessels of rats with streptozotocin-induced latent diabetes. *Diabète Métab., 7*, 77-86.

ROUILLER, Ch. (1964): Experimental toxic injury of the liver. In: Ch. Rouiller (Ed.), *The Liver, Vol. 2*, Chap. 22, pp. 335-476. Academic Press, New York.

ROUX, M.E., McWILLIAMS, M., PHILLIPS-QUAGLIATA, J.M. and LAMM, M.E. (1981): Differentiation pathology of Peyer's patch precursors of IgA plasma cells in the secretory immune system. *Cell Immunol., 61*, 141-153.

ROWLATT, U.F. (1967): Pancreatic neoplasms of rats and mice. In: E. Cotchin and F.J.C. Roe (Eds), *Pathology of Laboratory Rats and Mice*, Chap. 4, pp. 85-101. Blackwell Scientific, Oxford.

ROWLATT, U.F. and ROE, F.J.C. (1967): Epithelial tumors of the rat pancreas. *J.Natl Cancer Inst., 39*, 18-32.

RUBEN, Z., ROHRBAUKER, E. and MILLER, J.E. (1983): Esophageal impaction in BHE rats. *Lab.Anim.Sci., 33*, 63-65.

SACCHI, T.B., CORTESINI, C. and DOMENICI, L.L. (1982): The endocrine pancreas of the rat following portacaval shunt. *J.Submicrosc.Cytol., 14*, 655-671.

SAITO, A., WILLIAMS, J.A. and KANNO, T. (1980): Potentiation of cholecystokinin-induced exocrine secretion by both exogenous and endogeneous insulin in isolated and perfused rat pancreata. *J.Clin.Invest., 65*, 777-782.

SATOH, H., INADA, I., HIRATA, T. and MAKI, Y. (1981): Indomethacin produces gastric antral ulcers in the refed rat. *Gastroenterology, 81*, 719-725.

SCHAUER, A. and KUNZE, E. (1976): Tumours of the liver. In: V.S. Turusov (Ed.), *Pathology of Tumours in Laboratory Animals, Vol. 1, Tumours of the Rat, Part 2*, pp. 41-72. IARC Scientific Publ. No. 6, Lyon.

SCHEUER, P.J. (1980): Examination of the abnormal biopsy. In: *Liver Biopsy Interpretation, 3rd Ed.*, Chap. 4, pp. 27-35. Baillière Tindall, London.

SCHNEEMAN, B.O., RICHTER, B.D. and JACOBS, L.R. (1982): Response to dietary wheat bran in the exocrine pancreas and intestine of rats. *J.Nutr., 112*, 283-286.

SEEMAYER, T.A., OLIGNY, L.L., TANNENBAUM, G.S., GOLDMAN, H. and COLLE, E. (1980): Animal model: Spontaneous diabetes mellitus in the BB Wistar rat. *Am.J.Pathol., 101*, 485-488.

SEEMAYER, T.A., TANNENBAUM, G.S., GOLDMAN, H.Y. and COLLE, E. (1982): Dynamic time course studies of the spontaneously diabetic BB Wistar rat. *Am.J. Pathol., 106*, 237-249.

SELBY, W.S., JANOSSY, G. and JEWELL, D.P. (1981): Immunohistological characterization of intraepithelial lymphocytes of the human gastrointestinal tract. *Gut, 22*, 169-176.

SENAY, E.C. and LEVINE, R.J. (1967): Synergism between cold and restraint for rapid production of stress ulcers in rats. *Proc.Soc.Exp.Biol.Med., 124*, 1221-1223.

SHAMSUDDIN, A.K.M. and TRUMP, B.F. (1981a): Colon epithelium. I. Light microscopic, histochemical, and ultrastructural features of normal colon epithelium of male Fischer 344 rats. *J.Natl Cancer Inst., 66*, 375-388.

SHAMSUDDIN, A.K.M. and TRUMP, B.F. (1981b): Colon epithelium. II. In vivo studies of colon carcinogenesis. Light microscopic, histochemical and ultrastructural studies of histogenesis of azoxymethane-induced colon carcinomas in Fischer 344 rats. *J.Natl Cancer Inst., 66*, 389-401.

SHERLOCK, S. (1975): The liver in infancy and childhood. In: *Diseases of the Liver and Biliary System, 5th Ed.*, Chap. 23, pp. 533-569. Blackwell Scientific, Oxford.

SHINOZUKA, H. and KONISHI, Y. (1974): Degenerative and hyperplastic changes in rat pancreatic acinar cells induced by 4-hydroxyaminoquinoline-1-oxide. *Am.J.Pathol., 74*, 59a.

SHINOZUKA, H., POPP, J.A. and KONISHI, Y. (1976): Ultrastructure of atypical acinar cell nodules in rat pancreas induced by 4-hydroxyaminoquinoline-1-oxide. *Lab.Invest., 34*, 501-509.

SHRIVER, D.A., WHITE, C.B., SANDOR, A. and ROSENTHALE, M.E. (1975): A profile of the rat gastrointestinal toxicity of drugs used to treat inflammatory diseases. *Toxicol. Appl.Pharmacol., 32*, 73-83.

SINGH, M., LA SURE, M.M. and BOCKMAN, D.E. (1982): Pancreatic acinar cell function and morphology in rats chronically fed an ethanol diet. *Gastroenterology, 82*, 425-434.

SMINIA, T. and PLESCH, E.C. (1982): An immunohistochemical study of cells with surface and cytoplasmic immunoglobulins in situ in Peyer's patches and lamina propria of rat small intestine. *Virchows Arch.Cell.Pathol., 40*, 181-189.

SMITH, P.A., SUNTER, J.P. and CASE, R.M. (1982): Progressive atrophy of pancreatic acinar tissue in rats fed a copper-deficient diet supplemented with D-penicillamine or triethylene tetramine: Morphological and physiological studies. *Digestion, 23*, 16-30.

SNELL, K.C. (1967): Renal disease of the rat. In: E. Cotchin and F.J.C. Roe (Eds), *Pathology of Laboratory Rats and Mice*, Chap. 5, pp. 105-145. Blackwell Scientific, Oxford.

SNIPES, R.L. (1981): Anatomy of the cecum of the laboratory mouse and rat. *Anat.Embryol., 162*, 455-474.

SÖLING, H.D. and UNGAR, K.O. (1972): The role of insulin in the regulation of alpha-amylase synthesis in the rat pancreas. *Eur.J.Clin.Invest., 2*, 199-212

SPICER, S.S. (1965): Diamine methods for differentiating mucosubstances histochemically. *J.Histochem.Cytochem., 13*, 211-234.

SPJUT, H.J. and SMITH, M.N. (1967): A comparative electron microscopic study of human and rat colonic polyps and carcinomas. *Exp.Mol.Pathol., 6*, 11-24.

SPJUT, H.J. and SPRATT, S.S.Jr (1965): Endemic and morphological similarities existing between spontaneous colonic neoplasms in man and 3-2'-dimethyl-4-aminodiphenyl induced colonic neoplasms in rats. *Ann.Surg., 161*, 309-324.

SQUIRE, R.A. and LEVITT, M.H. (1975): Report of a workshop on classification of specific hepatocellular lesions in rats. *Cancer Res., 35*, 3214-3223.

SQUIRE, R.A., GOODMAN, D.G., VALERIO, M.G., FREDRICKSON, T.N., STRANDBERG, J.D., LEVITT, M.H., LINGEMAN, C.H., HARSHBARGER, J.C. and DAWE, C.J. (1978): Tumours. In: K. Benirschke, F.M. Garner and T.C. Jones (Eds), *Pathology of Laboratory Animals, Vol. 2*, Chap. 12, pp. 1051-1283. Springer-Verlag, New York.

STEVENS, R.E. and MOORE, G.E. (1983): Inadequacy of APUD concept in explaining production of peptide hormones by tumours. *Lancet, 1*, 118-119.

STEWART, H.L., SNELL, K.C., MORRIS, H.P., WAGNER, B.P. and RAY, F.E. (1961): Carcinoma of the glandular stomach of rats ingesting N,N'-2,7,fluorenylbisacetamide. *Natl Cancer Inst.Monogr., 5*, 105-139.

STEWART, H.L., WILLIAMS, G., KEYSSER, C.H., LOBARD, L.S., and MONTALI, R.J. (1980): Histological typing of liver tumours of the rat. *J.Natl Cancer Inst., 64*, 179-206.

STROMBERG, P.C., WILSON, F. and CAPEN, C.C. (1983): Immunocytochemical demonstration of insulin in spontaneous pancreatic islet cell tumors of Fischer rats. *Vet.Pathol., 20*, 291-297.

SUNTER, J.P., APPLETON, D.R. and WATSON, A.J. (1981): Acute changes occurring in the intestinal mucosae of rats given a single injection of 1,2-dimethylhydrazine. *Virchows Arch.Cell.Pathol., 36*, 47-57.

TEEBOR, G.W. and BECKER, F.F. (1971): Regression and persistance of hyperplastic nodules induced by N-2-fluorenylacetamide and their relationship to hepatocarcinogenesis. *Cancer Res., 31*, 1-3.

TRIMBLE, E.R., HALBAN, P.A., WOLLHEIM, C.B. and RENOLD, A.E. (1982): Functional differences between rat islets of ventral and dorsal pancreatic origin. *J.Clin.Invest., 69*, 405-413.

TSIFTSIS, D., JASS, J.R., FILIPE, M.I. and WASTELL, C. (1980): Altered patterns of mucin secretion in precancerous lesions induced in the glandular part of the rat stomach by the carcinogen N-methyl-N'-nitro-N-nitrosoguanidine. *Invest.Cell Pathol., 3*, 399-408.

UCHIDA, Y., SCHLAKE, W., ROESSNER, A., RÜHLAND, D., THEMANN, H. and GRUNDMANN, E. (1976): Development of tumors in the glandular stomach of rats after oral administration of carcinogens. *Z.Krebsforsch., 87*, 199-212.

UTSUMI, K., ISHIKAWA, T., MAEDA, T., SHIMIZU, S., TATSUMI, H. and FUJIWARA, K. (1980): Infectious sialodacryoadenitis and rat breeding. *Lab.Anim., 14*, 303-307.

VANE, J.R. (1971): Inhibition of prostaglandin synthesis as a mechanism of action for aspirin-like drugs. *Nature (London), New Biol., 231*, 232-239.

VESSELINOVITCH, S.D. (1982): Development of spontaneous liver tumors and their relationship to tumor induction. In: *Abstract Volume, International Symposium of the Society of Toxicologic Pathologists: Rodent Liver Nodules Significance to Human Cancer Risk, Reston, VA, May 10–12, 1982.*

VIRCHOW, R. (1862): Die pathologishen Gewebe. In: *Die Cellularpathologie*, Chap. 3, p. 62. Hirschwald, Berlin.

VISSCHER, G.E., ROBISON, R.L. and HARTMAN, H.A. (1980): Chemically induced lipidosis of the small intestinal villi in the rat. *Toxicol.Appl.Pharmacol., 55*, 535-544.

VITAL, A., BIOULAC-SAGE, P., IRON, A. and BALABAUD, C. (1982): Morphologic structure of bile canaliculi after bile duct ligation in the rat. *Arch. Pathol.Lab.Med., 106*, 464-467.

WALKER, N.I. and POUND, A.W. (1983): An autoradiographic study of the cell proliferation during involution of the rat pancreas. *J.Pathol., 139*, 407-418.

WARD, J.M. (1981): Morphology of foci of altered hepatocytes and naturally occurring hepatocellular tumors in F344 rats. *Virchows Arch.Pathol. Anat., 390*, 339-345.

WEINBREN, K. (1978): The liver. In: W.St.C. Symmers (Ed.), *Systemic Pathology, Vol. 3*, Chap. 21, pp. 1199-1301. Churchill Livingstone, Edinburgh.

WEINBREN, K. and WASHINGTON, S.L.A. (1976): Hyperplastic nodules after portacaval anastomosis in rats. *Nature (London), 264*, 440-442.

WEISBROTH, S.H. (1979): Bacterial and mycotic diseases. In: H.J. Baker, J.R. Lindsey and S.H. Weisbroth (Eds), *The Laboratory Rat, Vol. 1, Biology and Diseases*, Chap. 9, pp. 193-241. Academic Press, New York.

WEISBROTH, S.H. and PERESS, N. (1977): Ophthalmic lesions and dacryoadenitis: a naturally occurring aspect of sialodacryoadenitis virus infection of the laboratory rat. *Lab.Anim. Sci., 27*, 466-473.

WELLS, G.A.H. (1971): Mucinous carcinoma of the ileum in the rat. *J.Pathol., 103*, 271-275.

WEXLER, B.C. (1970): Arteriosclerosis of the pancreas and changes in the islets of Langerhans of repeatedly bred rats. *Br.J.Exp.Pathol., 51*, 107-113.

WEXLER, B.C., IAMS, S.G. and McMURTRY, J.P. (1980): Pathophysiological differences between obese and non-obese spontaneously hypertensive rats. *Br.J.Exp.Pathol., 61*, 195-206.

WHITTLE, B.J.R. (1977): Mechanisms underlying gastric mucosal damage induced by indomethacin and bile salts and the action of prostaglandins. *Br.J. Pharmacol., 60*, 455-460.

WINKLER, K. and POULSEN, H. (1973): Liver disease with periportal sinusoidal dilatation: a possible complication to contraceptive steroids. *Scand.J. Gastroenterol., 10*, 699-704.

YU, B.P., MASORO, E.J., MURATA, I., BERTRAND, H.A. and LYND, F.T. (1982): Life span study of SPF Fischer 344 male rats fed ad libitum or restricted diets: Longevity, growth, lean body mass and disease. *J.Gerontol., 37*, 130-141.

ZIMMERMAN, H.M. (1978): The expressions of hepatotoxicity. In: *Hepatoxicity. The Adverse Effects of Drugs and other Chemicals on the Liver*, Chap. 4, pp. 47-90. Appleton Century Crofts, New York.

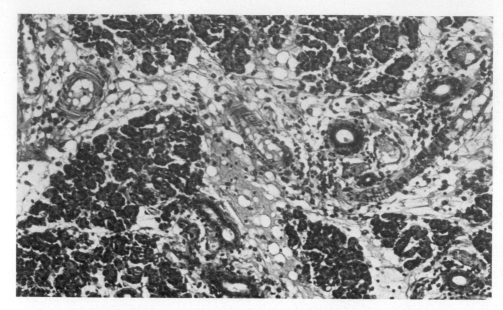

Fig. 64   Sialoadenitis in an 8-month-old female Sprague-Dawley rat. Several rats were affected in a similar way in the same study. The lobules and acini are separated by oedema fluid
and there is a sprinkling of acute and chronic inflammatory cells. (HE, × 105)

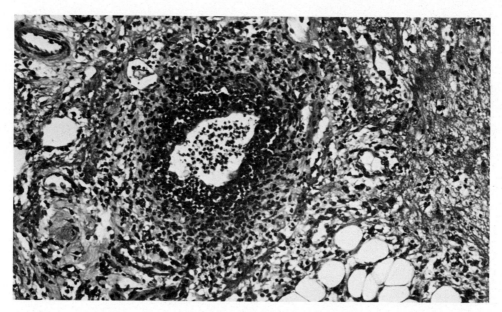

Fig. 65   Sialoadenitis. Same case as in Figure 64, showing heavy involvement of ducts by
active inflammation. (HE, × 105)

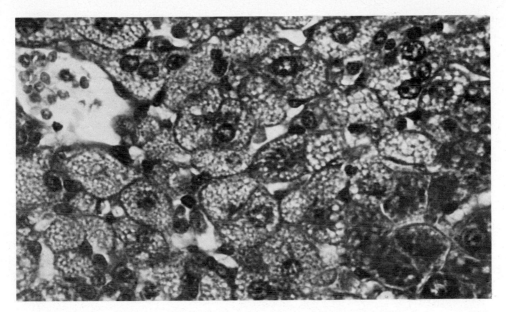

Fig. 66   Centrilobular fatty change in a moribund, 20-month-old Sprague-Dawley rat. This high power view clearly shows the finely vacuolated nature of this change. This rat had metastatic neoplasm in the abdominal cavity and there was thrombosis of the hepatic vein. Similar changes can be produced by drugs and chemicals. (HE, × 450)

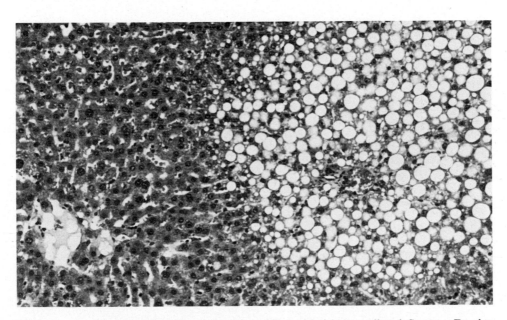

Fig. 67   Periportal fatty change (mainly large fat vacuoles) in a moribund, Sprague-Dawley female rat, 24 months old, that had a large pituitary adenoma. (HE, × 105)

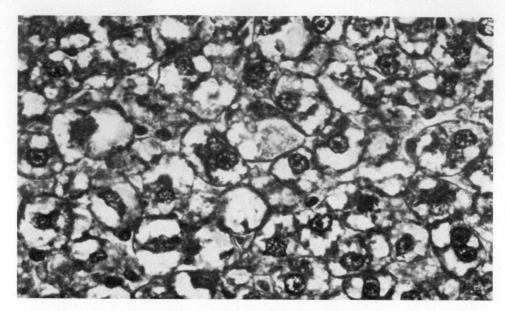

Fig. 68   Diffuse hepatic clear cell change in a male Sprague-Dawley rat, 25 months old. The cytoplasm of the hepatocytes is clear and the nuclei centrally situated. The PAS stain was positive in this case. (HE, × 450)

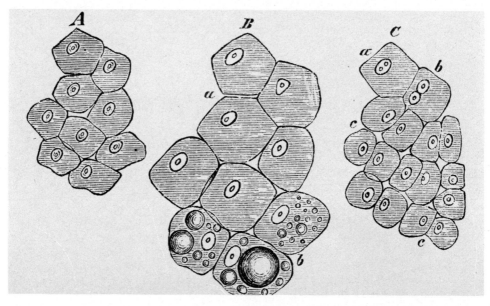

Fig. 69   Liver cell alterations as clearly illustrated by Virchow in 1862. A: Normal. B: Hypertrophy, a: simple hypertrophy, b: with fatty change. C: Hyperplasia, a: cell with dividing nucleus, b: cell with two nuclei, c: divided cells. Woodcut.

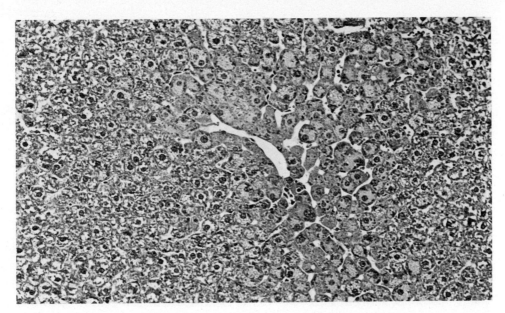

Fig. 70   Mild hepatic centrilobular hypertrophy in the liver of a rat treated for 1 month with phenobarbital. The hepatocyte cytoplasm in the centrilobular zone shows a 'ground glass' appearance. (HE, × 105)

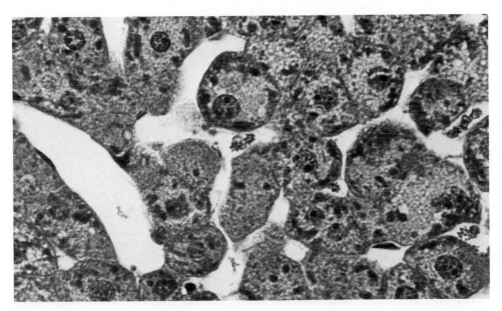

Fig. 71   Hepatic centrilobular hypertrophy, same case as in Figure 70. Centrilobular zone; the cytoplasmic 'ground glass' appearance is clearly evident. (HE, × 450)

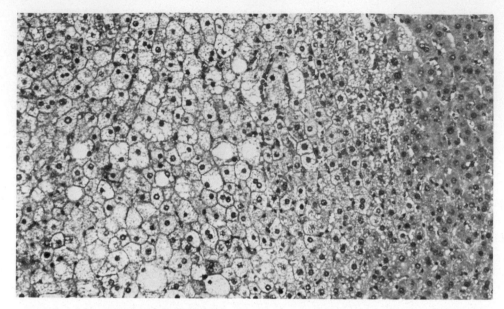

Fig. 72 Fatty (vacuolated) focus in a 26-month-old Sprague-Dawley male rat. A small, pale focus was observed at autopsy, situated in the medial lobe close to the median fissure. Histologically, a well-defined focus of fatty changes is present but it shows no convincing evidence of compression of surrounding liver tissue (HE, × 105)

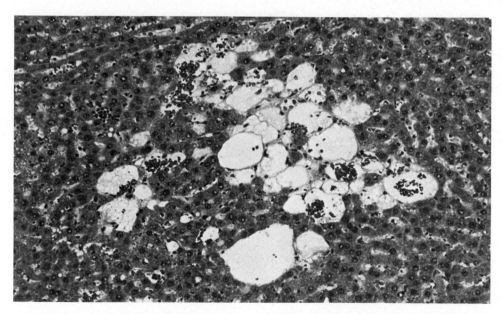

Fig. 73 Focal cystic degeneration (focal cystic change, cystic focus) found incidentally in a male Sprague-Dawley rat, 25 months of age. (HE, × 105)

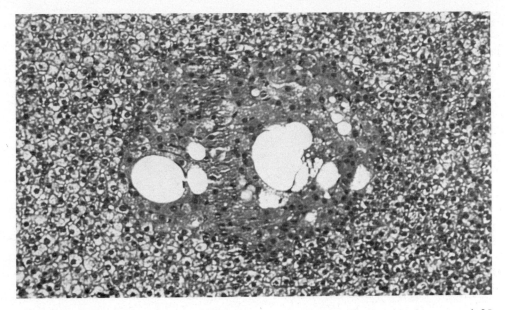

Fig. 74 A predominantly eosinophilic focus in a Sprague-Dawley female rat aged 25 months. (HE, × 105)

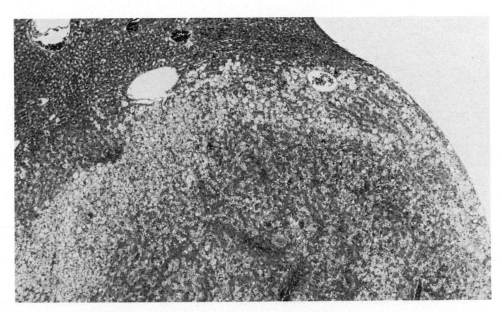

Fig. 75 Hyperplastic nodule in a male Sprague-Dawley rat. The cells are extensively foamy in character and there is distortion of adjacent liver tissue. (IIE, × 26)

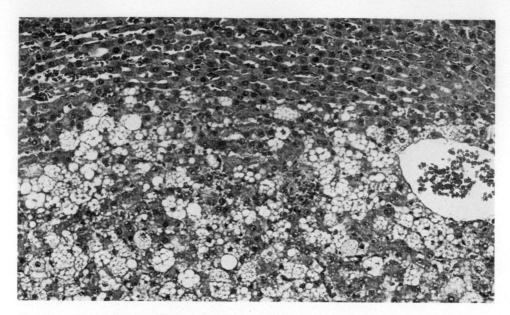

Fig. 76 Hyperplastic nodule, same case as in Figure 75, showing the edge of the lesion. Adjacent hepatocytes show early compression. (HE, × 105)

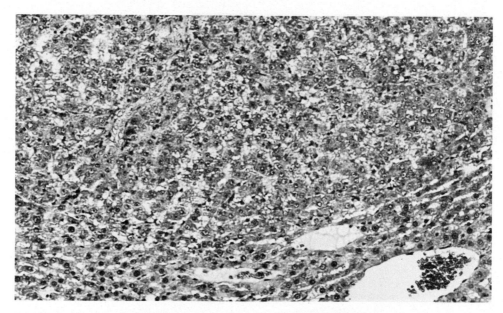

Fig. 77 Another hyperplastic nodule, in a 25-month-old male Sprague-Dawley rat. The nodule is composed of moderately large hepatocytes showing different tinctorial characteristics to the surrounding parenchyma. It is sharply demarcated and there is early compression of adjacent hepatocytes. (HE, × 105)

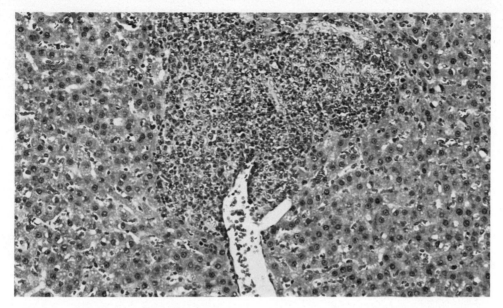

Fig. 78   Lymphoma. This lymphoblastic lymphoma infiltrated numerous organs in this male Sprague-Dawley rat, 25 months of age. There is focal infiltration sharply localized around portal tracts. (HE, × 105)

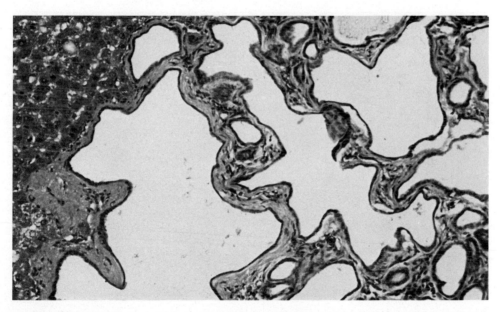

Fig. 79   Cystic change in the portal tract of an otherwise normal male Sprague-Dawley rat, 25 months of age. (HE, × 105)

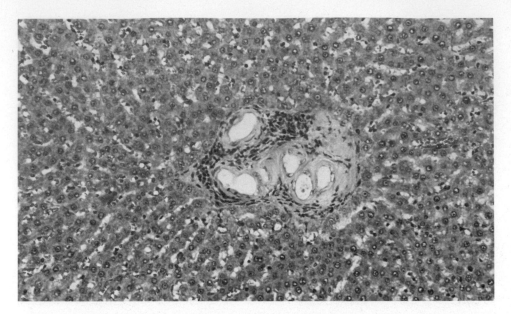

Fig. 80   Sclerosis (focal fibrosis) of the portal tract, an incidental finding in a Sprague-Dawley male rat aged 22 months. A small chronic inflammatory infiltrate is also present in the portal tract. (HE, × 105)

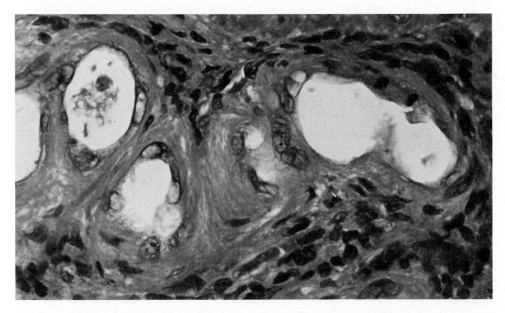

Fig. 81   Sclerosis (focal fibrosis) of the portal tract. Same case as in Figure 80. The biliary epithelium shows degenerative change. (HE, × 450)

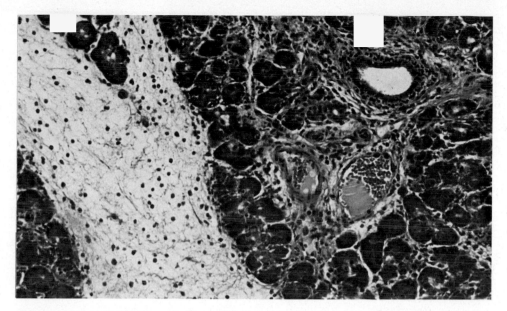

Fig. 82   Acute pancreatitis found as a spontaneous lesion in a 25-month-old Sprague-Dawley female rat. There is an acute inflammatory infiltrate, and oedema of the connective tissue stroma. (HE, × 105)

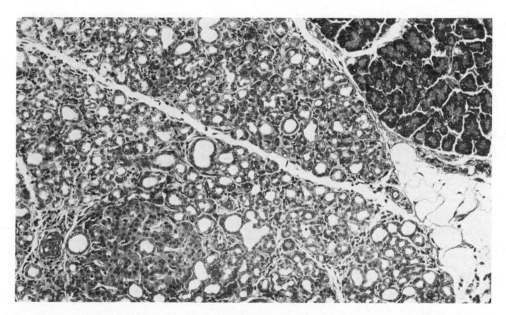

Fig. 83   Chronic pancreatitis (chronic relapsing pancreatitis) in a 26-month-old male Long-Evans rat. In this case, inflammation was minor in extent and atrophy was the major component. Acini are degenerative and show microcystic change. There is little disruption of the islets of Langerhans. Part of an adjacent normal lobule is visible for comparison. (HE, × 105)

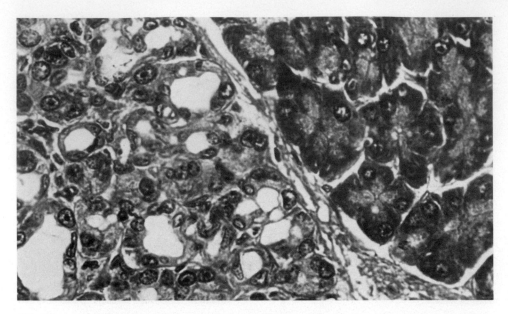

Fig. 84   Chronic pancreatitis, same case as in Figure 83, showing the microcystic change (small duct cells) in the affected lobule. (HE, × 450)

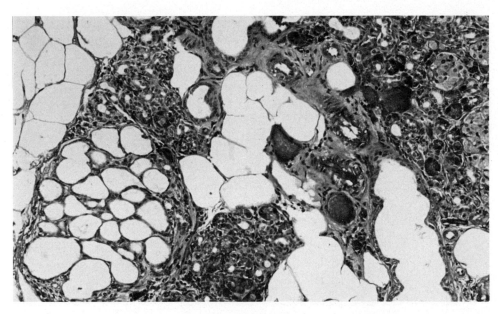

Fig. 85   Pancreatic atrophy in a 26-month-old male Long-Evans rat. In this case much of the gland is replaced by adipose tissue (fatty atrophy). (HE, × 105)

136

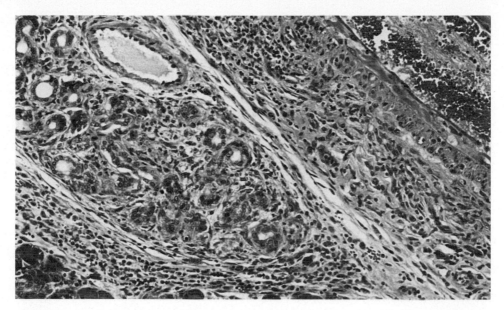

Fig. 86   Arteritis in the pancreas of a male Sprague-Dawley rat, 24 months of age. In the artery, at the top right hand corner of the photomicrograph, fibrin is present in the subendothelial zone and the surrounding pancreatic parenchyma shows active inflammation. Haemorrhagic peritonitis was found at autopsy. (HE, × 105)

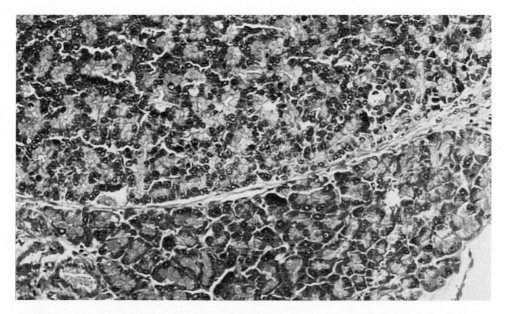

Fig. 87   Focal hyperplasia (hyperplastic nodule) in the exocrine pancreas of a Sprague-Dawley male rat. The nodule in the upper part of the photomicrograph is sharply defined and cytologically slightly different from the surrounding parenchyma. There is only mild condensation of connective tissue around this lesion. (HE, × 105)

137

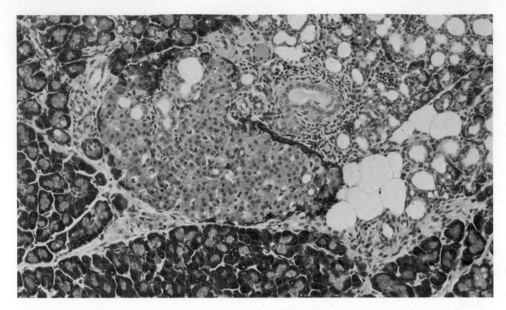

Fig. 88 Focal chronic pancreatitis is present in this section from the pancreas of a 26-month-old Long-Evans female. The large islet in the centre of the field contains a rim of cells staining for glucagon. (Immunoperoxidase-glucagon stain, counterstained with haematoxylin, × 105)

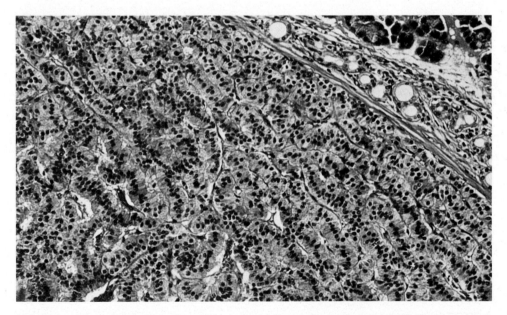

Fig. 89 Islet cell adenoma in a 26-month-old female Long-Evans rat. The tumour compresses exocrine tissue giving rise to a narrow rim of atrophic tissue. It possesses a well-defined fibrous capsule. The ribbon-like arrangement of cells is prominent in this case. (HE, × 105)

138

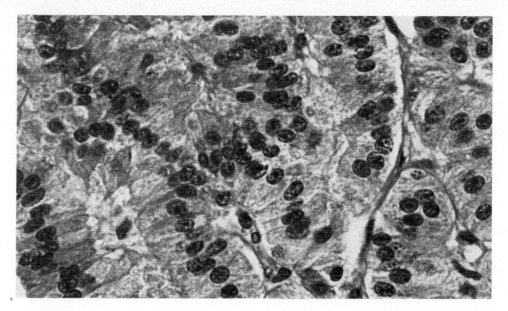

Fig. 90   Islet cell adenoma, same case as in Figure 89. High power view shows the ribbon-like structure of fairly uniform cells. (HE, × 450)

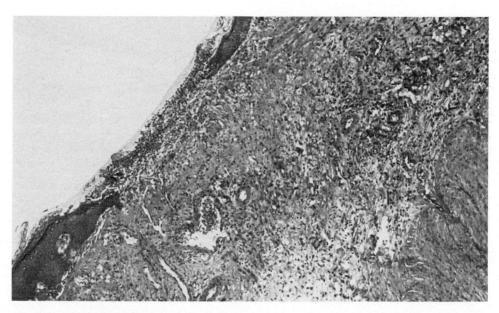

Fig. 91   Ulceration in the forestomach in a male Long-Evans rat, moribund at 22 months of age. Inflammation and fibrosis is present in the submucosa, features indicating an ulcer of some duration. (HE, × 34)

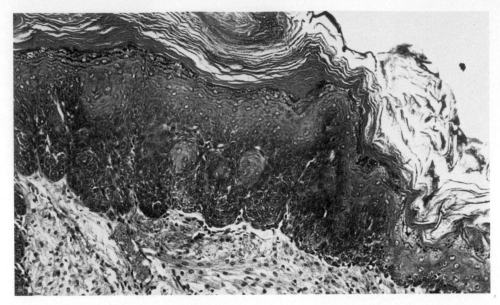

Fig. 92   Focal hyperplasia of the forestomach mucosa in a female Sprague-Dawley rat, 26 months of age. There is hyperkeratosis and moderate acanthosis but little evidence of dysplasia. (HE, × 105)

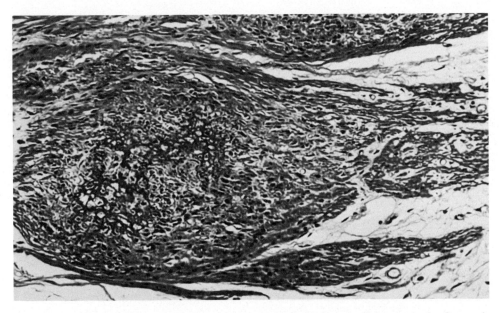

Fig. 93   Mineralization (calcification) in the muscularis externa of the stomach of a moribund Sprague-Dawley rat, 24 months of age. (HE, × 130)

Fig. 94   Gastric hyperplasia (gastric hypertrophy) found as a spontaneous change in a 25-month-old female Sprague-Dawley rat. There is lengthening of the glands, hyperplasia of foveolar and mucus-secreting cells and mild cystic dilatation of deep glands. (HE, × 26)

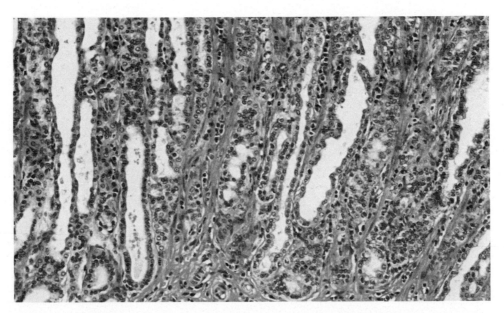

Fig. 95   Gastric hyperplasia, same case as in Figure 94. These deep glands are mildly dilated and there is loss of specialized gastric glandular cells. Fibromuscular tissue is increased. (HE, × 105)

141

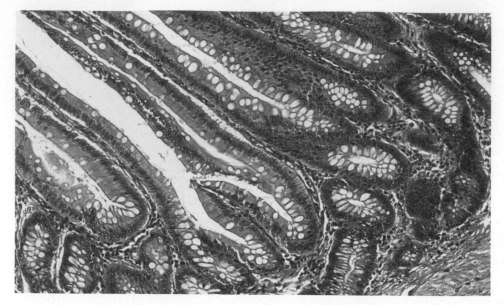

Fig. 96 Mucosal hyperplasia of the jejunum, found adjacent to an infiltrating adenocarcinoma (see Fig. 97). There is elongation of villi and crypts. (HE, × 105)

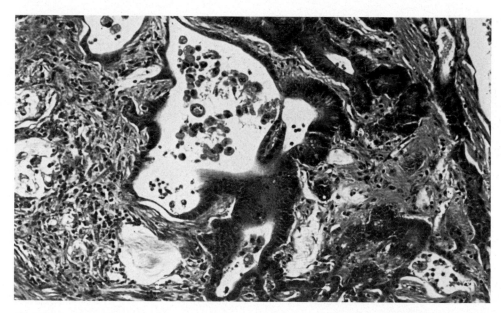

Fig. 97 Adenocarcinoma of the small bowel presenting as a mass 6 cm diameter in the jejunal region of a 26-month-old Sprague-Dawley rat. It is a poorly differentiated, mucin-secreting adenocarcinoma which infiltrates the full thickness of the bowel wall. Local lymph node metastases were also found. (HE, × 105)

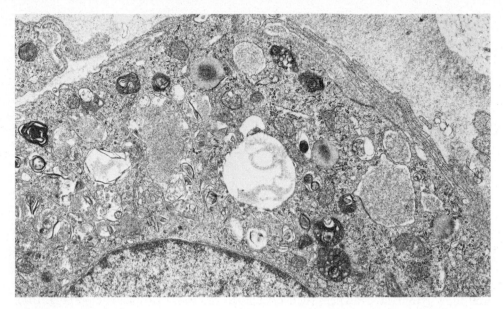

Fig. 98   Adenocarcinoma of the small bowel, same case as in Figure 97. This electron micrograph shows the mucin droplets within the cell cytoplasm. (E/M, × 13,500)

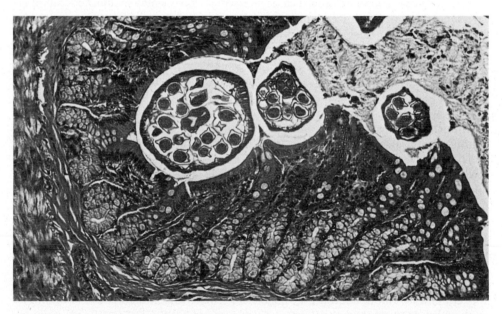

Fig. 99   Nematode. Section through the right side of the colon in a 26-month-old Sprague-Dawley male, showing the commonly observed pin-worm (*Syphacia species*). Note the lack of any inflammatory or reactive response. (HE, × 105)

VII. Urinary tract

KIDNEY

Non-neoplastic lesions

Glomerulonephrosis (glomerulonephropathy, chronic progressive nephrosis, progressive renal disease in rats, chronic nephritis)

This is the most important renal disease in adult and aged rats (Casey et al., 1978). In its established form in senile rats, the kidneys are enlarged and pale and cystic spaces may be visible to the naked eye. Microscopically, tubules are dilated and many contain densely pink-staining proteinaceous material (casts, hyaline casts) (Fig. 100). Tubular epithelial cells may be flattened and atrophic or they may be hyperplastic and show cytoplasmic changes such as vacuolar or hyaline droplet change (Fig. 101). The tubular basement membranes are often thickened. The glomeruli show a wide variety of changes. There is usually focal glomerulosclerosis which may be segmental (part of the tuft involved) or global (all of the tuft involved). Periglomerular fibrosis may be evident. Some workers report basement membrane thickening (Gray et al., 1974, 1982). In addition, the interstitium contains variable amounts of chronic inflammatory cells and in advanced cases interstitial fibrosis may be marked. Small arteries may become hyalinized late in the disease.

The potential for this condition to cause confusion in toxicity studies occurs with the initial phase of the disease. Although the disease is age-related (Durand et al., 1964), the onset may commence before six months especially with such accelerating factors as high protein diet and transient potassium deficiency (see below). The initial lesion is focal and affects a few isolated cortical tubules which show a basophilia, dilatation and basement membrane thickening accompanied by an adjacent round cell infiltrate. These changes are very similar to those induced by aminoglycoside antibiotics and heavy metals (Faccini, 1982) (see Acute tubular necrosis, below).

The pathogenesis of glomerulonephrosis in rats is uncertain, but it is probably primarily related to basement membrane dysfunction (Couser and Stilment, 1975). Biochemical studies suggest there are compositional changes in basement membrane structure, possibly due to increased synthesis or decreased degradation of the more collagen-like polypeptide components (Hoyer and Spiro, 1978). Its onset can be accelerated by a variety of factors such as diet (Bras and Ross, 1964), hormonal changes, irradiation and increased renal demand (Bolton et al., 1976). The distribution of changes may also be influenced by renal haemodynamics (Couser and Stilment, 1975). Under the housing and dietary conditions employed at Amboise and Lyon, this condition is more common in male than female rats and somewhat commoner in the OFA-ICO rat than the Sprague-Dawley (Crl:COBS-CD(SD)BR). A comparison of incidence in a separate life time study between Sprague-Dawley and Long-Evans rats at Amboise showed an incidence respectively in males of 56% against 74% and in females 13% against 44% (Greaves and Rabemampianina, 1982).

Although glomerulonephrosis complicates an assessment of potential nephrotoxicity of a compound under test, it is generally not a life-limiting condition unless studies are run beyond two years. The more severe nature of the condition in the OFA-ICO rat is related to a higher incidence of hyperparathyroidism with an accompanying osteitis fibrosa in this strain (see Bone in Chapter III and Parathyroid gland in Chapter X).

Owing to the importance of the diet in the aetiology of glomerulonephrosis, it is especially important in long-term studies on food additives which considerably modify the composition of the diet, to employ a grading system for the assessment of the severity of the glomerulonephrosis observed.

Other glomerular changes

Bowman's capsule may be lined by a high cuboidal epithelium resembling the proximal tubule in some strains of rats (Jakowski, 1982). It has been suggested that this change may be a response to an increase in systemic blood pressure because it is found more commonly in spontaneously hypertensive rats (Haensley et al., 1982). It has variously been described as metaplasia, hyperplasia, adenomatoid transformation and replacement. Bowman's capsule metaplasia appears the most appropriate term, although in most cases it is best regarded as a normal variation. Certain chemical compounds may also become deposited in the glomerular tuft (Figs 102 and 103.)

Simple cortical cyst

Large cysts formed from dilated tubules may accompany renal nephrosis (cystic change). Solitary cysts are also occasionally found, usually in the cortex. Their pathogenesis is uncertain.

Inflammation – mucous membrane of renal pelvis

A variety of mild inflammatory changes may be seen in the mucous membrane of the renal pelvis (focal chronic inflammation, acute focal inflammation), associated with changes such as mineralization, hydronephrosis or in apparent isolation.

Pyelonephritis

Severe inflammation, either acute or chronic, in the urinary outflow tract is associated with inflammatory changes within the renal parenchyma. The lesions are linear, extending to broad-based fan shapes in severe cases. They are distinguished from the focal lesions of glomerulonephrosis by the presence of polymorphonuclear leucocytes (Fig. 104).

Renal mineralization (calcification, calcium deposition)

Mineral deposits are relatively common in the urinary bladder and renal pelvis of the laboratory rat (Casey et al., 1978), and they are also found within the renal tubules. In the aged rat, flocculent or linear mineral deposits may be seen in the peripheral parts of the renal papillae (papilla or mucous membrane, renal pelvis – calcification, calcium deposition, mineralization) (Fig. 105). These deposits are often accompanied by focal fibrosis, granuloma formation in the surrounding papillary tissue, and the overlying transitional epithelium may show ulceration and hyperplasia. The chemical composition of these deposits is not certain but some workers have shown them to be composed of ammonium magnesium phosphate (Magnusson and

Ramsay, 1971). However, deposits seen around the renal pelvis in rats at Amboise and Lyon do show positive histochemical staining for calcium. Occasionally, younger rats may develop lesions in the papilla.

Intratubular lithiasis may be a distinct entity with a different histogenesis to lithiasis seen in the pelvis. It may be seen in young rats (Silverman and Riverson, 1980). These deposits are generally small concretions situated at the corticomedullary junction. Ultrastructural observations suggest they are formed from shed, vesiculated microvilli and microvesicles which initiate intraluminal microurolith formation (Nguyen and Woodard, 1980). These deposits contain calcium as shown by histochemical stains. They are more common in female rats and their presence correlates with the calcium/phosphorus ratio in the diet (Clapp, 1980).

The administration to rats of a number of chemical compounds, particularly carbonic anhydrase inhibitors (e.g. acetazolamide) which alter urinary pH and citrate excretion, may also precipitate the deposition of calcium salts in the urinary tract under certain dietary conditions (Fig. 106). The distribution of such mineralization within the kidney may also be dependent on the dietary calcium/phosphorus ratio (Harrison and Harrison, 1955).

Note:

In view of the assocation of urinary calculi with reactive urothelial hyperplasia and an as yet ill-understood relationship with urothelial neoplasia, it is advisable to record the presence of mineralization in the genito-urinary tract in toxicity and carcinogenicity experiments (see Hicks et al., 1976, and under Urinary bladder, below).

Pelvis dilatation (hydronephrosis)

Hydronephrosis is described in rats and appears to be of various types (Casey et al., 1978; Burton et al., 1979). It may be hereditary in nature or be related to the compression of the right ureter between the ovarian or spermatic artery and the ileolumbar artery. It may also be a function of the protein content of the diet (Clapp, 1980). In older animals, it can be difficult to distinguish true hydronephrosis from an apparent dilatation as a result of the renal parenchymal atrophy associated with advanced nephrosis.

Where possible, these are distinguished by the terms hydronephrosis and dilatation respectively.

Hyperplasia, mucous membrane of renal pelvis

Focal thickening of the urothelium may be seen in the renal pelvis particularly in association with renal mineralization (see above). It may also be seen as a reactive phenomenon in association with any pelvic inflammation or irritation (see also under Urinary bladder, below).

Tubular changes

A variety of cytoplasmic changes such as fine or coarse vacuolation or hyaline droplet change may be seen in the cytoplasm of renal tubular cells. These cellular inclusions are frequently P.A.S.-positive and they are not uncommon in the untreated rats examined at Amboise and Lyon. Their aetiology is unknown. Pigment may also be found in renal tubular epithelial cells of untreated rats even in the first year of life; it is usually found to stain positively for iron and is thought to reflect the metabolism of that mineral in the kidney (Ward and Reznik-Schüller, 1980).

Acute tubular necrosis

Necrosis of proximal convoluted tubules of the rat renal cortex can be induced by hypotension (Dobyan et al., 1977) and a wide variety of nephrotoxins, the most important of which are the heavy metals and aminoglycoside and cephalosporin antibiotics (Faccini, 1982). This lesion is an important one and should be looked for in toxicity studies on all agents that are principally excreted by the kidney or have a pharmacological action on the renal circulation. The evolution of the lesion has been extensively studied in the rat using aminoglycoside antibiotics. It can be demonstrated by both light and electron microscopy and is easily reproducible.

The acute changes, or those induced by mildly toxic doses, can only be detected by electron microscopy but with chronic administration or moderately toxic doses, lesions are evident by light microscopy. The established lesion, which is one of acute proximal tubular necrosis, comprises epithelial flattening with cytoplasmic basophilia and nuclear pyknosis with evidence of regeneration manifested by mitoses; amorphous deposits are present in the lumina and there is some tubular dilatation. With chronic dosing, foci of fibroblastic proliferation and lymphocytic infiltration of the interstitium appear. These changes need to be carefully distinguished from the early lesion of glomerulonephrosis which can appear in young rats (see Glomerulonephrosis, above): the differential diagnosis rests on the finding of several foci of tubular degeneration together with the presence of mitoses. In this respect, it is essential to ascertain that the mitoses observed represent regenerating tubular epithelial cells and not adjacent endothelial cells.

The severity and extent of such lesions lend themselves to a form of grading using light microscopy and haematoxylin and eosin sections. This grading can be useful in assessing the nephrotoxicity of new antibiotics and comparing them in a semi-quantitative manner with marketed compounds (Faccini, 1982). Such an assessment is augmented by enzyme histochemistry. One of the earliest targets of nephrotoxic agents such as heavy metals and aminoglycoside antibiotics is the brush border of the proximal convoluted tubule. As alkaline phosphatase is a brush border enzyme, a reduction in its activity can be shown histochemically. Conversely, as the proximal convoluted tubule is rich in lysosomal acid phosphatase and just as electron microscopy demonstrates increased numbers of lysosomes with nephrotoxins, so the reaction for this enzyme is seen to be diffusely increased. However, with the ensuing necrosis of cortical tubules resulting from prolonged dosage, a total loss of this enzyme from the cortex occurs (Faccini, 1982).

Renal papillary necrosis

This is the characteristic lesion associated with non-steroidal anti-inflammatory agents. The rat is especially sensitive to the effects of this class of compounds and the sensitivity has been shown to vary with different strains (Bokelman et al., 1971). Macroscopically the papilla is pale, while microscopically the tissue is necrotic with merely the outline of the collecting tubules apparent with a few remaining vesicular nuclei. A clear demarcation between the necrotic papilla and the surviving medullary tissue is usually seen. An associated cortical inflammatory reaction occurs with this

147

phenomenon but this can be prevented by surgical removal of the papilla prior to treatment (Hardy, 1970).

Extramedullary haemopoiesis

At times of increased demand, foci of haemopoiesis may be observed in the renal parenchyma of the adult rat (see Haemopoietic and Lymphatic Systems, Chapter II).

Neoplastic lesions

Adenoma and adenocarcinoma

Renal adenomas and adenocarcinomas are occasionally found in untreated rats of most strains and they can be induced by treatment with chemical carcinogens (Murphy et al., 1966; Hard, 1976). A rat model of renal adenoma and adenocarcinoma has also been recently described, in which tumour development is dependent on an autosomal dominant gene (Eker et al., 1981).

These tumours are strikingly similar to those described in man, being circumscribed, rounded tumours, frequently projecting from the cortex and ranging in size from microscopic lesions to neoplasms several centimetres in diameter (Hard, 1976).

Solid and cystic types have been described and individual cells may show a wide variety of appearances. Clear cells may predominate or cells may be eosinophilic, (oncocytic) basophilic, vacuolated and frankly fatty in type. They often retain their resemblance to renal tubular cells from which these tumours are thought to arise (Eker et al., 1981). However, there seems little point in separating these tumours into different sub-groups for they occur so uncommonly in the usual routine situation.

Adenomas are generally small, well-circumscribed lesions showing no haemorrhage, no necrosis and little or no cellular pleomorphism or mitotic activity. They obviously exhibit no evidence of tissue infiltration. By contrast, carcinomas are usually larger, infiltrative, and contain atypical cells, numerous mitoses and often show focal haemorrhage and necrosis. Metastases to lungs, lymph nodes and liver may occur (Eker et al., 1981). It should be noted, however, that the distinction between adenoma and adenocarcinoma is not always very sharp, in that some small tumours exhibit foci of necrosis, haemorrhage and cellular pleomorphism (Hard, 1976). Each tumour has to be assessed on its individual characteristics.

Rats bearing these tumours may be hypertensive (Murphy et al., 1966).

Lipomatous tumours (lipoma, lipomatous hamartoma, angiolipoma, myolipoma, angiomyolipoma, hamartoma, mixed tumours)

Benign tumours of fat and smooth muscle are the most common mesenchymal tumours of the kidney found in man, and they occur in the older population (Bennington and Beckwith, 1975). Similar tumours are found spontaneously in the aged rat and some authors group these lesions as lipomatous tumours as the lipid element is usually prominent (Hard, 1976). However, as in man, these tumours are often characterized by a variable admixture of mature adipose tissue, tangles or tortuous thick-walled vessels and collarettes and sheets of smooth muscle (Figs 107 and 108). Occasionally, lipoblasts are seen. The cells may show considerable nuclear pleomorphism and mitotic activity. In man at least, they are regarded as benign, but in the rat malignant varieties have been described (malignant mixed tumours, liposarcomas). These destroy renal parenchyma, invade adjacent structures and occasionally metastasize, especially to the lung (Goodman et al., 1980). The histogenesis of these tumours is not well understood but they are regarded by some authors as choristomas, i.e. composed of heterotopic but normal tissue (Bennington and Beckwith, 1975). A variety of different names are used for these tumours, dependent on type of tissues present and the user's view of their histogenesis.

Nephroblastoma

A satisfactory definition of nephroblastoma is hindered by unresolved controversies as to the classification of certain tumours composed entirely of one tissue pattern but otherwise typical of nephroblastoma (Bennington and Beckwith, 1975). The literature concerning induced nephroblastomas in the rat is particularly confusing due to the varied criteria used by different investigators for the diagnosis of nephroblastoma. In agreement with Bennington and Beckwith (1975), the term nephroblastoma is used both for the classical mixed renal tumour, composed of metanephric blastema and its recognized stromal and epithelial derivatives as well as mono-typic variants. Ultrastructural study has recently confirmed that in the rat nephroblastoma can be a purely epithelial neoplasm (Hard and Noble, 1982). Nephroblastoma is a malignant tumour found particularly in younger animals, thought to arise from metanephric blastema. It occasionally occurs spontaneously in the rat. It usually completely replaces renal tissue unilaterally and is typically composed of an admixture of three components, epithelial, stromal and blastematous although any one may be predominant. The blastemal elements are composed of closely packed, slightly ovoid cells with scanty cytoplasm, often arranged in nodules or in a trabecular fashion. Epithelioid differentiation may be predominantly tubular in character, mimicking various stages of foetal nephronic differentiation. Stromal constituents usually include fibroblastic and myxoid regions although smooth or striated muscle elements may also be seen. Rarely, fat, osteoid, lymphoid tissue and neural elements may also be present (Bennington and Beckwith, 1975).

Metastatic depositions are sometimes found especially in the lungs of rats (Iida et al., 1981). It has been suggested that hypertension may accompany nephroblastoma for this tumour has been associated with rupture (tear) of an aortic aneurysm in the rat (Bresnahan and Wagner, 1982).

We have not observed in untreated rats a definite case of the so-called mesenchymal tumour described in the rat after administration of dimethylnitrosamine (Hard and Butler, 1970; Hard, 1976).

Tumours of the renal pelvis (and ureter)

Soft tissue tumours may occasionally arise from connective tissue elements situated around the renal pelvis (see Skin/Subcutaneous tissue in Chapter I). Epithelial tumours can also develop from the transitional epithelium lining the upper urinary tract. These are similar to those found in the bladder (see Urinary bladder, below).

URINARY BLADDER

Non-neoplastic lesions

Cystitis (acute and chronic inflammation)

Inflammation of the urinary bladder is not a colony problem in most species of laboratory animals and most cases occur as isolated phenomena (Casey et al., 1978). An exception is the brown Norway rat (BN/Bi) which has a high frequency of bladder inflammation, probably secondary to ureteric or bladder tumours or urolithiasis (see below, and Burek, 1978). It has also been described in association with bladder infestation with *Trichosomoides crassicauda* in the rat (Zubaidy and Majeed, 1981). Cystitis is also found in association with pyelonephritis or prostatitis. A reactive hyperplasia (focal or diffuse hyperplasia) of the urothelium in chronic cystitis may mimic a transitional cell tumour (Fig. 109). Conversely, it is important to note that inflammatory cells are often present within the epithelium of induced transitional cell tumours (Hicks et al., 1976).

Mucous (proteinaceous) plugs, mucous retention, casts, proteinaceous droplets

Mucinous, hyaline amorphous or proteinaceous material is sometimes seen in the bladder and urethra of rats, mice and hamsters, and this material is generally not regarded as pathological unless there is evidence of urinary obstruction (Casey et al., 1978). These mucous plugs probably form from seminal fluid and secretions of the coagulating glands, and it may be that their development depends on the method used for euthanasia (Rapp, 1962). More recently, workers have suggested that they are present in life for they have been observed immediately after decapitation and these workers have also noted their similarity to the vaginal plug formed in female rats and mice after mating (Kunstyr et al., 1982). They should not be confused with calculi (see below).

Other small rounded eosinophilic (proteinaceous) droplets may also be observed in the normal rat bladder. These appear to arise from the urothelium itself and probably represent mucoprotein or mucopolysaccharide which is normally present in superficial cells of the bladder epithelium. They are of no pathological significance.

Dilatation

The urinary bladder may become dilated under a variety of pathological circumstances, although usually simple dilatation merely represents distension of the bladder with normal urine and is of no pathological significance.

Squamous metaplasia

Simple squamous metaplasia of the rat bladder epithelium has been described in rats on vitamin A deficient diet. We have observed it occasionally in chronically inflamed bladders of aged untreated rats. It cannot be regarded as a neoplastic change (Hicks et al., 1976).

Urothelial hyperplasia (bladder hyperplasia)

The transitional epithelium of the rat bladder is a mere three layers deep; the basal cells are smaller than those of the surface which are often binucleate.

In response to an irritant stimulus – infectious, mechanical or other – a localised or diffuse reaction can occur. This takes the form of a thickening of the epithelium which may not be associated with obvious cellular hypertrophy – a situation akin to acanthosis in cutaneous epithelium (Fig. 109). When there is a localised projection of the epithelium into the bladder lumen, the term nodular hyperplasia has been suggested (Hicks et al., 1976). The same authors used the designation papillary hyperplasia for more florid papillary outgrowths arising on a single stalk. They employed this diagnosis for a phenomenon which they observed in rats treated with bladder carcinogens and they considered it as a preneoplastic process, furthermore, they included this item under the general heading of 'papillary tumours'. It would seem advisable, however, given the finding of an occasional papillary outgrowth of the urothelium in a toxicity or carcinogenicity study, to use the term papilloma for these lesions (Figs 110 and 111) (see below).

Mineralization, calcification, calculi, stones

Rats may develop bladder calculi spontaneously and some strains are particularly prone to do this (Burek, 1978). Dietary factors may be important and compounds such as carbonic anhydrase inhibitors (including sulphonamides) may also precipitate the production of bladder calculi (Hicks et al., 1976). In view of the possible relationship between the mere presence of calculi, hyperplasia and neoplasia, the presence of calculi in the bladder should be recorded (see Kidney, above). The remnants of the bladder parasite *Trichosomoides crassicauda* may also act as a nidus for calculus formation (Garner and Patton, 1971).

Neoplasia

Tumours of the bladder are uncommon in untreated rats: the only types that we have observed in control rats have been papillary tumours; these need to be differentiated from papillary hyperplasia resulting from irritation due to infection or stones. Furthermore, if bladder neoplasia is found in treated rats in a carcinogenicity study, it is imperative to know whether calculi have been provoked by the test compound, and they should be searched for diligently at necropsy (Carter, 1978). Implantation of calcium oxalate calculi from the bladders of adult rats into young recipients has been shown to induce tumours in the latter (Weil et al., 1967). Substances which cause calculi formation in the bladder risk being labelled as carcinogens, therefore, unless this phenomenon is taken into account.

A simple classification of bladder tumours in the rat can be adopted from those seen in man:
papilloma
transitional cell carcinoma
squamous cell carcinoma
adenocarcinoma
undifferentiated carcinoma.
Bladder carcinogenesis has been extensively studied in the rat by Hicks and her

co-workers (1976) who have proposed further subdivisions of the above classification according to growth patterns. In a situation where statistically significant numbers of bladder tumours are found in treated rats, the adoption of their system would prove a useful means of evaluating the tumours with reference to the published data on known bladder carcinogens. For the discovery of the occasional tumour, a simpler classification (as below) would be in order.

Papilloma

This is a pedunculate tumour projecting from the mucosal surface with a narrow base and delicate branching villi. The main stalk and each villus has a narrow cone of connective tissue containing blood vessels and smooth muscle fibres. The surface is covered by transitional cell epithelium which is uniform and does not show any invasion of the stalk. The stroma may be focally oedematous. Inflammatory cells are usually present in the epithelium and stroma (Figs 110 and 111).

Transitional cell carcinoma

This may take the form of a papillary growth (as above) and is distinguished from a papilloma by the degree of cellular atypia of the surface epithelium, metaplastic, squamous or adenomatous epithelium and invasion of the stalk.

Solid growths are differentiated from localised hyperplasia by evidence of penetration of the muscle coat of the bladder and, eventually, the presence of tumour at the serosal surface. In such circumstances, regional lymph node metastases may be observed, although this is unusual, while haematogenous metastases are seldom observed (Hicks et al., 1976).

Squamous cell carcinoma

These tumours tend to be clearly malignant, demonstrating clear invasive qualities. They have only been described in studies reporting the effects of bladder carcinogens (Hicks et al., 1976).

Adenocarcinoma

Adenomatous metaplasia, like squamous metaplasia, may be observed in transitional cell carcinomas. Adenocarcinoma and undifferentiated carcinoma are, as with the case of squamous carcinoma, tumours associated with the administration of bladder carcinogens to rats.

REFERENCES

BENNINGTON, J.L. and BECKWITH, J.B. (1975): Mesenchymal tumors of the kidney. In: *Tumors of the Kidney, Renal Pelvis and Ureter. Atlas of Tumor Pathology, Second Series, Fascicle 12*, p. 201. AFIP, Washington, DC.

BOKELMAN, D.L., BAGDON, W.J., MATTIS, P.A. and STONIER, P.F. (1971): Strain-dependent renal toxicity of a nonsteroidal anti-inflammatory agent. *Toxicol.Appl.Pharmacol., 19*, 111-124.

BOLTON, W.K., BENTON, F.R., MACLAY, J.G. and STURGILL, B.C. (1976): Spontaneous glomerulosclerosis in aging Sprague-Dawley rats. I. Lesions associated with mesangial IgM deposits. *Am.J.Pathol., 85*, 277-302.

BRAS, G. and ROSS, M.H. (1964): Kidney disease and nutrition in the rat. *Toxicol.Appl. Pharmacol., 6*, 247-264.

BRESNAHAN, J.F. and WAGNER, J.E. (1982): Nephroblastoma with associated aortic rupture in the rat. *Lab.Anim.Sci., 32*, 189-197.

BUREK, J.D. (1978): Age-associated pathology. In: *Pathology of Aging Rats*, Chap. 4, pp. 29-167. CRC Press, West Palm Beach, FL.

BURTON, D.S., MARONPOT, R.R. and HOWARD, F.L. (1979): Frequency of hydronephrosis in Wistar rats. *Lab.Anim., 29*, 642-644.

CARTER, R.L. (1978): Long-term tests for carcinogenicity: the pathologist's view. In: A.D. Dayan and R.W. Brimblecombe (Eds), *Carcinogenicity Testing: Principles and Problems*, Chap. 1, pp. 1-15. MTP Press, Lancaster, England.

CASEY, H.W., AYERS, K.M. and ROBINSON, F.R. (1978): The urinary system. In: K. Benirschke, F.M. Garner and T.C. Jones (Eds.), *Pathology of Laboratory Animals, Vol. 1*, Chap. 3, pp. 115-173. Springer-Verlag, New York.

CLAPP, M.J.L. (1980): The effect of diet on some parameters measured in toxicological studies in the rat. *Lab.Anim., 14*, 253-261.

COUSER, W.G. and STILMENT, M.M. (1975): Mesangial lesions and focal glomerular sclerosis in the aging rat. *Lab.Invest., 33*, 491-501.

DOBYAN, D.G., NAGLE, R.B. and BULGER, R.E. (1977): Acute tubular necrosis in the rat kidney following sustained hypotension. *Lab.Invest., 37*, 411-422.

DURAND, A.M.A., FISHER, M. and ADAMS, M. (1964): Histology in rats as influenced by age and diet. I. Renal and cardiovascular systems. *Arch.Pathol., 77*, 268-277.

EKER, R., MOSSIGE, J., JOHANNESSEN, J.V. and AARS, H. (1981): Hereditary renal adenomas and adenocarcinomas in rats. *Diagn.Histopathol., 4*, 99-110.

FACCINI, J.M. (1982): A perspective on the pathology and cytochemistry of renal lesions. In: P.H. Bach, F.W. Bonner, J.W. Bridges and E.A. Lock (Eds), *Nephrotoxicity Assessment and Pathogenesis*, pp. 82-97. John Wiley and Sons, Chichester.

GARNER, F.M. and PATTON, C.S. (1971): Helminthic diseases of laboratory animals (rats and mice). In: R.A. Marcial-Rojas (Ed.), *Pathology of Protozoal and Helminthic Diseases*, pp. 960-969. Williams and Wilkins, Baltimore.

GOODMAN, D.G., WARD, J.M., SQUIRE, R.A., PAXTON, M.B., REICHARDT, W.D., CHU, K.C. and LINHART, M.S. (1980): Neoplastic and non-neoplastic lesions in aging Osborne-Mendel rats. *Toxicol.Appl.Pharmacol., 55*, 433-447.

GRAY, J.E., WEAVER, R.N. and PURMALIS, A. (1974): Ultrastructural observations of chronic progressive nephrosis in the Sprague Dawley rat. *Vet.Pathol., 11*, 153-164.

GRAY, J.E., VAN ZWIETEN, M.J. and HOLLANDER, C.F. (1982): Early light microscopic changes of chronic progressive nephrosis in several strains of aging laboratory rats. *J.Gerontol., 37*, 142-150

GREAVES, P. and RABEMAMPIANINA, Y. (1982): Choice of rat strain: A comparison of the general pathology and the tumour incidence in 2-year old Sprague-Dawley and Long-Evans rats. In: New Toxicology for Old. *Arch.Toxicol., Suppl. 5*, 298-303.

HAENSLEY, W.E., GRANGER, H.J., MORRIS, A.C. and CIOFFE, C. (1982): Proximal tubule-like epithelium in Bowman's capsule in spontaneously hypertensive rats. Changes with age. *Am.J.Pathol., 107*, 92-97.

HARD, G.C. (1976): Tumours of the kidney, renal pelvis and ureter. In: V.S. Turusov (Ed.), *Pathology of Tumours in Laboratory Animals, Vol. 1, Tumours of the Rat, Part 2*, pp. 73-101. IARC Scientific Publ. No. 6, Lyon.

HARD, G.C. and BUTLER, W.H. (1970): Cellular analysis of renal neoplasia: Induction of renal tumors in dietary-conditioned rats by dimethylnitrosamine, with a reappraisal of morphological characteristics. *Cancer Res., 30*, 2796-2805.

HARD, G.C. and NOBLE, R.L. (1982): Spontaneous rat nephroblastoma. Ultrastructure of a transplant line. *Arch.Pathol.Lab.Med., 106*, 418-422.

HARDY, T.L. (1970): Partial renal papillectomy and the study of drug induced renal papillary necrosis in the rat. *Br.J.Exp.Pathol., 51*, 591-596.

HARRISON, H.E. and HARRISON, H.C. (1955): Inhibition of urine citrate excretion and the production of renal calcinosis in the rat by acetazolamine (Diamox) administration. *J.Clin.Invest., 34*, 1662-1670.

HICKS, R.M., WAKEFIELD, J.St.J., VLASOV, N.N. and PLISS, G.B. (1976): Tumour of the bladder. In: V.S. Turusov (Ed.), *Pathology of Tumours in Laboratory Animals, Vol. 1, Tumours of the Rat, Part 2*, pp. 103-134. IARC Scientific Publ. No. 6, Lyon.

HOYER, J.R. and SPIRO, R.G. (1978): Studies on the rat glomerular basement membrane: age-related changes in composition. *Arch.Biochem.Biophys., 185*, 496-503.

IIDA, M., YASUBA, H. and ITAKURA, C. (1981): Spontaneous nephroblastoma in the rat. *Exp.Anim., 30*, 31-34.

JAKOWSKI, R.M. (1982): Renal tubular epithelium lining parietal layer of Bowman's capsule in adult Long-Evans rats. *Vet.Pathol., 19*, 212-215.

KUNSTYR, I., KÜPPER, W., WEISSER, H., NAUMANN, S. and MESSOW, C. (1982): Urethral plug – a new secondary male sex characteristic in rat and other rodents. *Lab. Anim., 16*, 151-155.

MAGNUSSON, G. and RAMSAY, C.H. (1971): Urolithiasis in the rat. *Lab.Anim., 5*, 153-162.

MURPHY, G.P., MIRAND, E.A., JOHNSON, G.S., SCHMIDT, J.D. and SCOTT, W.W. (1966): Renal tumours induced by a single dose of dimethylnitrosamine: morphological, functional, enzymatic and hormonal characteristics. *Invest.Urol., 4*, 39-56.

NGUYEN, H.T. and WOODARD, J.C. (1980): Intranephronic calculosis in rats. *Am.J.Pathol., 100*, 39-56.

RAPP, J.P. (1962): Terminal formation of urethral plugs in male mice. *Proc. Soc.Exp. Biol.Med., 111*, 243-245.

SILVERMAN, J. and RIVERSON, A. (1980): Nephrocalcinosis in 2 young rats. *Lab.Anim., 14*, 241-242.

WARD, J.M. and REZNIK-SCHÜLLER, H. (1980): Morphological and histochemical characteristics of pigments in aging F344 rats. *Vet.Pathol., 17*, 678-685.

WEIL, C.S., CARPENTER, C.P. and SMYTH, H.F. (1967): Urinary bladder calculus and tumour response following either repeated feeding of diethylene glycol or calcium oxalate stone implantation. *Ind.Med.Surg., 36*, 55.

ZUBAIDY, A.J. and MAJEED, S.K. (1981): Pathology of the nematode *Trichosomoides crassicauda* in the urinary bladder of laboratory rats. *Lab. Anim., 15*, 381-384.

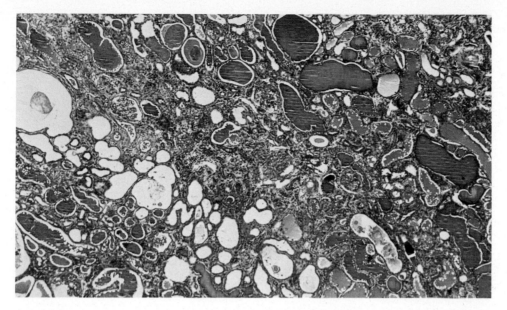

Fig. 100   Glomerulonephrosis (nephrosis) in a 24-month-old male Sprague-Dawley rat. There is moderate cystic dilatation of tubules, proteinaceous intratubular casts and interstitial inflammation. (HE, × 105)

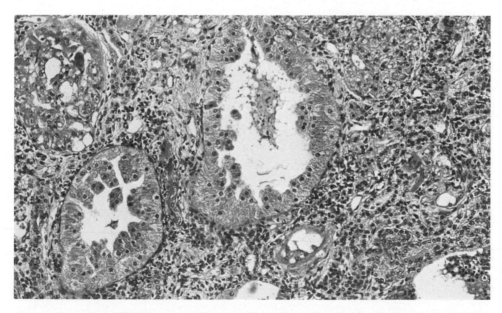

Fig. 101   Glomerulosclerosis, high power view of the same case as in Figure 100 showing sclerosis of the glomerular tuft, vascular hyaline change and interstitial inflammation. In this field, hyperplastic tubular cells are present. (HE, × 450)

155

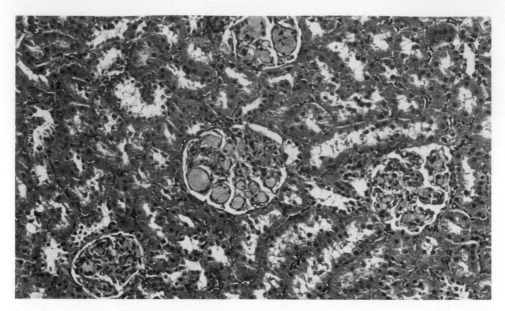

Fig. 102   Glomerular deposits (deposition of foreign material) in the kidney of a rat treated for 6 months by repeated intravenous injection of a soluble synthesis polymer (same case as in Fig. 51). Foamy deposits appear to be present predominantly in mesangial cells. (HE, × 105)

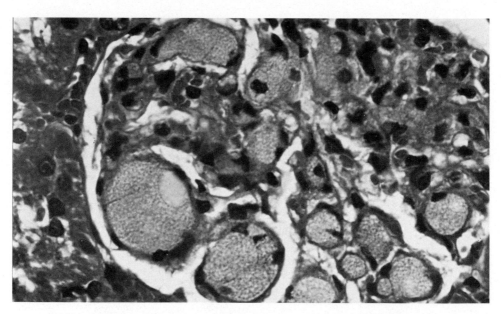

Fig. 103   Glomerular deposits (deposition of foreign material), high power view of a glomerulus seen in Figure 102. Foamy deposits are clearly visible. (HE, × 450)

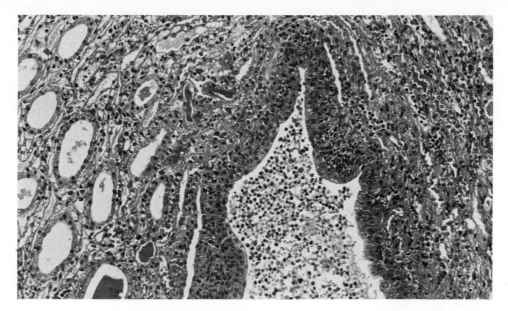

Fig. 104   Pyelonephritis in a moribund female Long-Evans rat, 13 months of age. There is marked acute inflammation in the pelvis and adjacent renal parenchyma. (HE, × 105)

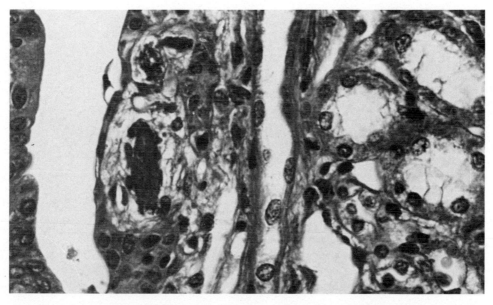

Fig. 105   Renal mineralization (minimal) in a 22-month-old Sprague-Dawley female rat. A small deposit of mineral is present in or just below the urothelium. (HE, × 105)

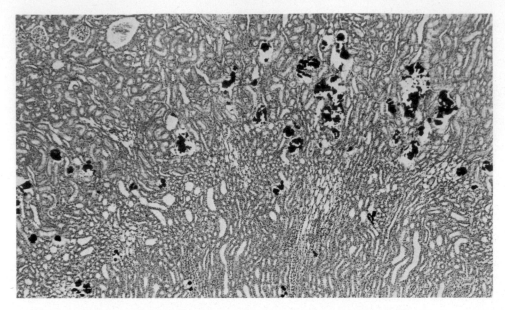

Fig. 106   Renal mineralization (calcification) at the corticomedullary junction in a 4-month-old Sprague-Dawley female rat treated with a carbonic anhydrase inhibitor. These deposits are present in a similar distribution to those sometimes found spontaneously in rats. (HE, × 105)

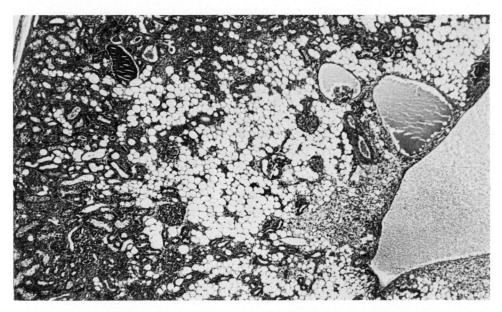

Fig. 107   Lipomatous tumour (angiolipoma) in the kidney of a Long-Evans rat, 25 months of age. An ill-defined pale focus was observed on the cut surface of the kidney at autopsy. The renal parenchyma is partly replaced by a poorly circumscribed mass of mature adipose tissue with an admixture of blood vessels and more immature cells, some of which are lipoblasts. (HE, × 105)

158

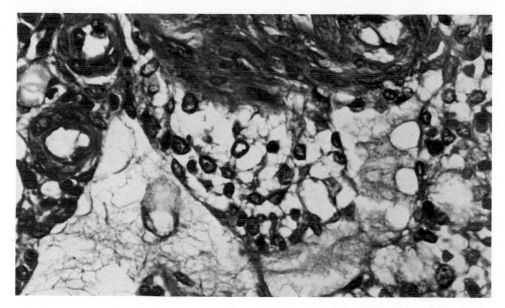

Fig. 108 Lipomatous tumour, same case as in Figure 107. This high power view shows the mixture of mature adipose cells, lipoblasts and thick-walled blood vessels. (HE, × 450)

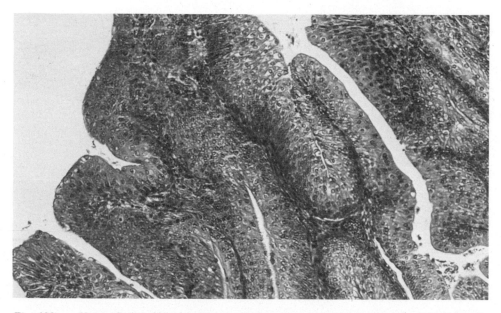

Fig. 109 Hyperplasia of the bladder urothelium in a female Long-Evans rat, 26 months of age. Active inflammation (pyelonephritis) was present elsewhere in the urinary tract. The urothelium is polypoid and thicker than the 2-3 cell layer normally observed. (HE, × 105)

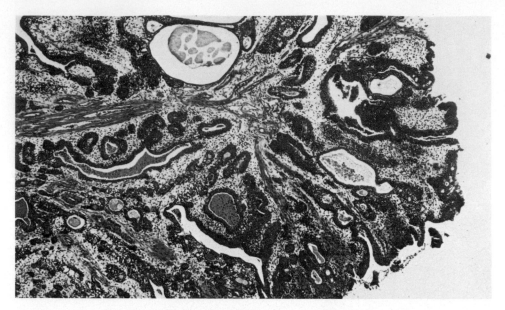

Fig. 110   Papilloma of the bladder which presented as a small, mobile mass filling the bladder in a female Sprague-Dawley rat, 25 months old. It comprises a papillomatous formation of mildly to moderately thickened urothelium and a loose connective tissue stroma which contains smooth muscle and a scattering of chronic inflammatory cells. No tissue invasion was observed. (HE, ×26)

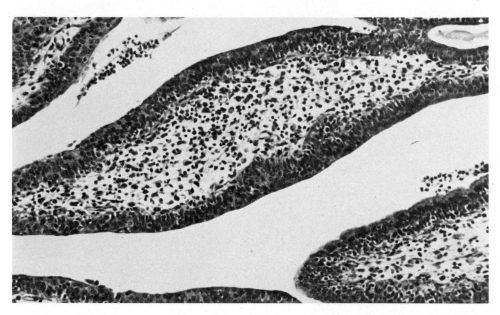

Fig. 111   Papilloma of the bladder. Same case as in Figure 110, showing the slightly thickened urothelium and chronic inflammatory infiltrate predominantly of plasma cells. (HE, ×105)

160

VIII. Male genital tract

INTRODUCTION

The normal structure of the testis has been reviewed by Mostofi and Bresler (1976). The accessory male sex organs comprise the prostate (and coagulating glands), seminal vesicles, bulbourethral glands and preputial glands. The normal structure of the accessory glands has been described in detail by Franks (1967).

PROSTATE GLAND

Non-neoplastic lesions

Inflammation
Acute and chronic inflammation (acute and chronic prostatitis) may be commonly found in the aged rat prostate gland and this is often seen in association with inflammation in the other accessory glands (see below). Concomitant inflammation may also be found in the urinary bladder, the ureter and renal pelvis. There are generally no specific features, but the offending organisms are thought to be pathogens of the urinary tract, and include *E. coli*, *Proteus vulgaris*, Staphylococci and Streptococci (King, 1978). The prostatic glandular epithelium may respond to chronic inflammation by undergoing squamous metaplasia (Fig. 112) (Reznik and Reznik-Schüller, 1980).

Small foci of chronic inflammation (minimal focal chronic inflammation), focal necrosis and fibrosis may be seen in glands of aged rats.

Oedema
Oedema may be observed in the interstitium of the rat prostate gland in association with inflammation as well as in the absence of other pathology. The latter may represent an agonal change.

Atrophy
Atrophy of the prostate glandular epithelium occurs in the aged rats. It is characterized histologically by flattening of the epithelium and dilatation of the alveoli. Large quantities of secretions may be also observed in histological sections (retention of content). Small concretions (corpora amylacea) are also commonly observed in the lumen of the alveoli. Foci of chronic inflammation, fibrosis and accumulation of lipid- and pigment-(iron)laden macrophages may be also seen.

Hyperplasia
Reactive hyperplasia of the prostatic glandular epithelium is observed in severe prostatitis. Foci of thickened and mildly proliferative glandular epithelium are also

observed in the prostate gland of our aged Sprague-Dawley rat population in the absence of inflammation. These foci are very small, and produce no distortion of glandular architecture, either by expansion or compression. Polypoid growth within glands or ducts is not seen and there is no evidence of marked mitotic activity or cytological atypia. These foci, therefore, are considered to be hyperplastic (focal hyperplasia) in nature, although no sharp distinction between hyperplasia and neoplasia exists. These foci are to be distinguished from the infolding of normal prostatic glandular epithelium.

Neoplasia

Carcinoma

In contrast to previous studies, prostatic carcinomas have been recently reported occurring in a significant number of aging rats of certain strains. It occurs in a particularly high percentage of ACI/SegHap BR rats (Ward et al., 1980) but it has also been reported to occur in Fischer 344 rats (Reznik et al., 1981). It usually develops in the ventral lobe only, and this fact may explain the low incidences previously reported. Quite often in routine studies, the prostate is sampled in other anatomical areas or not even routinely examined histologically (Reznik et al., 1981). The prostate gland has been histologically examined routinely at Amboise for a number of years, and although focal hyperplasia of the acinar epithelium is not uncommon, carcinoma is. Although carcinoma may evolve through a stage of atypical hyperplasia (Ward et al., 1981), in our opinion the presence of a few atypical glands is not sufficient evidence for the presence of carcinoma and the usual general criteria for this diagnosis should be used. These include the presence of cellular atypia, irregular glandular architecture, compression and infiltration of surrounding tissues.

Predominantly squamous carcinomas of the rat prostate gland have been induced by nitrosamine (Pour, 1981).

Sarcoma

The usual variety of soft tissue tumours also arises in and around the prostate gland. At Amboise, malignant histiocytomas have been observed in the prostate as well as other types of sarcoma (undifferentiated sarcoma, cystic sarcoma, angiosarcoma).

OTHER ACCESSORY MALE SEX GLANDS

Non-neoplastic lesions

A great variety of minor non-neoplastic changes may be observed in these glands including acute and chronic inflammation, granulomatous inflammation, oedema and necrosis often associated with similar alterations elsewhere in the genito-urinary tract. Abscesses may also be occasionally seen.

Atrophy of the acinar epithelium of preputial glands of the aging male rat is occasionally reported (Reznik and Reznik-Schüller, 1980), as is focal hyperplasia or focal cystic hyperplasia of the preputial glandular epithelium (Reznik and Ward, 1981).

Atrophy of the seminal vesicles commonly occurs in association with diffuse testi-cular atrophy (see below). Similarly, inflammation is seen in the seminal vesicles in association with testicular inflammation.

Tumours of preputial glands

These are infrequently described in the preputial glands of the rat, but they are usually of epithelial origin, arising from acinar or ductal cells. They may be classified as adenomas, adenocarcinomas, squamous cell or basal cell carcinomas. Carcinomas of mixed cell type may also occur (Reznik and Ward, 1981).

TESTIS

Non-neoplastic lesions

Atrophy

Tubular atrophy is a well described and common age-associated change in one or both testes of aging male rats (Burek, 1978). In our experience, it already commences in the first year of life. It needs to be carefully evaluated as the testis is sensitive to drugs which may act either directly on spermatogenesis or produce effects secondari-ly by interfering with the testicular blood supply or the general nutrition of the ani-mal. It is important when evaluating the effects of drugs on the rodent testis for even-tual extrapolation to possible effects in man, to bear in mind that the human testis is comparatively resilient to the adverse effects of drugs. For example, the testes of young men who have received large doses of cytotoxic agents for the treatment of leukaemia or lymphoma have been shown to be fibrotic with loss of spermatogonia and even a 'Sertoli cell only picture', yet with cessation of such treatment, testicular function – as measured by the tubular fertility index (see Appendix) – is eventually restored to normal (Lendon et al., 1978).

Expanding lesions in the testicular parenchyma also produce pressure atrophy (Fig. 115); such atrophy should be considered separately from the types described below.

Focal atrophy   The atrophy associated with ageing, whether enhanced by the ef-fects of drugs or not, usually commences as a focal lesion. The grading of such lesions is related to problems of sampling error (see Appendix) and usually it is advisable to note the presence or absence of the lesion only. It is characterized by a reduction in number or an absence of the various layers of the seminiferous tubule. In compari-son, the unaffected tubules contain spermatogonia adjacent to the basement mem-brane and usually several layers of spermatocytes between them and the spermatids which surround the lumen. It is noteworthy, incidentally, that spermatogenesis is a cyclical phenomenon with an average duration of around 13 days (Clermont and Harvey, 1965).

The initial stages of focal atrophy affect the spermatozoa and spermatids; with advancement of the lesion, only the Sertoli cells remain. Providing the lesion remains localised, as is often the case, it is justified, even in the absence of all germ cells in the affected region, to designate the process as focal atrophy – the term diffuse atrophy being reserved for those cases affecting 50% or more of the seminiferous tubules (see below).

Diffuse atrophy   The line drawn between focal and diffuse atrophy is a matter of definition by the individual pathologist concerned with the assessment – an arbitrary definition would comprise 50% or more of affected tubules.

Usually, the lesion affects the whole of one or both testes, often leaving only Sertoli cells in the tubules – the Sertoli cell-only syndrome (Fig. 113). Frequently, giant cells are associated with the degenerating tubular epithelium, the tubules themselves are shrunken and calcium deposits may be apparent together with thickening of the tunica albuginia of the testis. Interstitial cell hyperplasia and cystic degeneration may be associated with both diffuse and focal atrophy (see below). Arteritis (periarteritis, periarteritis nodosa), as seen in other organs is sometimes observed in testicular vessels (Fig. 61).

Experimental ischaemic damage (ligation of the blood supply) of the rat testis also produces testicular degeneration and atrophy. Initial changes include degeneration of the germinal epithelium and Sertoli cells, exfoliation of cells into the lumen of the tubules and frank tissue necrosis. Eventually, the tubules atrophy and the tubular basement membrane becomes thickened by collagen deposition (fibrosis) (Oettlé and Harrison, 1952). It should be noted, however, that ischaemic damage in one testis may induce damage in the contralateral one, an effect mediated by an immunological mechanism (Harrison et al., 1981). Focal haemorrhagic necrosis of seminiferous tubules has been described following natural parvovirus infection in adult rats (Coleman et al., 1983).

Oedema
Any testicular damage may be accompanied by interstitial oedema. However, true oedema should be distinguished from apparent oedema produced in the central parts of the testis as a result of fixation artefact, particularly marked with formalin.

Dilatation
Care must be taken to distinguish true atrophy of the testis from simple dilatation of the seminiferous tubules.

Cystic degeneration
The accumulation of fluid-filled cystic spaces within one or both testes. This is observed as an age-related change in the rats and is usually associated with focal atrophy.

Spermatogenic granuloma (granulomatous orchitis)
This condition is an occasional, spontaneous finding in the testis or epididymus in rats. It comprises either a focal or more diffuse reaction involving epithelioid cells, inflammatory cells and occasional giant cells. It is thought to be due to the escape of spermatozoa into the interstitial tissue.

Interstitial cell hyperplasia (Leydig cell hyperplasia)
This condition may be seen in apparently otherwise normal testes (Fig. 114), although it is usually associated with testicular atrophy (Burek, 1978). The interstitial cells are pleomorphic and nuclear acidophilic inclusions may be present. Mostofi and Bresler (1976) consider that this condition precedes a true Leydig cell tumour. Differentiation from a Leydig cell tumour may be difficult. The usual criteria for distinguishing between tumours and hyperplasia in endocrine tissue apply; hyperplasia is usually diffuse, there is no compression of surrounding testicular tissue, instead the seminiferous tubules may be included within the area affected.

Congenital abnormality
Gonadal dysgenesis has been described under ovary. The most frequent testicular congenital anomaly is undescended or absent testis.

Neoplasia

Introduction
As a basis for the classification of testicular tumours of the rat, Mostofi and Bresler (1976) described the human testicular tumours in considerable detail. As is usually the case with neoplasms of the ovary, testicular tumours are also classified into those of germ cell origin, those of specialized gonadal (sex cord) stroma, those of the adnexae and covering membranes and metastatic neoplasms.

Interstitial cell tumour (Leydig cell tumour)
These tumours are the most common testicular tumours in the rat (Mostofi and Bresler, 1976). Their incidence increases with age and they can be bilateral. Microscopically, they are usually composed of regular cells with fairly uniform but hyperchromatic, rounded nuclei and eosinophilic cytoplasm reminiscent of the normal Leydig cell (Fig. 115). Vacuolated or spindle cells may also be seen. Using the criteria of cellular anaplasia, increased and abnormal mitotic figures, extension to adjacent structures and invasion of vessels, about 10% are regarded as malignant, although benign looking tumours may also metastatize (Mostofi and Bresler, 1976).
A non-metastatic, but transplantable Leydig cell tumour of Fischer rats which causes hypercalcaemia has been recently described and it is believed that this effect is mediated by a tumoral factor which activates osteoclasts and causes monocytes to differentiate into osteoclasts (Troyer et al., 1982).

Sertoli cell tumour
This tumour has been rarely reported arising in the testes of rats (Mostofi and Bresler, 1976; Abbott, 1983). We have observed these and other sex cord tumours in abnormal gonads (see under Ovary and oviducts in Chapter IX).

Mesothelioma (adenomatoid tumour)
This is, in point of fact, a tumour of the adnexae usually being located in the epididymus, capsule or spermatic cord and considered to be mesothelial in origin (Mostofi and Bresler, 1976). It has been observed in the Sprague-Dawley rats maintained at Amboise. It consists of papillary processes or numerous spaces and clefts covered

165

or lined by cells resembling endo- or mesothelium (Figs 116 and 117). The supporting fibrous stroma may contain smooth muscle cells.

Other tumours

Germ cell tumours have been described in the rat (Mostofi and Bresler, 1976) but are extremely rare. Primitive tumours of probable germ cell origin (yolk sac carcinoma, parietovisceral yolk sac carcinoma) have been produced in inbred rats by transplanting extra-embryonic portions of 8-9 day old egg cylinder or by performing foetectomies of 12-13 day pregnant dams without removal of foetal membranes (Damjanov, 1980). We have not observed an unequivocal germ cell tumour arising in the rat testes.

Occasionally, lymphoma cells or leukaemic cells may infiltrate the testes. True malignant histiocytoma (histiocytic sarcoma) is particularly liable to involve the testis and its coverings (see Skin/Subcutaneous tissue in Chapter I).

Angiomas are occasionally seen within the testicular tissue in our experience, as are soft tissue sarcomas.

REFERENCES

ABBOTT, D.P. (1983): A malignant Sertoli cell tumour in a laboratory rat. *J.Comp.Pathol., 93,* 339-342.

BUREK, J.D. (1978): Age-associated pathology. In: *Pathology of Aging Rats,* Chap. 4, pp. 29-167. CRC Press, West Palm Beach, FL.

CLERMONT, Y. and HARVEY, S.C. (1965): Duration of the cycle of the seminiferous epithelium of normal, hypophysectomized and hypophysectomized-hormone treated albino rats. *Endocrinology, 76,* 80-89.

COLEMAN, G.L., JACOBY, R.O., BHATT, P.N., SMITH, A.L. and JONAS, A.M. (1983): Naturally occurring lethal parvovirus infection of juvenile and young-adult rats. *Vet.Pathol., 20,* 49-56.

DAMJANOV, I. (1980): Animal model: Parietovisceral yolk sac carcinoma in the rat. *Am.J. Pathol., 98,* 569-572.

FRANKS, L.M. (1967): Normal and pathological anatomy and histology of the genital tract of rats and mice. In: E. Cotchin and F.J.C. Roe (Eds), *Pathology of Laboratory Rats and Mice,* Chap. 15, pp. 469-496. Blackwell, Oxford.

HARRISON, R.G., LEWIS-JONES, D.I., MORENO DE MARVAL, M.J. and CONNOLLY, R.C. (1981): Mechanism of damage to the contralateral testis in rats with an ischaemic testis. *Lancet, 2,* 723-725.

KING, N.W. (1978): The reproductive tract. In: F.M. Benirschke and T.C. Jones (Eds), *Pathology of Laboratory Animals, Vol. 1,* Chap. 7, pp. 509-580. Springer-Verlag, New York.

LENDON, M., HANN, I.M., PALMER, M.K., SHALET, S.M. and JONES, P.H. (1978): Testicular histology after combination chemotherapy in childhood for acute lymphoblastic leukaemia. *Lancet, 2,* 439-441.

MOSTOFI, F.K. and BRESLER, V.M. (1976): Tumours of the testis. In: V.S. Turusov (Ed.), *Pathology of Tumours in Laboratory Animals, Vol. 1, Tumours of the Rats, Part 2,* pp. 135-150. IARC Scientific Publ. No. 6, Lyon.

OETTLE, A.G. and HARRISON, R.G. (1952): The histological changes produced in the rat testis by temporary and permanent occlusion of the testicular artery. *J.Pathol.Bacteriol., 64,* 273-297.

POUR, P. (1981): A new prostatic cancer model: Systemic induction of prostatic cancer in rats by a nitrosamine. *Cancer Lett., 13,* 303-308.

REZNIK, G. and REZNIK-SCHÜLLER, H. (1980): Pathology of clitoral and preputial glands in aging F344 rats. *Lab.Anim.Sci., 30*, 845-850.

REZNIK, G. and WARD, J.M. (1981): Morphology of hyperplastic and neoplastic lesions in the clitoral and preputial gland of the F344 rat. *Vet.Pathol., 18*, 228-238.

REZNIK, G., HAMLIN, M.H., WARD, J.M. and STINSON, S.F. (1981): Prostatic hyperplasia and neoplasia in aging F344 rats. *Prostate, 2*, 261-268.

TROYER, H., SOWERS, J.R. and BABACH, E. (1982): Leydig cell tumour induced hypercalcemia in the Fischer rat. Morphimetric and histochemical evidence for a tumoral factor that activates osteoclasts. *Am.J.Pathol., 108*, 284-290.

WARD, J.M., REZNIK, G., STINSON, S.F., LATTUADA, C.P., LONGFELLOW, D.G. and CAMERON, T.P. (1980): Histogenesis and morphology of naturally occurring prostatic carcinoma in the ACl/Seg Hap BR rat. *Lab.Invest., 43*, 517-522.

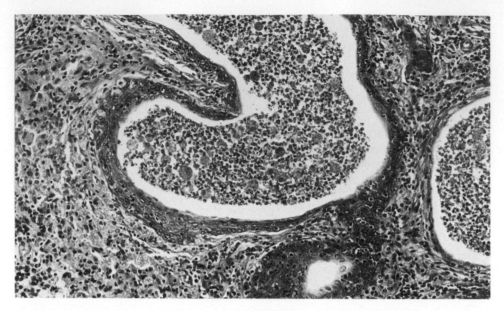

Fig. 112   Prostatitis in a Long-Evans rat, aged 26 months. The glandular lumen contains acute inflammatory cells and cellular debris. Squamous metaplasia of the glandular epithelium is evident and the connective tissue stroma contains many chronic inflammatory cells. (HE, ×105)

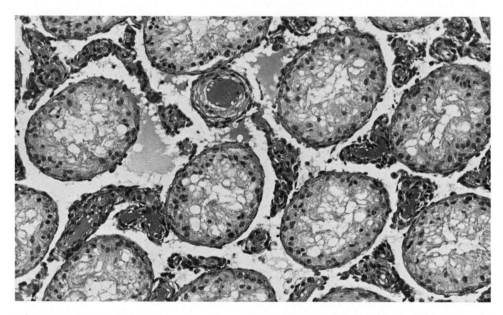

Fig. 113   Testicular atrophy in a 26-month-old Sprague-Dawley male rat. Total loss of spermatogonia, spermatids and spermatocytes has occurred although Sertoli cells remain ('Sertoli-only syndrome'). The interstitial blood vessels show fibromuscular sclerosis. (HE, ×105)

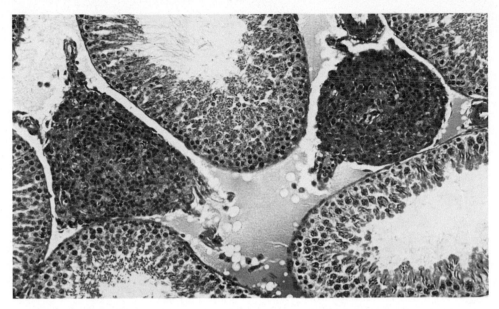

Fig. 114   Interstitial cell hyperplasia found in a macroscopically normal testis of a 26-month-old Long-Evans rat. Aggregation of interstitial (Leydig) cells such as those seen in the figure were present throughout the testis. (HE, × 105)

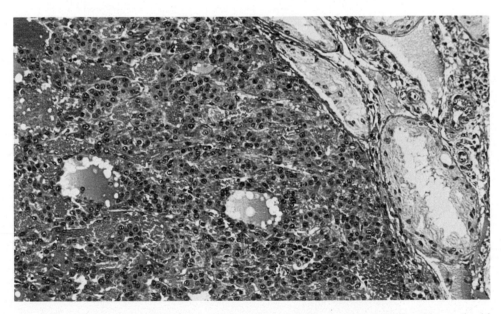

Fig. 115   Interstitial cell (Leydig cell) tumour occurring in the testis of a 26-month-old Sprague-Dawley rat. It is a vascular tumour composed of fairly uniform cells with moderately abundant eosinophilic cytoplasm. No metastatic deposits were found in this case but there is compression atrophy of adjacent seminiferous tubules. (HE, × 105)

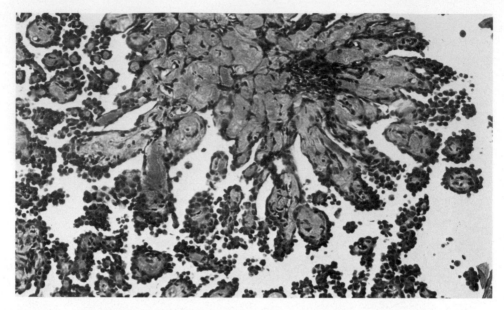

Fig. 116   Mesothelioma found in the right testis of a 25-month-old Sprague-Dawley rat. At autopsy, the testis appeared of normal size but its surface appeared roughened. The tumour is composed of papillary processes covered by cells resembling mesothelium. The stroma is mainly fibrous in nature. (HE, × 105)

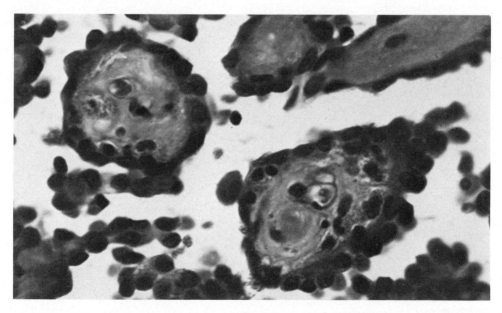

Fig. 117   Mesothelioma, same case as in Figure 116, showing the fibrovascular stalks and overlying mesothelial cells in detail. (HE, × 450)

IX. Female genital tract

INTRODUCTION

There are a number of important phenomena that reflect effects on these organs collectively, the most important of which are the oestrous cycle, pituitary function and aging. Drugs which affect the hypothalamic-pituitary axis will have effects on all three. A knowledge of the changes observed with oestrus and with aging in these tissues, therefore, provides an opportunity of evaluating possible changes in pituitary function due to drugs.

Morphology of the uterus is dependent on ovarian hormonal factors. Cessation or reduction of ovarian hormonal stimulation results in atrophy of both the myometrium and endometrium. By contrast, excessive or prolonged stimulation by endogenous or exogenous ovarian hormones will cause an increase in uterine size, resulting from myometrial hypertrophy and endometrial hyperplasia (King, 1978).

With increasing age, the number of corpora lutea is usually progressively reduced and, in many cases, they will eventually disappear completely from the ovary – the extent of this phenomenon varies between strains (Burek, 1978; Russfield, 1967). In contrast, increased numbers of interstitial cells are apparent and when much of the stroma is replaced by these epithelioid cells, a diagnosis of interstitial cell hyperplasia or granulosa-theca cell tumour is justified (see below). Follicular cysts may also be present. This condition is associated with endometrial cystic hyperplasia, which consequently, in turn, is an age-related change.

A particularly important change that may occur in the aged female rat is cessation of the oestrous cycle. The primary fault appears to be a result of decreased responsiveness of the hypothalamus to stimuli that evoke the release of luteinizing hormone and follicle stimulating hormone, which is probably due to the presence of pituitary tumours in aged female rats (Meites et al., 1978).

Disturbances in hypothalamic-pituitary junction provoked by such agents as neuroleptic and beta-blockers will modify these phenomena. These compounds, which increase prolactin levels in the rat, are associated with disturbances in the oestrous cycle (Horowski and Gräf, 1979): they reduce the weight of the uterus (Janssen, 1968; Tuchmann-Duplessis and Mercier-Parot, 1968), and because prolactin is the major luteotrophic hormone in the rat (Neill and Smith, 1974), they increase the number and size of corpora lutea (Baker and Tucker, 1968; Janssen, 1968).

The profile of such an effect on animals maintained in a life-time study would consequently be a dose-related increase in the percentage of animals at final sacrifice with persistent corpora lutea, with an associated dose-related reduction in uterine weight and endometrial cystic hyperplasia. That is, the spontaneously occurring, age-related changes usually observed are reversed: the reduction in uterine weight is achieved by reversing the fluid retention in the uterus usually observed in aged untreated rats (Berg, 1967), together with endometrial cystic hyperplasia. The value of carefully recording these complex phenomena in a carcinogenicity study is consequently apparent.

It should be noted in this context, however, that not only is prolactin luteotrophic in the rat, probably by regulation of the luteal receptor for LH, but also has a distinct luteolytic effect during the oestrous cycle (Wuttke and Meites, 1971). Prolactin may also have other roles in the maintainance of the corpus luteum and maturation of the ovum (Dunaif et al., 1982).

VAGINA

Non-neoplastic lesions

Cyclical changes
The vaginal mucosa undergoes morphological changes during the oestrous cycle and these have been clearly reviewed by Baba and Von Haam (1976). In di-oestrus, the mucosa is characterized by basal and squamous cells covered by a superficial layer of mucus-secreting columnar cells and a leucocytic infiltration. In pro-oestrus, superficial cells desquamate and the epithelium consists of squamous cells which become keratinized in oestrus. Cells exfoliate and leucocytes appear again in met-oestrus. It may be difficult to distinguish pathological inflammation from cyclical changes (see below).

Inflammation
Frank suppurative change (acute and chronic inflammation) is occasionally seen in the vagina, usually in association with inflammation in the uterine body and cervix.

Imperforate vagina (vagina, dilatation)
An imperforate vagina is occasionally observed in an otherwise normal rat. There is massive cystic dilatation of the vagina which may be mistaken for a congenital cyst at autopsy. Inflammation may also be present.

Fibrosis
Increased deposition of collagen (fibrosis) has been reported to occur in the walls of the rat vagina with increasing age, although special stains for reticulin and collagen fibres may be necessary to demonstrate this change (Wolfe et al., 1942).

Neoplasia

Occasionally, squamous carcinomas have been reported arising from the vaginal mucosa in aged untreated rats (Goodman et al., 1979), and we have observed occasional cases arising in aged Sprague-Dawley rats (Figs 118 and 119). In our experience, mesenchymal tumours also arise from the soft tissues in and around the vagina, although the exact site of origin of large tumours within the female genital tract frequently remains a matter of conjecture. The usual range of sarcomas are observed. Large benign uterine polyps may also project from the uterine cavity into the vagina. Both epithelial and mesenchymal neoplasms can be induced in the rat vagina by application of carcinogens and sex hormones may affect their incidence (Baba and Von Haam, 1976).

CLITORAL GLANDS

These glands are bilateral and located at either side of the clitoris, immediately adjacent to the inguinal parts of the mammary glands. Like the preputial glands in the male rat, they too may show atrophy, fibrosis and suppurative inflammation as well as adenomas, adenocarcinomas, squamous cell and basal cell carcinomas (Reznik and Reznik-Schüller, 1980). These tumours have been well reviewed by Reznik and Ward (1981).

UTERUS
(including uterine horns and cervix)

Non-neoplastic lesions

Inflammation (acute and chronic endometritis, myometritis, pyometria)
Infectious diseases of the uterus do not constitute a major problem in laboratory animal colonies, although they may jeopardize the reproductive capacity of individual animals (King, 1978). Acute or chronic inflammation is found sporadically in the endometrium (endometritis, pyometria), sometimes associated with obstructive or neoplastic lesions of the genital tract. Bacterial infections probably account for the majority of natural uterine infections in laboratory animals (King, 1978). *Mycoplasma pulmonalis* also causes uterine inflammation in the rat (Cassell et al., 1979). Uterine inflammation may be accompanied by vaginal inflammation (see above).

Note:
It is normal to find some leucocytes in the epithelium of the endometrium during the oestrous cycle.

Atrophy
The endometrium and the myometrium may become thinned (atrophy) with advancing age and this is presumably due to reduced oestrogen secretion in the aged rat (Meites et al., 1978).

Cystic change
The endometrium may contain cystically dilated glands (cystic change) or even a large single cystic gland (cyst) in the absence of definite endometrial hyperplasia.

Hypertrophy and hyperplasia
Prolonged, unopposed stimulation of the uterus by oestrogen gives rise to cystic hyperplasia of the endometrium, and, in the rat, cystic endometrial hyperplasia regu-

173

larly accompanies ovarian follicular cysts and granulosa cell tumours (King, 1978). Histologically, the lesion presents a marked glandular proliferation – the superficial glands being more cystic. The supporting stroma is increased. The endometrium and myometrium may contain increased amounts of collagen (fibrosis) and hypertrophy of the myometrium is usually seen.

Dilatation (hydrometra)

During the rodent oestrous cycle, the uterine horns may become dilated because of accumulation of ovulatory intraluminal fluid (uterine ballooning) (Sheldon Bivin et al., 1979). Mucus may be observed and the uterine wall becomes thinned, oedematous and hyperaemic (Baba and Von Haam, 1976).

Chemical compounds administered to female rats may produce apparent dose-related increases in uterine dilatation. Whether such changes are a non-specific disturbance of the oestrous cycle or whether such compounds have direct hormonal effects is sometimes unclear.

Dilatation of the uterus (hydrometra) also occurs spontaneously in aged rats. This is possibly also related to ovarian hormonal factors.

Dysgenesis

Deformed or absent uterus or uterine horns are occasionally detected (see under Ovary and oviducts, below).

Endometrial polyps

Endometrial polyps are common lesions in the uterine horns (Goodman et al., 1979, 1980). They are generally composed of both stromal and glandular elements with often a preponderance of one or other element. Hence, polyps may be predominantly stromal in type (stroma polyp), glandular in type (glandular polyp) or intimate mixtures of both elements.

Many of these polyps are probably not true neoplasms but represent focal areas of hyperplasia, not all areas of the endometrium being equally responsive to hormonal influences.

Neoplasms

Adenoma/adenocarcinoma

Adenomas and adenocarcinomas of the rat uterus are occasionally observed in aged untreated rats. Histologically, they are composed of glandular, or tall columnar epithelium showing a papillary or acinar pattern with little or no stroma. Although they are often localized polypoid growths, nuclear pleomorphism and mitotic activity can be so marked as to warrant a diagnosis of carcinoma (Figs 120 and 121).

A variety of other epithelial neoplasms can be induced in the cervix and uterus of the rat, including squamous tumours (Baba and Von Haam, 1976). However, we have not observed any in our rat populations.

Leiomyomas

Tumours composed of benign looking smooth muscle are occasionally found in the rat female genital tract and may apparently extend into the vagina (see above).

There may be a considerable collagen component to these tumours (Figs 122 and 123).

Sarcomas

Spindle cell sarcomas are seen in the rat genital tract. They may show definite smooth muscle differentiation (leiomyosarcoma) or have an appearance resembling endometrial stroma (stromal sarcoma) (Figs 124 and 125). There is little information about the histological behaviour of smooth muscle tumours in the rat to warrant separating benign and malignant tumours on the basis of mitotic activity alone, as in human practice. The endometrial stromal sarcoma is one of the most frequently observed types of sarcoma induced by locally applied chemical carcinogens (Baba and Von Haam, 1976).

Less well-defined types of sarcoma also arise from mesenchymal tissue of the uterus and cervix. A fairly common varient is an undifferentiated sarcoma with a cystic appearance similar to that occurring in the subcutaneous tissue (cystic sarcoma). MacKenzie and Garner (1973) originally reported this sarcoma occurring in the uterus of one rat.

Fibromas and fibrosarcomas are also occasionally reported (Goodman et al., 1979), although it may be difficult to make a sharp distinction between these and tumours of smooth muscle origin, particularly as leiomyomas and leiomyosarcomas often contain fibrous components.

Haemangiomas and haemangiosarcomas are also rare tumours occurring in the uterus or uterine horns, structurally resembling their counterparts in the other soft tissues (see under Skin/Subcutaneous tissue in Chapter I). Care has to be taken to exclude the very vascular leiomyoma or leiomyosarcoma.

Lipomas have been occasionally observed in the female genital tract in Sprague-Dawley rats at Amboise.

OVARY AND OVIDUCTS

Non-neoplastic lesions

Cysts

Several cystic lesions are observed in and around the ovary. A dilated, but otherwise normal bursa may be mistaken for a true cyst at autopsy (capsule, bursa – dilatation). This would generally appear to vary with the oestrus cycle (cyclic alteration) (see also Uterus, above). Follicular and luteal cysts, and haematomas are occasionally seen, but most ovarian cysts are lined by simple cuboidal, flattened or tubular-type epithelium suggesting origin from ovarian mesothelium ('germinal' epithelium). The term used for these cysts is simple cyst. Similar cysts are seen in the tissues around the ovary and these are described as paraovarian cysts. These probably arise from remnants of the paramesonephric or mesonephric ducts. Simple cysts are commonly observed in untreated mature and aging female rats. It has been suggested that large or cystic follicles tend to develop in rats when oestrous cycles first become irregular with advancing age (Meites et al., 1978).

175

Female genital tract

Atrophy

Structural changes in the aging ovary vary from rat to rat even within the same strain (Carter and Ird, 1976). In a number of cases, simple atrophy of the ovary may be seen without any evidence of interstitial cell hyperplasia. Such ovaries are small and devoid of well-developed cysts and corpora lutea. Simple cysts may be seen but there is considerable stromal fibrosis. However, unlike the corresponding changes in man, some ova may still be visible (Meites et al., 1978). Tubular structures containing Sertoli-like cells are also occasionally observed in aged atrophic ovaries.

Inflammation

Inflammatory disease of the ovary (oophoritis) and oviduct (salpingitis) is uncommon but *Mycoplasma pulmonis* is implicated in some rat colonies as a pathogen causing a high incidence of genital inflammatory disease (Cassell et al., 1979).

Corpus luteum

Normal corpora lutea can appear quite large at autopsy and consequently risk being reported as ovarian nodules. In these cases, the histological diagnosis is simply corpus luteum. It may sometimes be difficult to make the distinction between a large, persistant corpus luteum in an aged female from a luteinized granulosa cell tumour (Carter and Ird, 1976).

Dysgenesis

Occasional adult animals are found in which the gonads show developmental abnormalities. The most common are unilateral gonads (either ovary or testis) and undescended testicles (see under Testis in Chapter VIII). More rarely, distinct ovotestes are observed, in which apparently female rats possess bilateral ovarian tissue and non-functional testicular elements and epididymides (Figs 126 and 127). These rats are prone to develop unusual ovarian/testicular tumours.

Interstitial cell hyperplasia

This is an aging change seen in the interstitial tissue which becomes hyperplastic with much of the stroma comprising epithelioid cells (Russfield, 1967). Normal follicles disappear and the proliferation of germinal epithelium is difficult to distinguish from the early stages of tumour formation – the distinction is made on size, evidence of expansive and invasive growth and the fact that theca-granulosa cell tumours are usually unilateral and may show compression of the surrounding stroma.

Neoplasia

Introduction

A wide variety of different histological types of neoplasm arise in the human ovary and even though they have been widely studied, the tissue from which many ovarian tumours arise is often uncertain and the mode of development is frequently open to dispute (Fox and Langley, 1976). Tumours of the rat ovary have been studied far less than those in man and except for a few well-described types of tumour, it may be impossible to make precise diagnoses. Particularly unusual tumours have been observed in association with dysgenic gonads in our Sprague-Dawley rats. In simple terms, ovarian tumours can be grouped into:

1) Serosal or epithelial tumours
2) Sex cord (specialized gonadal) stromal tumours
3) Germ cell tumours
4) Metastatic tumours or tumours arising from associated connective tissue

Serosal or epithelial tumours

Simple ovarian cysts may contain one or two polypoid excrescences but these cannot be regarded as true neoplasms. Occasionally, cystic lesions are lined by much more proliferative and papillomatous glandular tissue, the glandular cells being cuboidal or columnar. They may occasionally contain mucin. The terms adenoma or cystadenoma are used if cellular pleomorphism is not marked and there is no evidence of tissue invasion. When glandular tumours show more mitotic activity, cellular pleomorphism and infiltration of ovarian stroma and surrounding structures, these are regarded as adenocarcinomas or cystadenocarcinomas (Fig. 128). In cases where differentiation is poor and there are no other distinguishing histological features, the term carcinoma is preferred.

Tumours with similar histological appearances in man are generally thought to arise from ovarian serosal cells (Fox and Langley, 1976).

Sex cord tumours

Theca-granulosa cell tumours   These tumours are usually unilateral and show great variation in histological appearances, ranging from almost pure granulosa-cell lesions to pure theca-cell tumours (Carter and Ird, 1976). Theca elements are principally elongated, fibroblast-like cells showing whorling and accumulation of connective tissue. The granulosa cell tumours are composed of uniform, rounded cells with eosinophilic cytoplasm (Carter and Ird, 1976). They are generally benign in rats.

Sertoli/Leydig cell tumours (androblastoma, arrhenoblastoma) and other sex cord tumours   Very occasionally, less well-described types of sex cord tumours are observed in aged rats, particularly in those that prove to have abnormal (dysgenic) gonads. These tumours show considerable variability even within the same tumour but they are composed in general of cords or ribbons of cells (Fig. 129), sometimes with quite clear tubular or Sertoli-like differentiation (Fig. 130). Hyaline bodies have also been observed in these tubules. Spindle cell differentiation may be seen. In our experience, the few we have seen infiltrate the surrounding tissue and are frankly malignant in appearance. It may not always be possible to make a clear distinction between a tumour of sex cord type and a poorly differentiated teratoma or carcinoma.

Note:

The term androblastoma is used for a neoplasm in the human ovary composed of Sertoli cells, Leydig cells or precursors of, either alone or in combination (Scully, 1968). Formerly employed was the term arrhenoblastoma, but this implies a virilizing tumour and is now not so commonly used (Fox and Langley, 1976).

Germ cell tumours

No mature ovarian teratoma (dermoid) has been observed in Sprague-Dawley rats housed at Amboise. However, the situation is less clear with poorly differentiated tumours, and it may be difficult to decide whether a tumour does contain primitive teratomatous elements or not. However, some neoplasms do appear to contain poorly differentiated or immature teratomatous tissue (malignant teratoma).

Metastatic tumours or tumours arising from associated connective tissue
The usual variety of mesenchymal tumours can be found in and around the ovary: the malignant histiocytoma (histiocytic sarcoma) commonly spreads in the peritoneal cavity to involve the ovary. Metastatic carcinoma is also occasionally observed.

REFERENCES

BABA, N. and VON HAAM, E. (1976): Tumours of the vagina, uterus, placenta and oviduct. In: V.S. Turusov (Ed.), *Pathology of Tumours in Laboratory Animals, Vol. 1, Tumours of the Rat, Part 2*, pp. 161-188. IARC Scientific Publ. No. 6, Lyon.

BAKER, S.B. de C. and TUCKER, M.J. (1968): Changes in the reproductive organs of rats and dogs treated with butyrophenones and related compounds. In: S.B. de C. Baker, J.R. Boissier and W. Koll (Eds), *Toxicity and Side-Effects of Psychotropic Drugs, Vol. 9*, pp. 113-118. ICS No. 145, Excerpta Medica Foundation, Amsterdam.

BERG, B.N. (1967): Longevity studies in rats. II. Pathology of aging rats. In: E. Cotchin and F.J.C. Roe (Eds), *Pathology of Laboratory Rats and Mice*, Chap. 23, pp. 749-785. Blackwell Scientific, Oxford.

BUREK, J.D. (1978): Age-associated pathology. In: *Pathology of Aging Rats*, Chap. 4, pp. 29-167. CRC Press, West Palm Beach, FL.

CARTER, R.L. and IRD, E.A. (1976): Tumours of the ovary. In: V.S. Turusov (Ed.), *Pathology of Tumours in Laboratory Animals, Vol. 1, Tumours of the Rat, Part 2*, pp. 189-200. IARC Scientific Publ. No. 6, Lyon.

CASSELL, G.H., LINDSEY, J.R., BAKER, H.J. and DAVIS, J.K. (1979): Mycoplasmal and rickettsial diseases. In: M.J. Baker, J.R. Lindsey and S.H. Weisbroth (Eds), *The Laboratory Rat, Vol. 1*, Chap. 10, pp. 243-269. Academic Press, New York.

DUNAIF, A.E., ZIMMERMAN, E.A., FRIESEN, H.G. and FRANTZ, A.G. (1982): Intracellular localization of prolactin receptor and prolactin in the rat ovary by immunocytochemistry. *Endocrinology, 110*, 1465-1471.

FOX, H. and LANGLEY, F.A. (1976): The classification and incidence of ovarian tumours. In: *Tumours of the Ovary*, Chap. 3, pp. 19-28. William Heinemann, London.

GOODMAN, D.G., WARD, J.M., SQUIRE, R.A., CHU, K.C. and LINHART, M.S. (1979): Neoplastic and non-neoplastic lesions in aging F344 rats. *Toxicol.Appl. Pharmacol., 48*, 237-248.

GOODMAN, D.G., WARD, J.M., SQUIRE, R.A., PAXTON, M.B., REICHARDT, W.D., CHU, K.C. and LINHART, M.S. (1980): Neoplastic and non-neoplastic lesions in aging Osborne-Mendel rats. *Toxicol.Appl.Pharmacol., 55*, 433-447.

HOROWSKI, R. and GRÄF, K.J. (1979): Neuroendocrine effects of neuropsychotropic drugs and their possible influence on toxic reactions in animals and man. The role of the dopamine-prolactin system. In: Mechanisms of Toxic Action on some Target Organs. *Arch.Toxicol., Suppl. 2*, 93-104.

JANSSEN, P.A. (1968): Toxicology and metabolism of butyrophenones. In: S.B. de C. Baker, J.R. Boissier and W. Koll (Eds), *Toxicity and Side-Effects of Psychotropic Drugs, Vol. 9*, pp. 107-112. ICS No. 145, Excerpta Medica Foundation, Amsterdam.

KING, N.W. (1978): The reproductive tract. In: F.M. Benirschke, F.M. Garner and T.C. Jones (Eds), *Pathology of Laboratory Animals, Vol. 1*, Chap. 7, pp. 509-580. Springer-Verlag, New York.

MacKENZIE, W.F. and GARNER, F.M. (1973): Comparison of neoplasms in six sources of rats. *J.Natl Cancer Inst., 50*, 1243-1257.

MEITES, J., HUANG, H.H. and SIMPKINS, J.W. (1978): Recent studies on neuroendocrine control of reproductive senescence in rats. In: E.L. Schneider (Ed.), *The Aging Reproductive System (Aging, Vol. 4)*. Raven Press, New York.

NEILL, S.H. and SMITH, M.S. (1974): Pituitary-ovarian inter-relationships in the rat. In: V.H.T. James and L. Martini (Eds), *Current Topics in Experimental Endocrinology, Vol. 2*, p. 73. Academic Press, New York.

REZNIK, G. and REZNIK-SCHÜLLER, H. (1980): Pathology of clitoral and preputial glands in aging F344 rats. *Lab.Anim.Sci., 30*, 845-850.

REZNIK, G. and WARD, J.M. (1981): Morphology of hyperplastic and neoplastic lesions in the clitoral and preputial gland of the F344 rat. *Vet.Pathol., 18*, 228-238.

RUSSFIELD, A.B. (1967): Pathology of the endocrine glands, ovary and testis of rats and mice. In: E. Cotchin and F.J.C. Roe (Eds), *Pathology of Laboratory Rats and Mice*, Chap. 14, pp. 391-466. Blackwell Scientific, Oxford.

SCULLY, R.E. (1968): Sex cord-mesenchyme tumours. In: F. Gentil and A.C. Junqueira (Eds), *Ovarian Cancer. UICC Monograph Series, Vol. 2*, pp. 40-57. Springer-Verlag, Berlin.

SHELDON BIVIN, W., CRAWFORD, M.P. and BREWER, N.R. (1979): Morphophysiology. In: H.J. Baker, J.R. Lindsey and S.H. Weisbroth (Eds), *The Laboratory Rat, Vol. 1*, Chap. 4, pp. 73-103. Academic Press, New York.

TUCHMANN-DUPLESSIS, H. and MERCIER-PAROT, L. (1968): Endocrine effects of some neurotropic drugs. In: S.B. de C. Baker, J.R. Boissier and W. Koll (Eds), *Toxicity and Side-Effects of Psychotropic Drugs, Vol. 9*, pp. 128-133. ICS No. 145, Excerpta Medica Foundation, Amsterdam.

WOLFE, J.M., BURAK, E., LENSING, W. and WRIGHT, A.W. (1942): The effects of advancing age on the connective tissue of the uterus, cervix and vagina of the rat. *Am.J.Anat., 70*, 135-165.

WUTTKE, W. and MEITES, J. (1971): Luteolytic role of prolactin during the oestrous cycle of the rat. *Proc.Soc.Exp.Biol.Med., 137*, 988-991.

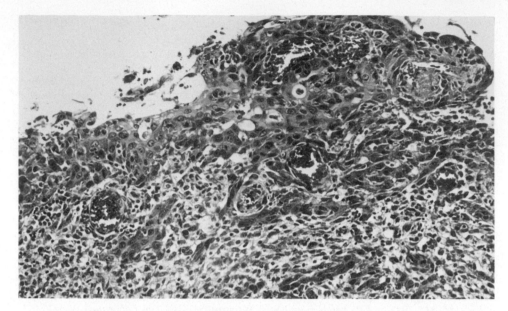

Fig. 118 Squamous carcinoma of the vagina in a female Sprague-Dawley rat found dead at the age of 24 months. A firm, red mass 1.5 cm diameter found in the vagina proved to be a poorly differentiated, inflamed squamous carcinoma, widely infiltrating surrounding tissues. This view shows the superficial part of the neoplasm. (HE, ×105)

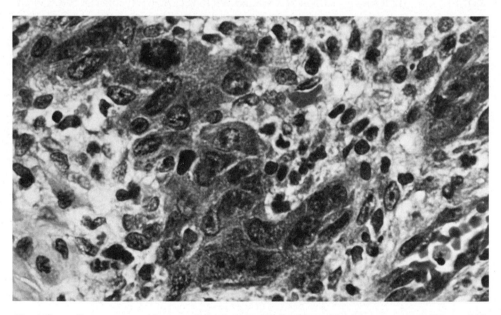

Fig. 119 Squamous carcinoma of the vagina. High power view, same case as in Figure 118. The cells are poorly differentiated, and an abnormal mitosis is present. (HE, ×450)

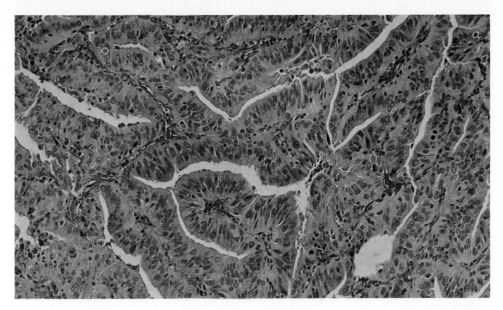

Fig. 120 Papillary endometrial carcinoma in a 25-month-old Sprague-Dawley rat. A mass in the left uterine horn proved to be this well-differentiated papillary carcinoma showing moderate cellular pleomorphism and mitotic activity. (HE, × 105)

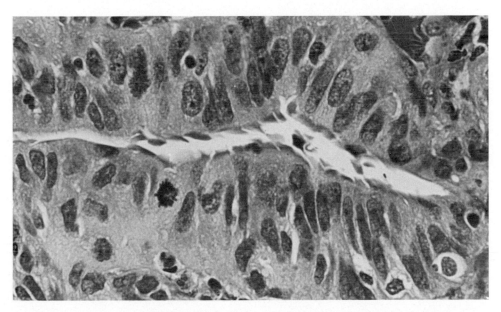

Fig. 121 Papillary endometrial carcinoma, same case as in Figure 120. This high power view shows the nuclear pleomorphism and mitotic activity. (HE, × 450)

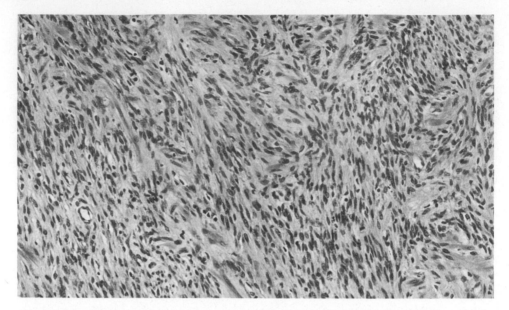

Fig. 122   Leiomyoma of the uterus which presented as a prolapsed mass in the vagina, 1.5 cm in diameter, in a 23-month-old Sprague-Dawley rat. The tumour is composed of fairly uniform spindle cells showing smooth muscle differentiation. Mitotic activity was low in this example. (HE, × 105)

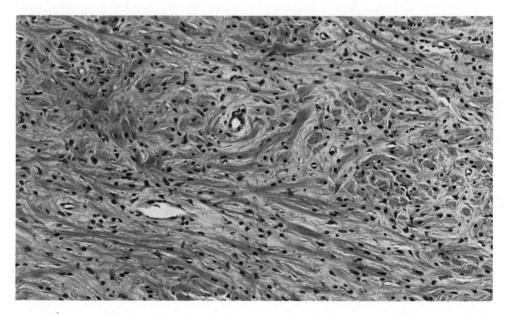

Fig. 123   A leiomyoma found as a large uterine mass in a 26-month-old female Long-Evans rat. This tumour is particularly well differentiated with large smooth muscle cells surrounded by collagen stroma. (HE, × 105)

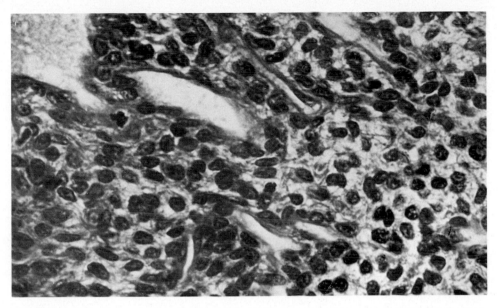

Fig. 124 Stromal sarcoma of the uterus in a Sprague Dawley rat, aged 12 months. This tumour widely infiltrated the uterus and in many areas resembled endometrial stroma. This view is taken from an area of round-cell differentiation resembling endometrial stroma (stromal sarcoma). (HE, × 450)

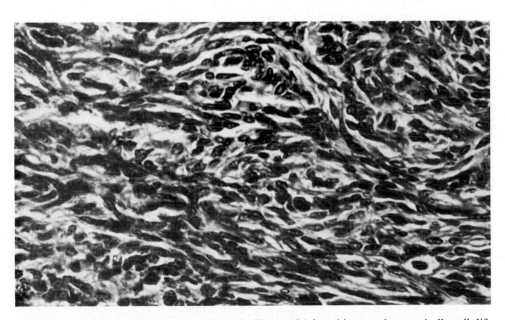

Fig. 125 Stromal sarcoma, same case as in Figure 124, but this area shows spindle-cell differentiation. (HE, × 450)

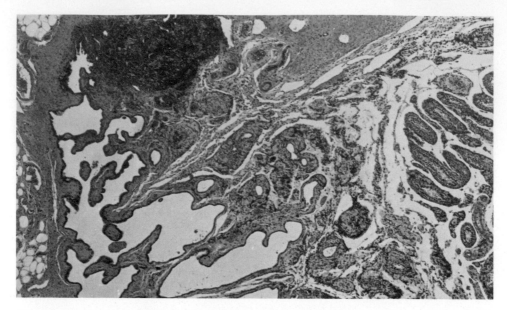

Fig. 126   Ovarian dysgenesis in an apparently normal female Sprague-Dawley rat, 25 months old. Both uterine horns were present but atrophic. This is the section of the left gonad showing both ovarian stroma (upper left) and atrophic seminiferous tubules (right). The left ovary contained a neoplasm (Fig. 129). (HE, × 26)

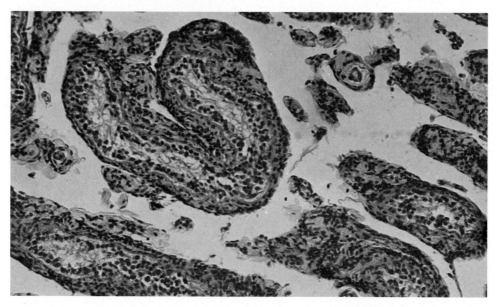

Fig. 127   Ovarian dysgenesis. Higher power view of atrophic testicular tissue seen in Figure 126. (HE, × 105)

184

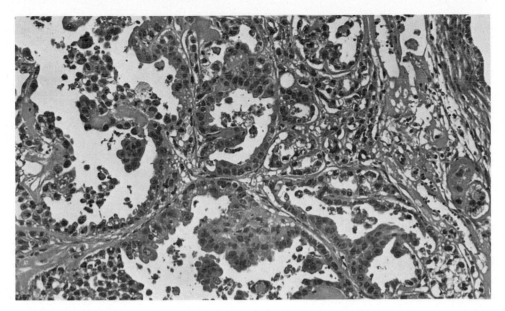

Fig. 128 Ovarian carcinoma. This papillary adenocarcinomatous appearance was found in a cystic mass 6 cm diameter replacing the right ovary in a 20-month-old Sprague-Dawley rat. (HE, × 105)

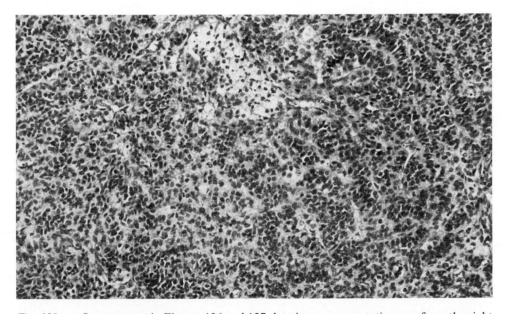

Fig. 129 Same case as in Figures 126 and 127 showing a representative area from the right gonad which measured 2.0 cm diameter. This is an infiltrative neoplasm composed of cords and ribbons of hyperchromatic cells, features highly suggestive of a malignant sex cord tumour. (HE, × 105)

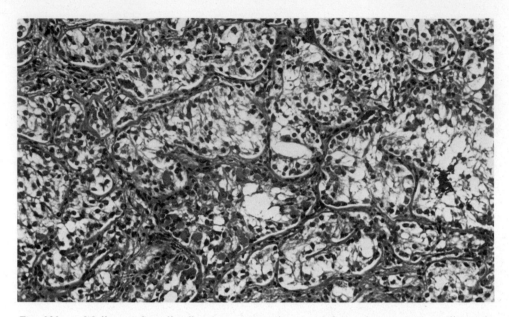

Fig. 130　　Malignant Sertoli cell tumour presenting as a left ovarian mass, 4 cm diameter, in a 25-month-old Sprague-Dawley rat. It is composed of cords of Sertoli-like cells in a sparse fibrous stroma. Local tissue invasion was seen but there were no distant metastases. (HE, × 105)

X. Endocrine glands

PITUITARY GLAND

Introduction

The pituitary gland is a rounded organ composed of the adenohypophysis which develops from the hypophyseal recess (Rathke's pouch) and the neurohypophysis, arising from neuroectoderm as a downgrowth of the floor of the mid-brain.

The adenohypophysis comprises the anterior lobe (pars distalis), intermediate lobe (pars intermedia) and the pars infundibularis (pars tuberalis). Classically, the anterior lobe contains acidophil, basophil and chromophobe cells as observed in haematoxylin and eosin sections. Various special dye techniques have been used to delineate the various cellular subtypes secreting pituitary hormones, but to a certain extent these classical stains must be considered obsolete because they have been superseded by more specific immunohistochemical methods (Furth et al., 1976). Ultrastructural examination also remains a valid method for distinguishing various cell types (Majeed et al., 1980; Yoshimura and Nogami, 1981).

The intermediate lobe which probably secretes melanocyte stimulating hormone is well developed in the rat and is composed of densely packed, pale eosinophilic polygonal cells which, on ultrastructural examination, contain numerous secretory granules (Rhodin, 1974).

The neurohypophysis, composed of the infundibulum (stalk) and posterior lobe (pars nervosa) contains numerous nerve fibres, the cell bodies of which are located in the hypothalamus, capillaries, connective tissue stroma and pituicytes (a form of glial cell).

Non-neoplastic lesions

A variety of atrophic changes may be seen in the pituitary gland from aged mammals, including hyaline degeneration of the stroma, sclerosis of the reticular elements and calcium deposition (Anderson and Capen, 1978). Simple atrophy in the absence of other features is also occasionally seen in the aged, untreated rat. Lipofuscin and other pigments (grouped as pigmentation) may also accumulate in the adenohypophysis and the neurohypophysis. A highly vascular organ such as the pituitary may develop circulatory changes such as congestion, cystic change, haemorrhage, necrosis and infarction. In the rat, these lesions are not common, except as secondary changes in vascular tumours.

Fibrosis
Focal fibrosis is sometimes present in non-tumorous glands. The additional presence of iron pigment suggests previous focal haemorrhage or necrosis in some cases. However, in old age, there is normally a marked increase in connective tissue in the rat pituitary (Russfield, 1967).

Cysts

Simple cysts are occasionally seen in the pituitary gland, thought to be remnants of the hypophyseal cleft (Rathke's pouch). They are usually lined by ciliated columnar epithelium and may be distended with mucoid substances or even cholesterol crystals (cholesterol deposition) (Fig. 131).

Hyperplasia, focal

Ill-defined foci of cellular alteration or proliferation are grouped together as focal hyperplasia. These foci show no nodularity, no compression of surrounding normal gland or undue mitotic activity to warrant the diagnosis of adenoma. A helpful histological feature is the presence of normal pituitary cells within the hyperplastic foci. The anterior or intermediate lobes can be affected. Similar cellular changes have been described in relation to hormonal and dietary modifications, stress, light and temperature (Russfield, 1967). Some of these changes may precede true adenomas.

Note:

The neurohypophysis is far less commonly considered in toxicity and carcinogenicity studies than is the adenohypophysis. Recent study in the rat has, however, shown that the neurohypophysis does undergo structural changes with increasing age. These changes include a depletion of hormone-containing vesicles from axon terminals and Herring bodies, an increase in connective tissue around nerve terminals, axons and capillaries and lipid accumulation in the pituicytes (Lechardt and Hervonen, 1982). The neurohypophysis is also compressed by expanding adenomas of the adenohypophysis.

Pituitary tumours

Spontaneous tumours in the pituitary gland are very common in the rat and may be the main factor limiting life-span, death being preceded by lethargy, anorexia and neurological abnormalities (Squire et al., 1978). Pituitary tumours are generally described as chromophobe adenomas, but modern immunocytochemical and ultrastructural studies have shown that most of these tumours are prolactin-containing cells (acidophils) (Berkvens et al., 1980; Kovacs et al., 1977). They are probably functional tumours and appear to be chromophobic either because they produce very little hormone or because they rapidly discharge the hormones they produce as a result of hyperstimulation or neoplastic transformation (Furth et al., 1976). Recent study of Wistar-Furth rats has shown that many rats with larger pituitary adenomas do have high levels of circulating prolactin and that the increases observed are related to the size of the tumour (Trouillas et al., 1982). However, tumours composed of cells containing other hormones have been described (Berkvens et al., 1980) and it does appear that more than one hormone can be present in any single tumour-cell type (McComb et al., 1981).

Adenoma

An adenoma is defined as cellular proliferation of pituitary cells (anterior or intermediate lobe) which may be small, but showing definite compression or displacement of surrounding normal tissue (Figs 132 and 133). Such lesions are usually without capsules and there may be two or three adenomas in the same gland. Although adenomas can show considerable cellular pleomorphism and nuclear atypia, only lesions showing frank infiltration of surrounding structures are described as carcinomas (see below). Most adenomas are extremely vascular, containing numerous blood-filled spaces (Fig. 134). They also may appear cystic; smaller adenomas tend to be solid in nature. Tumours do appear to occasionally develop from the intermediate lobe. In our laboratory, a considerable proportion of these adenomas contain immunereactive prolactin.

Carcinoma

Any glandular pituitary tumour showing frank infiltration of the surrounding tissue (brain) is regarded as malignant (carcinoma). However, these lesions are not sharply separable from non-invasive adenomas; they are merely more aggressive members of the same species (Willis, 1960). Such invasive tumours are rare (Magnusson et al., 1979). Occasionally, malignant craniopharyngiomas composed of squamous epithelium are observed (Fitzgerald et al., 1971).

Note:

The pituitary gland is also a site for metastatic tumour deposits and it may also be infiltrated by tumours arising from nearby structures (e.g. meninges, brain). This is however rare (Furth et al., 1976).

ADRENAL GLAND

The aged rat adrenal cortex is the site of a variety of focal cellular changes and these foci may be nodular in character (Burek, 1978). Such lesions in the rodent have not been well characterized and the literature concerning hyperplastic nodules and adenomas is particularly confusing (Anderson and Capen, 1978). Indeed, because of these difficulties, some workers describe any circumscribed group of apparently proliferating cells which compress the surrounding tissue as adenomas (Hollander and Snell, 1976). However, these changes in the rat are not only associated with increasing age but also with the chronic adrenocortical stimulation associated with repeated breeding (Wexler, 1964). There also appears to be a definite correlation between arteriopathy and adrenal nodularity both in man and in rat (Wexler, 1964; Dobbie, 1969). On this basis, most adrenal nodules are, therefore, probably not true neoplasms but are best regarded as a variation of adrenal structure occurring as part of the ageing process and/or in response to adrenal vascular changes (Neville, 1978).

Non-neoplastic adrenal changes – cortex

Accessory cortical nodule (rest)

This is a portion of normal cortex either detached from the main gland or attached to the gland but separated from it by a complete fibrous capsule. It must be distinguished from an extruded hyperplastic nodule of abnormal cortex not completely surrounded by a capsule (Dobbie, 1969).

Focal cortical lesions (cytoplasmic alterations)

The following terms are used to describe focal cortical lesions not thought to be neoplastic:

Clear cell foci are small aggregates of cortical cells with pale cytoplasm commonly seen in the zona glomerulosa of aged rats (Figs 135 and 136). Eosinophilic and basophilic foci consist of groups or collections of cortical cells showing eosinophilic (Fig. 136) or basophilic cytoplasm usually located in the zona fasciculata. Basophilic foci are infrequently observed (Burek, 1978). Some foci of altered cells are finely or grossly vacuolated (focal fatty change) (Fig. 137). Some of these foci may show mixed appearances (mixed cell focus).

Careful clinicopathological study of those focal lesions in the adrenal glands of two strains of aged rats housed at Amboise has shown little biological difference between any of these different cytological types. The only exceptions were the clear cell foci located in the zona glomerulosa. These foci were strikingly more common in Sprague-Dawley male rats when compared with Sprague-Dawley females and Long-Evans rats of both sexes (Greaves and Rabemampianina, 1982) and this does imply some functional difference.

The term focal hyperplasia, therefore, is reserved for focal nodular lesions in the adrenal cortex not regarded as true neoplasms.

Diffuse fatty change

Rats may show diffuse cytoplasmic vacuolation of the adrenal cortical cells and this is thought to be a functional or age-related change (Russfield, 1967; Liebegott, 1958; Anderson and Capen, 1978). At Amboise it is also seen in young rats, particularly males.

Diffuse hyperplasia (lipid depletion)

Lipid depletion of the adrenal cortex occurs under various conditions, in animals subjected to stress (particularly natural disease), following treatment with ACTH and certain drugs, and in rats bearing functional hormone-producing tumours (Hollander and Snell, 1976). The cells of the cortex (zona fasciculata) are depleted of lipid and show a dense eosinophilic cytoplasm in haematoxylin and eosin stained sections. These changes may be associated with increased adrenal weight (see review by Sloper, 1978).

Cortical atrophy

Cortical atrophy is characteristically disuse atrophy, usually related to administration of adrenocortical steroids or the presence of an adrenocortical steroid producing neoplasm. There is a reduction in the thickness of the cortex, and the cortical fibrous capsule is characteristically thickened (Figs 138 and 139). There may be associated brown atrophy.

Brown atrophy (pigmentation, brown degeneration, ceroid deposition, haemosiderin)

This is a common feature of the mouse adrenal gland, although it has been described in a few other species (Dunn, 1970). There is a deposition of ceroid pigment within the cells of the cortex or medulla. In the rat, it may be associated with severe hormone-induced atrophy or as a result of compression of the adrenal gland by a space-occupying lesion, such as a pheochromocytoma. It is suggested that brown atrophy is a sign of degeneration, characteristic of lipid-producing cells (Russfield, 1967). Small amounts of pigment in the deep cortex, however, may stain positively for iron in the aged rat.

Cystic degeneration of the cortex (cystic change, peliosis of the adrenal cortex)

This distinctive abnormality may be found in the cortex of old rats (Burek, 1978) and has been reported particularly in female breeder rats (Wexler, 1964). Its morphological similarity to peliosis hepatis has been noted (Dhom et al., 1981), which explains the use of the term adrenal peliosis. Electron microscopic data suggest that the primary lesion occurs in the capillary system, possibly as a consequence of continual oestrogenic stimulation (Dhom et al., 1981). The cells of the cortex show considerable cystic change, congestion with blood, haemorrhage, thrombosis and inflammation (Fig. 140). Foci of iron deposition may also be present. The histological appearances of early or minimal cystic degeneration are difficult to distinguish from the simple congestion of the adrenal cortex that may arise as an agonal phenomenon. Therefore, minimal cystic change can be included under the term congestion of the adrenal gland.

Inflammation

Acute focal inflammation (acute adrenalitis) is occasionally seen as a non-specific accompaniment to severe generalized inflammatory disease, such as pneumonia. It may also be the result of specific infective agents localized in the gland (Anderson and Capen, 1978).

Haemorrhage and congestion

Haemorrhage and congestion of the adrenal gland may accompany cystic degeneration of the adrenal cortex, inflammation or necrosis (see above). However, in view of the great vascularity of the gland and the delicacy of its connective tissue stroma, it is particularly prone to vascular changes and foci of haemorrhage and congestion are often incidental findings in rats.

Necrosis

Foci of necrosis may also be seen in the adrenal gland associated with diverse conditions such as haemorrhage, inflammation and cystic degeneration. Some chemical agents have a direct action on the adrenal cortical cells and may cause focal or diffuse necrosis (Sloper, 1978; Ciocca et al., 1982).

Extramedullary haemopoiesis

Foci of haemopoietic tissue are seen occasionally in the rat adrenal gland (see Haemopoietic and Lymphatic Systems, Chapter II). They need to be distinguished from true inflammation.

Adrenal medulla: non-neoplastic changes

Focal hyperplasia

Small, ill-defined foci of cells showing slightly larger, pleomorphic nuclei and basophilic cytoplasm are observed in the rat adrenal medulla. These foci show no evidence of compression of surrounding tissue. In view of the difficulty in distinguishing these foci from true pheochromocytomas, some authors regard them as micropheochromocytomas (Hollander and Snell, 1976). However, in the routine situation, there seems no good reason for grouping small aggregates of basophilic cells together with expansile and potentially malignant tumours (see below). These foci are preferably designated as focal hyperplasia.

Neoplasia

Cortical tumours

Many of the cortical tumours have a well-differentiated structure, closely resembling that of the adrenal cortex but they show *clear* evidence of compression of surrounding normal tissue and unequivocal cytological features of cellular proliferation. When such tumours are well circumscribed and devoid of metastases, no objection can be raised to calling them adenomas. Tumours of similar structure may metastatize and distinction between benign and malignant growths is, therefore, arbitrary (Willis, 1960) (Figs 141, 142 and 143). In view of these difficulties, adrenal cortical tumours are divided into adenomas and carcinomas simply on the basis of absence or presence of metastases or unequivocal local invasion. They are probably best regarded nonetheless as one biological entity.

Medullary tumours

Some of the commonest tumours described in the rat adrenal gland are pheochromocytomas (Hollander and Snell, 1976). At Amboise, they occur more commonly among Long-Evans than Sprague-Dawley rats (Greaves and Rabemampianina, 1982). These are generally composed of fairly uniform cells with hyperchromatic nuclei and more densely staining basophilic cytoplasm than normal medullary cells and they may be arranged in sheets, alveoli or cords (Glaister et al., 1977). They displace surrounding structures, may invade blood vessels and may occasionally produce distant metastases (Fig. 144). Their incidence, aetiology, morphology and functional activity have been recently reviewed by Cheng (1980).

Ganglioneuromas may be found occasionally in the adrenal gland (MacKenzie and Garner, 1973) and are often associated with pheochromocytomas (Reznik et al., 1980). These neoplasms are composed of various mixtures of mature ganglion cells, immature or primitive cells and supporting cells of spindle cell type (Figs 145, 146 and 147). The primitive cells are thought to be neoplastic pheochromocytes, whereas the spindle cell stroma includes Schwann cells and capsular or satellite cells (Reznik et al., 1980).

THYROID GLAND

Non-neoplastic conditions

Inflammation

Focal active (acute inflammation) is only occasionally observed in the rat thyroid gland, usually in association with cysts or isolated degenerate thyroid follicles. Very occasionally, foci of chronic inflammatory cells are observed (focal chronic inflammation).

More severe inflammation of the thyroid gland is in our experience very rare, although frank chronic (lymphocytic) thyroiditis (diffuse chronic inflammation) has been reported in certain strains of rat (Penhale et al., 1973). It has been described more recently in Wistar rats after treatment with an immunosuppressive compound (Kitchen et al., 1979). It was postulated that immune depression, particularly depletion of suppressor T-lymphocytes, could lead to autoimmune thyroid damage, mediated at least in part by an anti-thyroglobulin antibody.

Histologically, chronic thyroiditis is characterized by infiltrates of lymphocytes, plasma cells and macrophages and disruption, degeneration or hyperplasia of follicular epithelial cells (Kitchen et al., 1979).

Cysts (cystic change)

Cysts lined by stratified squamous epithelium are very occasionally found in the thyroid gland of rats. These are embryological rests arising from the ultimobranchial body. The occasional islands of squamous epithelium also found in the rat thyroid probably also have a similar origin.

The size of follicles varies considerably and quite large follicles up to 300 microns in diameter may be observed in mature rats. It is inappropriate to designate single large follicles of this type as cysts, colloid cysts when they do occur, which is rare, are large and are usually in close proximity to the capsule (Napalkov, 1976).

Pigmentation

Iron pigment is occasionally seen in the thyroid gland but usually located in large dilated follicles containing cellular debris (Ward and Reznik-Schüller, 1980).

Neoplasia

In the thyroid, as in many other organs, no sharp separation of epithelial hyperplasia, benign tumours and malignant tumours is possible (Willis, 1960). In man, the behaviour of these neoplasms is fairly well known, and the experienced pathologist can usually assign them to a well-defined group. However, in the rat, biological behaviour of thyroid neoplasms is not well known and distinction between hyperplasia, adenoma and carcinoma is somewhat arbitrary. Thus, although the distinction is made according to criteria used in human pathology, uncertainties remain. For instance, a true neoplasm with a papillary structure in the human thyroid is known to behave in a malignant manner and thus such a tumour is always described as a papillary carcinoma. A papillary tumour in the rat thyroid is often, however, designated as a benign adenoma (Napalkov, 1976). Information is not available to say whether this diagnosis in the rat is appropriate, or whether such a tumour behaves as its human counterpart and should be regarded as a carcinoma.

Follicular (nodular) hyperplasia, and follicular adenoma of the thyroid

It is usual to distinguish a true adenoma from the adenoma-like nodules which are found in human nodular goitres (Gowing, 1970). As Warren and Meissner (1953)

suggest, the following criteria are regarded as indicative of a true adenoma:
   a) A solitary nodule
   b) Good encapsulation
   c) Uniform structure
   d) A different microscopic appearance from the adjacent gland
   e) Compression of the surrounding thyroid by the expansive growth of the tumour.
Nodules not showing the above features are grouped as hyperplasia (nodular).

Follicular and papillary carcinoma

Follicular carcinoma is characterized microscopically by the formation of acinar structures with a varying colloid content and absence of a papillary architecture (Figs 148 and 149). Tumours are still classed as follicular if solid (trabecular) and Hürthle-cell features are present in addition to the neoplastic acini (Gowing, 1970). Necrosis and haemorrhage may be marked secondary features. A true capsule may be present but unlike adenomas, carcinomas show invasion of surrounding connective tissue and local structures (Fig. 148).

Papillary carcinomas show predominantly papillary differentiation.

C-cell hyperplasia and neoplasia

Introduction   In contrast to man, hyperplasia and neoplasia of the parafollicular, calcitonin-producing C cells is common in the rat. There are important strain differences, hyperplasia and neoplasia of these cells being frequent in Long-Evans rats (DeLellis et al., 1979). Considering the importance of calcitonin in the regulation of calcium metabolism, this may be a reflection of the higher incidence of glomerulo-nephrosis in this strain.

The parafollicular cells are easily discernable as 'light-cells' (Pearse, 1966). They can be selectively stained by acid toluidine blue and silver stains, but they can only conclusively be shown to be calcitonin-producing cells with immunofluorescent or immunoperoxidase techniques. They are readily identifiable by electron microscopy when they are seen within the follicular basement membrane but distinct from follicular cells; they are distinguished by their secretory granules which are smaller than those of the follicular cell.

C-cell hyperplasia   C-cell hyperplasia is characterized by an increase in number and size of parafollicular light-cells, either focally (focal hyperplasia) (Fig. 150) or diffusely (diffuse hyperplasia). As in man, hyperplasia is not only observed as a separate condition from neoplasia (Hodsman et al., 1976) but also in thyroid tissue adjacent to medullary carcinomas. The evolution of C-cell hyperplasia in the rat has been well described by DeLellis and his colleagues (1979). These workers also defined a group of more nodular forms of hyperplasia (focal hyperplasia, nodular hyperplasia) which show little or no nuclear or cellular pleomorphism and do not penetrate basement membrane, although these foci do compress adjacent thyroid follicles. Like these workers, we also prefer to regard these somewhat more nodular forms as focal hyperplasia (Fig. 150), reserving the term medullary carcinoma for infiltrative lesions (see below).

C-cell hyperplasia is associated with increased serum concentrations of calcitonin in the rat (DeLellis et al., 1979).

Medullary carcinoma   A diagnosis of medullary carcinoma is made when a proliferating mass composed of C cells exhibits evidence of stromal or vascular invasion (DeLellis et al., 1979). Microscopically, these tumours can closely resemble normal C cells possessing a rounded or polygonal outline. Nuclei are usually rounded, although nuclear pleomorphism may be quite marked. Some tumour cells are much more fusiform (Fig. 151). Fibrous septa may be prominent and occasionally amyloid is demonstrable in the tumour stroma. Medullary carcinomas can be multicentric. We have not observed distant metastases in our rat populations. Electron microscopic examination reveals characteristic intracytoplasmic granules (Fig. 152).

PARATHYROID GLAND

Fibrosis

Interstitial fibrosis is occasionally seen in the rat parathyroid gland, usually confined to one gland (Burek, 1978). Its significance is unknown.

Focal hyperplasia, adenoma

Grouped under the heading focal hyperplasia are those parathyroid glands containing small foci of cells showing tinctorial cytoplasmic alterations (Fig. 153). Such foci may be multiple and have a nodular appearance. Criteria fundamental to the diagnosis of parathyroid hyperplasia in man are loss of fat and enlargement of all four glands and, for adenoma, the enlargement of one gland with reduction in size or maintainance of normal size of the other three glands (Faccini, 1969). Lack of adipose tissue in the normal rat parathyroid gland, and the fact that not all glands are examined histologically routinely, enables assessment of hyperplasia and its distinction from true adenomas difficult in this species.

Parathyroid hyperplasia is described as a frequent occurrence in the rat, secondary to severe renal disease (MacKenzie and Garner, 1973). The high incidence of severe renal disease in the OFA rats at Lyon is associated with a high incidence of both parathyroid hyperplasia and secondary hyperparathyroidism affecting the skeleton (see Bone in Chapter III). Other authors consider, however, that parathyroid hyperplasia and C-cell lesions represent interrelated abnormalities which are under separate genetic control but which are frequently linked (DeLellis et al., 1979).

Parathyroid adenomas are rare (MacKenzie and Garner, 1973; Goodman et al., 1979, 1980). The diagnosis is reserved for those cases of unilateral enlargement of the gland producing displacement of adjacent thyroid tissue, thickening of the capsule and clear evidence that the contralateral gland is not hyperplastic. A recent study has confirmed that parathyroid adenomas, like thyroid tumours, can be induced in the rat by ionizing radiation and that the incidence of tumours following radiation is inversely related to the vitamin D content of the diet (Wynford-Thomas et al., 1983). These workers suggested that metabolites of vitamin D_3 may influence parathyroid growth and tumour formation in glands initiated by radiation. This is yet another example of tumour development in an endocrine organ which is influenced by chronic physiological stimuli or functional changes.

REFERENCES

ANDERSON, M.P. and CAPEN, C.C. (1978): The endocrine system. In: K. Benirschke, F.M. Garner and T.C. Jones (Eds), *Pathology of Laboratory Animals, Vol. 1*, Chap. 6, pp. 423-508. Springer-Verlag, New York.

BERKVENS, J.M., VAN NESSELROOY, J.H.J. and KROES, R. (1980): Spontaneous tumours in the pituitary gland of old Wistar rats. A morphological and immunocytochemical study. *J.Pathol., 130*, 179-191.

BUREK, J.D. (1978): Age-associated pathology. In: *Pathology of Aging Rats*, Chap. 4, pp. 29-167. CRC Press, West Palm Beach, FL.

CHENG, L. (1980): Pheochromocytoma in rats: Incidence, etiology, morphology and functional activity. *J.Environ.Pathol.Toxicol., 4*, 219-228.

CIOCCA, D.R., PARENTE, A. and RUSSO, J. (1982): Endocrinologic milieu and susceptibility of the rat mammary gland to carcinogenesis. *Am.J.Pathol., 109*, 47-56.

DeLELLIS, R.A., NUNNEMACHER, G., BITMAN, W.R., GAGEL, R.F., TASHJIAN, A.H.Jr, BLOUNT, M. and WOLFE, M.J. (1979): C-cell hyperplasia and medullary carcinoma in the rat. An immunohistochemical and ultrastructural analysis. *Lab.Invest., 40*, 140-154.

DHOM, G., HOHBACH, Ch., MUSLE, E., SCHERR, O. and VEBERBERG, H. (1981): Peliosis of the female adrenal cortex of the aging rat. *Virchow Arch. Cell.Pathol., 36*, 195-206.

DOBBIE, J.W. (1969): Adrenocortical nodular hyperplasia: the ageing adrenal. *J. Pathol., 99*, 1-18.

DUNN, T.B. (1970): Normal and pathologic anatomy of the adrenal gland of the mouse, including neoplasms. *J.Natl Cancer Inst., 44*, 1323-1389.

FACCINI, J.M. (1969): Fluoride and bone – a review. *Calcif.Tissue Res., 3*, 1-16.

FITZGERALD, J.E., SCHARDEIN, J.L. and KAUMP, D.H. (1971): Several uncommon pituitary tumors in the rat. *Lab.Anim.Sci., 21*, 581-584.

FURTH, J., NAKANE, P. and PASTEELS, J.L. (1976): Tumours of the pituitary gland. In: V.S. Turusov (Ed.), *Pathology of Tumours of Laboratory Animals, Vol. 1, Tumours of the Rat, Part 2*, pp. 201-237. IARC Scientific Publ. No. 6, Lyon.

GLAISTER, J.R., SAMUELS, D.M. and TUCKER, M.J. (1977): Ganglioneuroma-containing tumours of the adrenal medulla in Alderley Park rats. *Lab.Anim., 11*, 35-37.

GOODMAN, D.G., WARD, J.M., SQUIRE, R.A., CHU, K.C. and LINHART, M.S. (1979): Neoplastic and non-neoplastic lesions in aging F344 rats. *Toxicol.Appl. Pharmacol., 48*, 237-248.

GOODMAN, D.G., WARD, J.M., SQUIRE, R.A., PAXTON, M.B., REICHARDT, W.D., CHU, K.C. and LINHART, M.S. (1980): Neoplastic and non-neoplastic lesions in aging Osborne-Mendel rats. *Toxicol.Appl.Pharmacol., 55*, 433-447.

GOWING, N.F.C. (1970): Pathology and natural history of thyroid tumours. In: D. Smithers (Ed.), *Neoplastic Diseases at Various Sites, Vol. 6, Tumours of the Thyroid Gland*, Chap. 6, pp. 103-129. Churchill Livingstone, Edinburgh.

GREAVES, P. and RABEMAMPIANINA, Y. (1982): Choice of rat strain: A comparison of the general pathology and the tumour incidence in 2-year old Sprague-Dawley and Long-Evans rats. In: New Toxicology for Old. *Arch.Toxicol., Suppl. 5*, 298-303.

HODSMAN, A., DENT, C.E. and FACCINI, J.M. (1976): Medullary carcinoma of the thyroid gland in a girl aged 10 years. *Arch.Dis.Child., 51*, 223-226.

HOLLANDER, C.F. and SNELL, K.C. (1976): Tumours of the adrenal gland. In: V.S. Turusov (Ed.), *Pathology of Tumours in Laboratory Animals, Vol. 1, Tumours of the Rat, Part 2*, pp. 273-293. IARC Scientific Publ. No. 6, Lyon.

KITCHEN, D.N., TODD, G.C., MEYERS, D.B. and PAGET, C. (1979): Rat lymphocytic thyroiditis associated with ingestion of an immunosuppressive compound. *Vet.Pathol., 16*, 722-729.

KOVACS, K., HORWATH, E., ILSE, R.G., EZRIN, C. and ILSE, D. (1977): Spontaneous pituitary adenomas in aging rats. A light microscopic, immunocytological and fine structural study. *Beitr.Pathol., 161*, 1-16.

LECHARDT, L. and HERVONEN, H. (1982): Ultrastructural changes in the neurohypophysis of the aged male rat. *Cell Tissue Res., 226*, 51-62.

LIEBEGOTT, G. (1958): Nebennieren. In: P. Cohrs, R. Jaffé and H. Meesen (Eds), *Pathologie der Laboratoriumstiere, Vol. 1*, pp. 501-553. Springer-Verlag, Berlin.

MacKENZIE, W.F. and GARNER, F.M. (1973): Comparison of neoplasms in six sources of rats. *J.Natl Cancer Inst., 50*, 1243-1257.

MAGNUSSON, G., MAJEED, S.K. and GOPINATH, C. (1979): Infiltrating pituitary neoplasms in the rat. *Lab.Anim., 13*, 111-113.

MAJEED, S.K., GOPINATH, C. and MAGNUSSON, G. (1980): Ultrastructure of spontaneous pituitary neoplasms in the rat. *J.Comp.Pathol., 90*, 239-246.

McCOMB, D.J., RYAN, N., HORWATH, E., KOVACS, K., NAGY, E., BERCZI, I., DOMOKOS, I. and LASZLO, F.A. (1981): Five different adenomas derived from the rat adenohypophysis: Immunocytochemical and ultrastructure study. *J.Natl Cancer Inst., 66*, 1103-1111.

NAPALKOV, N.P. (1976): Tumours of the thyroid gland. In: V.S. Turusov (Ed.), *Pathology of Tumours in Laboratory Animals, Vol. 1, Tumours of the Rat*, pp. 239-271. IARC Scientific Publ. No. 6, Lyon.

NEVILLE, A.M. (1978): The nodular adrenal. *Invest.Cell Pathol., 1*, 99-111.

PEARSE, A.G.E. (1966): Cytochemistry of thyroid C-cells and their relationship to calcitonin. *Proc.Roy.Soc.B, 164*, 478-487.

PENHALE, W.J., FARMER, A., McKENNA, R.P. and IRVINE, W.J. (1973): Spontaneous thyroiditis in thymectomized and irradiated Wistar rats. *Clin.Exp.Immunol., 15*, 225-236.

REZNIK, G., WARD, J.M. and REZNIK-SCHÜLLER (1980): Ganglioneuromas in the adrenal medulla of F344 rat. *Vet.Pathol. 17*, 614-621.

RHODIN, J.A.G. (1974): *Histology. A Text and Atlas*, Chap. 20, pp. 428-436. Oxford University Press, New York.

RUSSFIELD, A.B. (1967): Pathology of the endocrine glands, ovary and testis of rats and mice. In: E. Cotchin and F.J.C. Roe (Eds), *Pathology of Laboratory Rats and Mice*, Chap. 14, pp. 391-466. Blackwell Scientific, Oxford.

SLOPER, J.C. revised by B. Fox (1978): The adrenal glands. In: W.St.C. Symmers (Ed.), *Systemic Pathology, Vol. 4, 2nd Ed.*, Chap. 30, pp. 1913-1974. Churchill Livingstone, Edinburgh.

SQUIRE, R.A., GOODMAN, D.G., VALERIO, M.G., FREDRICKSON, T.N., STRANDBERG, J.D., LEVITT, M.H., LINGEMAN, C.H., HARSHBARGER, J.C. and DAWE, C.J. (1978): Tumours. In: K. Benirschke, F.M. Garner and T.C. Jones (Eds), *Pathology of Laboratory Animals, Vol. 2*, Chap. 12, pp. 1051-1283. Springer-Verlag, New York.

TROUILLAS, J., GIROD, C., CLAUSTRAT, B., CURE, M. and DUBOIS, M.P. (1982): Spontaneous pituitary tumors in the Wistar/Furth/Ico rat strain: An animal model of human prolactin adenoma. *Am.J.Pathol., 109*, 57-70.

WARD, J.M. and REZNIK-SCHÜLLER, H. (1980): Morphological and histochemical characteristics of pigments in aging F344 rats. *Vet.Pathol., 17*, 678-685.

WARREN, S. and MEISSNER, W.A. (1953): Tumours of the thyroid gland. In: *Atlas of Tumour Pathology, Sect. 4, Fascicle 14*, p. 20. AFIP, Washington, DC.

WEXLER, B.C. (1964): Correlation of adrenocortical histopathology with arteriosclerosis in breeder rats. *Acta Endocrinol. (Copenhagen), 46*, 613-631.

WILLIS, R.A. (1960): Epithelial tumours of the thyroid gland. In: *Pathology of Tumours, 3rd Ed.*, Chap. 36, pp. 605-619. Butterworths, London.

WYNFORD-THOMAS, V., WYNFORD-THOMAS, D. and WILLIAMS, E.D. (1983): Experimental induction of parathyroid adenomas in the rat. *J.Natl Cancer Inst., 70*, 127-134.
YOSHIMURA, F. and NOGAMI, H. (1981): Fine structural criteria for identifying rat corticotrophs. *Cell Tissue Res., 219*, 221-228.

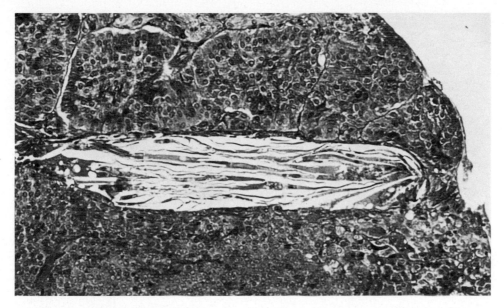

Fig. 131 A cyst (cystic change) present in the pituitary gland of a Long-Evans male, 26 months of age. It shows no definite lining epithelium but cholesterol clefts are present in the cavity. (HE, × 105)

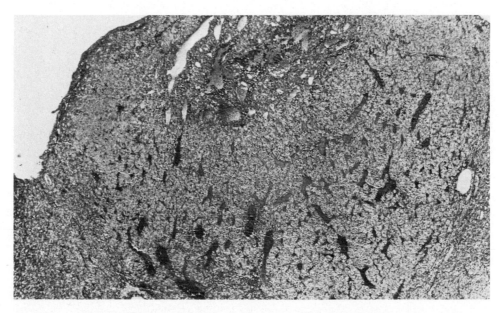

Fig. 132 Pituitary adenoma found in a 26-month-old Sprague-Dawley male rat. The tumour is unencapsulated, fairly solid but with a prominent vasculature. (IIE, × 26)

199

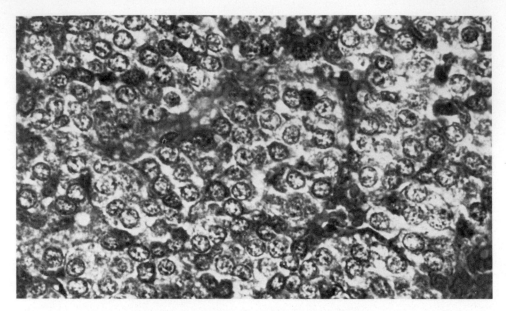

Fig. 133 Pituitary adenoma, same case as in Figure 132. High power view showing the fairly uniform cellular pattern, cells chromophobic in type. (HE, ×450)

Fig. 134 Pituitary adenoma, a common vascular or haemorrhagic type in a male Long-Evans rat, 26 months of age. (HE, ×105)

200

Fig. 135 A clear cell focus of typical appearance found incidentally in a 26-month-old Sprague-Dawley male rat. Pale staining cells are located in the zona glomerulosa. There is no unequivocal compression of surrounding gland. (HE, × 105)

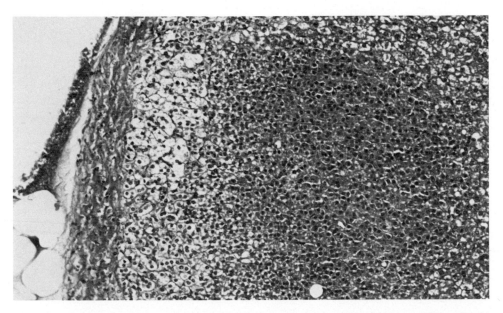

Fig. 136 Eosinophilic focus in the zona fasciculata in the adrenal gland in a 26-month-old Long-Evans male rat. It is not sharply demarcated and shows no evidence of compression of the adjacent gland. A small clear cell focus is also present in the zona glomerulosa. (HE, × 105)

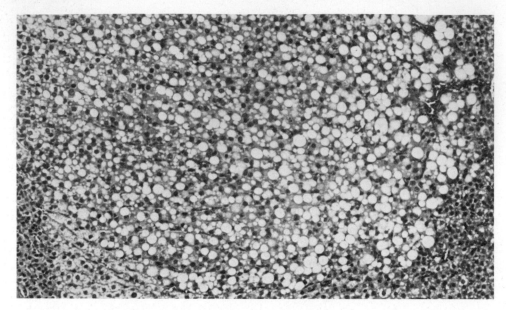

Fig. 137   A vacuolated or fatty focus in the zona glomerulosa of a Sprague-Dawley rat, aged 25 months. A well-defined focus of cells containing large, clear fat vacuoles is present. (HE, × 105)

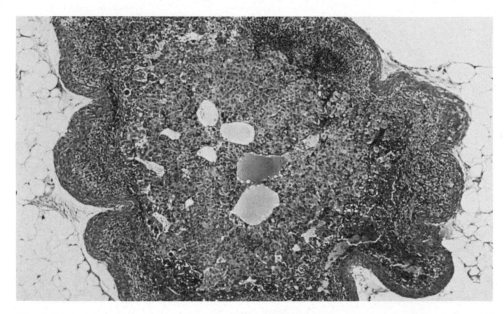

Fig. 138   Adrenal cortical atrophy in a 22-month-old Long-Evans rat, which possessed a large cortical adenoma in the contralateral adrenal gland. The cortex is reduced in thickness compared with normal, and the capsule shows marked fibrous thickening. (HE, × 26)

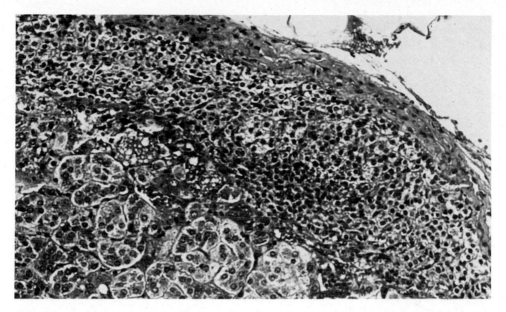

Fig. 139 Adrenal cortical atrophy, same case as in Figure 138. This higher power view shows the reduced thickness of the cortex and the thickened capsule. (HE, ×210)

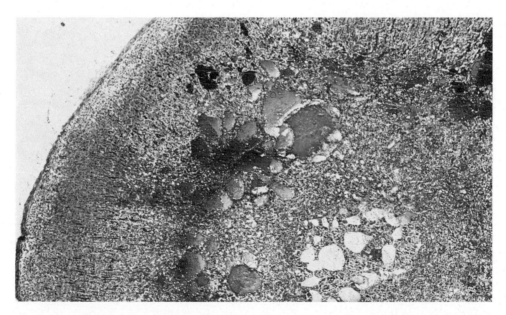

Fig. 140 Cystic degeneration (peliosis) of the adrenal cortex in a female Sprague-Dawley rat aged 26 months. The histological changes are moderate in severity but the congestion of the corticomedullary junction with dilated or cystic vascular channels is clearly seen. (HE, ×26)

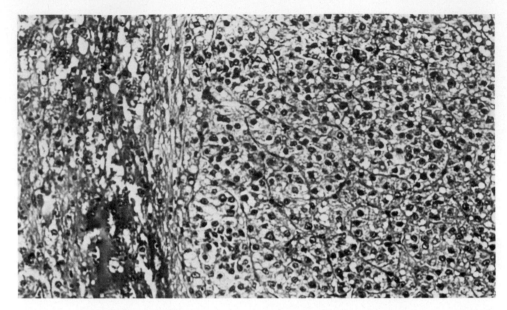

Fig. 141   A well-circumscribed adrenal cortical carcinoma in a 26-month-old Sprague-Dawley rat. There is a fibrous capsule but there was *no* clear evidence of local tissue invasion. However, metastases were found (see Fig. 143). (HE, ×210)

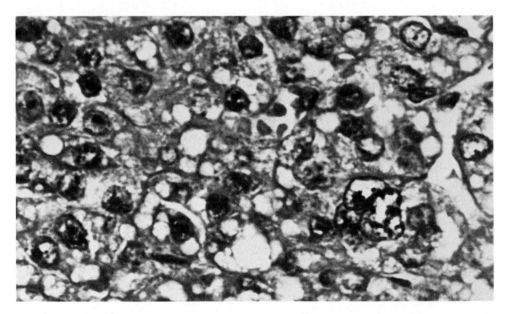

Fig. 142   Adrenal cortical carcinoma, same case as in Figure 141. Mild cellular pleomorphism is evident in this high power view. (HE, ×825)

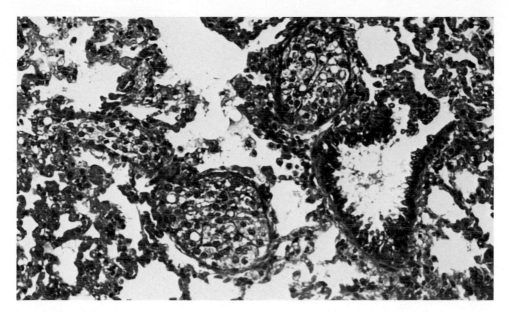

Fig. 143 Adrenal cortical carcinoma, same case as in Figures 141 and 142. Pulmonary intravascular metastases are seen. (HE, × 210)

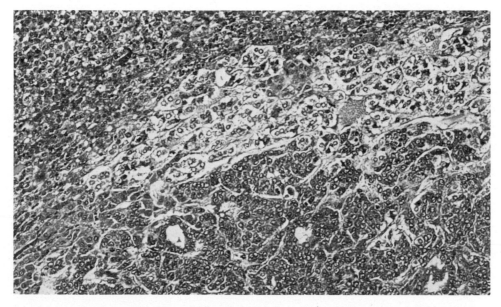

Fig. 144 A pheochromocytoma found in a Long-Evans male rat, 26 months old. This neoplasm, composed of cells more hyperchromatic than the normal medullary cells, compresses the adjacent gland. Metastases were not found in this case. (HE, × 105)

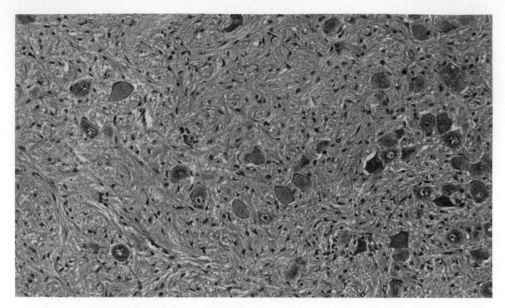

Fig. 145 Ganglioneuroma found in the adrenal gland of a 25-month-old Sprague-Dawley rat. The central zone is seen in this figure and is composed of mature ganglion cells embedded in a spindle or Schwann cell component. (HE, × 105)

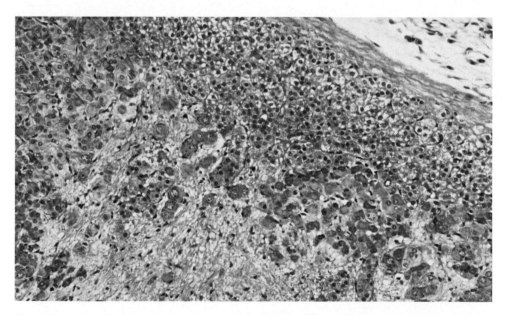

Fig. 146 Ganglioneuroma, same case as in Figure 145, but view of the periphery of the tumour. More primitive hyperchromatic cells are present at the junction between the adrenal cortex and the tumour, but the stroma is similar to that seen in Figure 145. (HE, × 105)

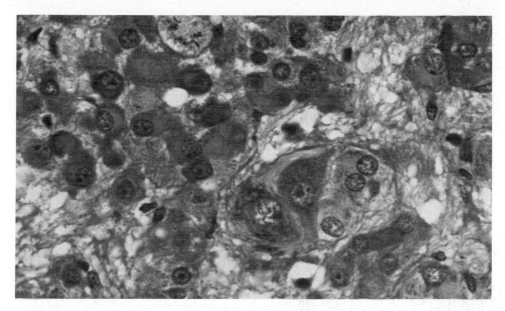

Fig. 147 Ganglioneuroma, high power view of the area seen in Figures 145 and 146 showing the primitive cells at the edge of the neoplasm. A mitosis is present at the top of the figure whereas the cells towards the lower part of the illustration show neuronal differentiation. (HE, × 450)

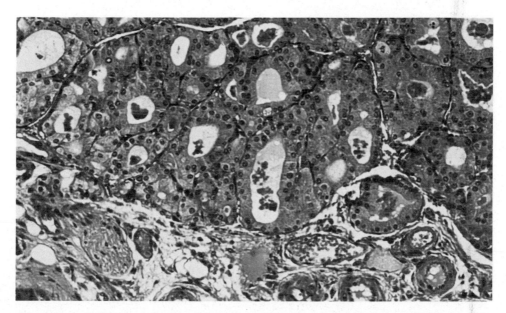

Fig. 148 Follicular carcinoma of the thyroid gland in a male Sprague-Dawley rat, 24 months of age. Although a well-differentiated neoplasm composed of acinar structures, it infiltrated local tissues and caused the death of the animal. (HE, × 130)

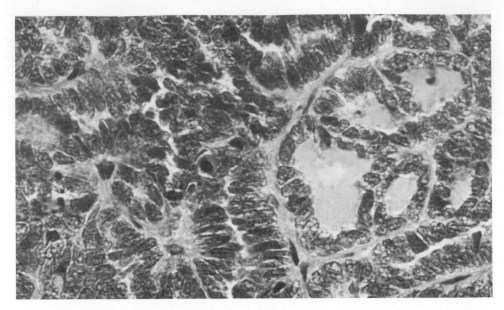

Fig. 149 Follicular carcinoma of the thyroid in a female Sprague-Dawley rat aged 25 months. This tumour is very cellular and it infiltrated the neck widely but differentiated colloid-containing acini are still present. (HE, × 450)

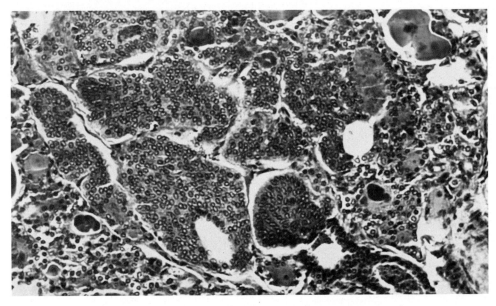

Fig. 150 C-cell hyperplasia, an incidental finding in a 26-month-old male Sprague-Dawley rat. (HE, × 210)

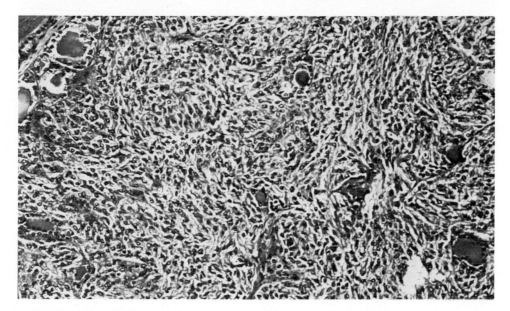

Fig. 151   Medullary carcinoma in a 26-month-old Long-Evans male rat. It replaced one lobe of the thyroid gland and it is composed principally of spindle cells in this field. (HE, × 105)

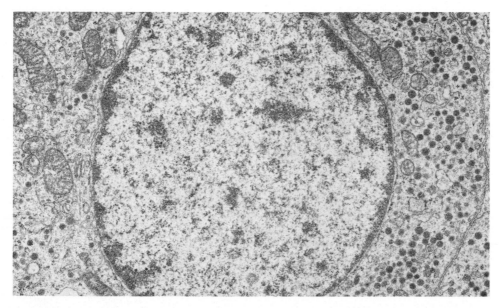

Fig. 152   Medullary carcinoma in a 25-month-old Sprague-Dawley male rat. This electron micrograph shows the numerous cytoplasmic granules pathognomic of this tumour. (E/M, × 13,500)

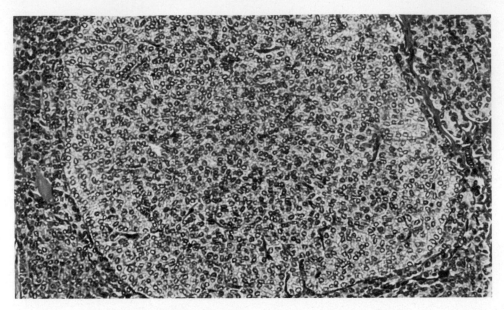

Fig. 153   Focal hyperplasia of the parathyroid gland in a 26-month-old Sprague-Dawley rat. This is a small focus showing tinctorial cytoplasmic changes but no definite compression of surrounding gland. (HE, × 130)

XI. Nervous system and special sense organs

BRAIN

Non-neoplastic changes

Brain and meninges – inflammation

Inflammatory disease of the brain and its coverings is uncommon in the rat. The usual spontaneous arteritis is occasionally seen in the cerebral arteries lying in the brain substance (Anver et al., 1982).

Occasionally, small foci of non-specific chronic inflammation are observed in the meninges or brain substance in the rats housed at Amboise.

Although obvious infectious disease affecting the brain and meninges is not commonly encountered in well-housed rat colonies, a certain number of microbiological agents do have the potential to cause inflammatory disease in the central nervous system. Under certain experimental conditions these may assume considerable importance.

Frank bacterial (purulent) inflammation of meninges (acute inflammation, acute meningitis) can be caused by bacteria normally pathogenic for the rat respiratory tract such as *Streptococcus pneumonia* (*Diplococcus pneumoniae*) currently regarded as a widespread and major primary bacterial pathogen in the laboratory rat (Weisbroth, 1979). In severe cases of bacterial meningitis, spread of the inflammation to the underlying cerebral tissue may occur, the grey and white matter also being diffusely infiltrated by acute inflammatory cells (purulent encephalitis). Suppurative inflammation may also be localized in brain tissue (abscess) (Jortner and Percy, 1978).

Viral encephalitis (encephalomyelitis) also occurs, particularly under conditions of stress when toxic chemicals are administered, although the number of viruses known to be naturally infectious for the laboratory rat is small (Jacoby et al., 1979). The rat parvovirus may produce intranuclear inclusions and it has a particular affinity for the vessel walls which may be a factor in the development of a haemorrhagic encephalomyelitis (Jacoby et al., 1979; Coleman et al., 1983).

Toxoplasma gondii, an ubiquitous coccidian parasite, has also been seen to give rise to chronic encephalitis in adult rats (Hsu, 1979). Focal granulomatous inflammation (focal granulomas, focal granulomatous encephalitis, glial nodules) consisting of perivascular accummulation of activated glial cells and lymphocytes in the absence of necrosis is also seen in apparently normal rats infected with *Encephalitozoon* (*Nosema*) *cuniculi*, a microsporidian parasite (Hsu, 1979).

Basophilic bodies

Rounded or irregular basophilic bodies or concretions are found occasionally in rat brains, although an incidence of up to 20% has been reported (Burek, 1978). They are often located in the thalamic area and show no evidence of glial reaction. These lesions are PAS-positive and contain some calcium (Fig. 154).

Haemorrhage

Cerebral haemorrhage occurs for a variety of reasons. It may be seen in the hypothalamus as a result of an expanding pituitary adenoma, particularly if this is of vascular or haemorrhagic type, and this precipitates the death of the animal. Focal intracerebral haemorrhage may also be found in rats dying of leukaemia. Massive haemorrhage may accompany gliomas and focal cerebral infarcts (see below). It has also been observed in association with vascular damage in the encephalomyelopathy caused by rat parvovirus infection (Jacoby et al., 1979).

Compression and hydrocephalus

Any expanding lesion in the cranial cavity may compress the brain. In the rat, this generally occurs as a result of an expanding pituitary adenoma, particularly if over 0.5 cm in diameter. With these tumours, there is considerable indentation and atrophy of the hypothalamus sometimes associated with localized oedema of brain tissue. There may be evidence of early hydrocephalus. This may precipitate the death of the animal (Squire et al., 1978; Greaves and Rabemampianina, 1982).

Infarcts

Focal infarcts of various ages are seen in the rat brain and they may show evidence of previous haemorrhage. Lipid and haemosiderin-containing microglia (macrophages, foam cells) are often numerous.

Vacuolation (vacuolar degeneration, vacuolar encephalopathy)

Vacuolation of the cerebral white and grey matter appears to be a spontaneous change occurring more commonly in aged rats. However, lack of staining reaction and lack of cellular reaction suggest it is simply artefact due to tissue processing (Burek, 1978). Such changes are usually disregarded by the experienced pathologist.

Pigmentation

Several different pigments (pigmentation) are observed in the brain or meninges of rats. P.A.S.-positive and Ziehl-Nielson acid-fast lipofuscin (ceroid pigment) is found within cerebral neurons with increasing age. Although lipofuscinosis, vacuolar degeneration and a number of other morphological alterations increase with age, these changes provide no *specific* indication of an aging brain (Meier-Ruge, 1982).

Perl's-positive iron pigment (haemosiderin) is found in macrophages associated with focal infarcts, haemorrhage, inflammation or around expanding neoplasms.

Melanin is commonly seen in the meninges and the pituitary gland of pigmented strains of rats of all ages, and is a normal finding.

Note:

The rat brain weight remains remarkably stable with increasing age in our experience and this appears to be generally the case in this species (Weil, 1970). However, *after* formalin fixation, an age-related decrease in rat brain weight and volume has been reported and it has been suggested that post-fixation weighing of the brain is a useful index of brain aging (Douglas et al., 1981).

Neoplasms

Most classifications of rodent intracranial tumours are based on the study of those induced by the appropriate administration of powerful carcinogens. These studies have shown that induced tumours bear a striking morphological resemblance to human neoplasms, and that classification used in human pathology is appropriate in the rodent (Zimmerman and Innes, 1979; Mennel and Zülch, 1976). Central nervous system tumours seen in the usual toxicological or carcinogenicity studies are uncommon and only a few of the types seen in man have been reported to arise spontaneously in the rat; incidences of over 5% have been reported to arise spontaneously in some colonies of rats (Sumi et al., 1976). Thus, in routine studies, a fairly simple classification is warranted. Primary tumours can be divided into those of neuroectodermal or neurogenic origin (principally tumours of neuroglial cells or gliomas) and those of mesodermal tissues (principally tumours of the meninges and their derivatives). To these must be added the tumours of cranial and spinal nerve roots and a variety of other rare tumours such as those originating in the pineal region.

Neuroectodermal tumours

The largest group of neuroectodermal tumours is that included under the term glioma, the word used to designate primary tumours of the brain and spinal cord that originate from the cells of the glial stroma (astrocytes, oligodendrocytes and ependymal cells). The classification adopted is based on the modification of Bailey and Cushing's (1926) classic cytogenic classification as modified by Rubinstein (1972). This classification is similar to that adopted by other authors for rat tumours of spontaneous type (Mawdesley-Thomas and Newman, 1974; Dagle et al., 1979).

The distinction between benign and malignant neoplasms is considerably less sharp among tumours of central neurogenic origin than among those arising in other systems, and criteria usually set for the definition of malignancy often break down when applied to the gliomas (Rubinstein, 1972). As gliomas often behave in a clinically malignant manner in the rat and usually show histological evidence of infiltrative behaviour, it would seem generally more appropriate to group all but the most well-differentiated gliomas with malignant neoplasms.

For practical routine purpose, these tumours can be grouped into astrocytomas (and glioblastoma multiforme), oligodendroglioma and ependymomas. Mixed tumours or unclassifiable tumours of gliomatous origin also occur in the rat (Mennel and Zülch, 1976). They are so poorly defined in the rat that it is probably more appropriate to simply use the generic term glioma for these.

Astrocytomas (astrocytic glioma, glioblastoma multiforme)　　These are neoplasms derived from, and composed of, astrocytes which show varying degrees of maturity (Rubinstein, 1972). Most glial tumours of the rat fall into this group (Dagle et al., 1979).

These tumours often occur in periventricular areas and are usually poorly circumscribed, merging gradually into the surrounding grey or white matter. In our experience, most of these tumours are very cellular being composed of proliferating cells often showing marked pleomorphism. For the most anaplastic forms, containing tumour giant cells and showing zonal necrosis surrounded by pseudopalisading tu-

213

mour cells, the term glioblastoma multiforme may be used (Fig. 155). This term is widely accepted to describe the extreme manifestation of anaplasia and dedifferentiation on the part of mature glial tumours, which are mostly astrocytomas (Rubinstein, 1972). However, usually even in poorly differentiated tumours, some microscopic fields contain recognizable astrocytic tumour cells with hyperchromatic nuclei. Vascular changes may also be prominent, comprising endothelial proliferation, increases in number of small vessels and thromboses. These proliferating capillaries may protrude through the ependymal surface.

Certain differential diagnostic difficulties may be encountered. Mawdesley-Thomas (1968) described 'ependymitis' of probably infectious origin which he later reclassified as astrocytoma (Mawdesley-Thomas and Newman, 1974). This highlights the fact that early gliomatous change occurring around the ventricles may appear of inflammatory nature. However, careful examination usually reveals lack of true inflammatory change and the presence of pleomorphic, proliferating astrocytes and abnormal vascular changes in keeping with the diagnosis of astrocytoma.

Oligodendrogliomas   These are uncommonly found in the rat brain and they show a much more uniform cellular appearance than astrocytic gliomas, being composed of regular cells with rounded nuclei and characteristically clear cytoplasm (Mawdesley-Thomas and Newman, 1974; Dagle et al., 1979) (Figs 156 and 157). Attempts to correlate the biological behaviour of oligodendrogliomas in man with histological appearances have been unrewarding (Rubinstein, 1972). It would seem, therefore, unwise to attempt to do so in the occasional oligodendroglioma found in the rat.

Ependymoma   These tumours have been described in the rat but they are rare and difficult to diagnose (Mennel and Zülch, 1976; Dagle et al., 1979). The recognition of ependymomas depends on the presence of cells that morphologically resemble mature ependymal elements or display rosettes with a well-defined central lumen (Rubinstein, 1972). Of special importance is the demonstration of cilia and blepharoblasts, the latter being small intracytoplasmic dots, best demonstrated with the phosphotungstic acid haematoxylin stain, which represent the basal bodies of cilia seen at electron microscopic level. Those arising spontaneously in the rat are composed of densely packed, large cells with evenly distributed nuclear chromatin and distinct cytoplasmic membranes, and which appear to arise from intact areas of ependymoma (Dagle et al., 1979).

Mesenchymal tumours

Meningiomas originate from the cells that form the meninges and their derivatives in the meningeal spaces. In man, they show highly variable microscopic appearances, probably due to the adaptive potential of the arachnoid cell from which most meningiomas are thought to arise (Rubinstein, 1972). This variability is also seen in rat meningiomas although they have not been well characterized. However, in some colonies, meningiomas are the commonest type of tumour in the central nervous system (Mawdesley-Thomas and Newman, 1974; Sumi et al., 1976).

Two major types of meningioma are described in the rat, syncytial and fibroblastic. The former is composed of epithelioid cells possessing regular ovoid nuclei and fairly dense eosinophilic cytoplasms, but these cells may be mixed with cells of more fibroblastic type. The fibroblastic meningioma is composed of bundles and whorls of fairly hyperchromatic spindle cells forming variable amounts of collagen and reticulin. Concentric concretions (psammoma bodies) have been described in rat meningiomas (Burek, 1978), and we have observed scatterings of benign-looking tumour giant cells in some tumours.

Whether the rat meningiomas which arise spontaneously in the aged rat are always the exact counterparts of the usual human meningiomas is open to some question. Macroscopically, the fibroblastic type of meningioma may spread diffusely over the cerebral surface in a way that is only occasionally seen in man ('en plaque' type). The fibroblastic cells may infiltrate into the Robin-Virchow sinus and in all types mitotic figures can be surprisingly common for a so-called benign tumour. However, nodular compressive forms are seen occasionally and have been reported in the literature (Dagle et al., 1979), and these do generally resemble human types.

Lack of information about the biological nature of these tumours in the rat constrains the pathologist to apply the general histological criteria for assessment of malignant potential.

Granular cell tumours (myoblastomas)   These are found in the cranial cavity of a number of rat strains (Sass et al., 1975; Hollander et al., 1976; Squire et al., 1978). In certain strains they are the most common tumour of the central nervous system (Burek, 1978).

These tumours are well circumscribed, generally attached to the meninges, and are composed of sheets or nests of polygonal or elongated cells with pink, finely granular cytoplasm and small uniform nuclei. The cytoplasmic granules are diastase-resistant, P.A.S.-positive, and ultrastructurally represent membrane-bound dense granules of variable size (Burek, 1978). Such granules probably represent lysosomes, and most ultrastructural studies of similar tumours in man have suggested they are of Schwann cell origin (Ghadially, 1960).

As a rule, they destroy brain tissue by compression only and, therefore, are considered benign. Aggressive cases have been described which show perivascular invasion into surrounding structures and these must be regarded as essentially malignant.

Other tumours

Other primary tumours of sarcomatous or lymphomatous nature have been described in the rat brain, and may occasionally pose diagnostic problems. Some of these can widely infiltrate the brain (Mawdesley-Thomas and Newman, 1974; Dagle et al., 1979) and may indeed be primary tumours of the cerebral lymphoreticular system (lymphoma, reticulosis, reticulum cell sarcoma, microgliomatosis, gliomatosis).

Metastatic tumours

Secondary tumours of the central nervous system in small laboratory animals are unusual (Jortner and Percy, 1978). Occasionally, the meninges are infiltrated by leukaemia or lymphoma cells, and this has been reported to be particularly common for some types of large cell (stem cell) leukaemia (Richter et al., 1972). Large invasive tumours of the head may also locally invade the brain or spinal cord.

PINEAL GLAND

In view of the accumulating evidence that the pineal gland, a neuroendocrine organ, has an important function in thyroid and reproductive physiology in rats, this gland should not be completely disregarded in chronic toxicity and carcinogenicity tests. It is postulated that it exerts anti-thyroid and anti-gonadal effects through the secretion of melatonin and that these effects are dependent on light restriction (Vriend, 1981).

The pineal gland, situated dorsally between the cerebral hemispheres and the cerebellum, is seen in routine histological sections of the rat brain. The frequency with which it is observed is somewhat dependent on the blocking procedure, but it is often sectioned tangentially. A normal gland may occasionally appear quite large if it is sectioned centrally and this may be mistaken for hyperplasia or a tumour. However, unless there is evidence of undue nuclear pleomorphism or mitotic activity or frank displacement of surrounding tissues, the diagnosis of hyperplasia or adenoma is probably not warranted. However, pineal tumours are occasionally observed.

The occasional example we have observed has been an expansive vascular mass compressing, but not infiltrating, adjacent cerebral and cerebellar cortex. The tumour cells are often quite large with moderately pleomorphic nuclei showing a little mitotic activity. Cells tend to be grouped into thick trabeculae with a somewhat organoid appearance, although glandular differentiation is not striking (Figs 158 and 159).

Note:
The term pinealoma, coined by Krabbe (1923) for a human tumour of the pineal region, now thought to be a primitive tumour of germ cell origin (germinoma), is probably not appropriate for a benign or malignant tumour thought to arise from pineal parenchymal cells, and the terms pineocytoma and pineoblastoma have been proposed (Rubinstein, 1972). Adenoma and carcinoma are probably less confusing in this situation.

SPINAL CORD

Pathology of the spinal cord is similar to that described in the brain (see under Brain, above). However, lesions are infrequently observed, perhaps due to the fact that the rodent cord is so small that it is infrequently examined in great detail (Zimmerman and Innes, 1979).

Degeneration
In association with the spontaneous degeneration of peripheral and spinal nerves in the aged rat (see Peripheral nerve, spinal nerve roots, below), there may be evidence of degeneration in the spinal cord and cauda equina. The lesions are limited to white matter and are most severe in the lateral and ventral funiculi or columns (Burek, 1978). Microscopically, changes are similar to those occurring in spinal roots and peripheral nerves – demyelinization, swelling of axon sheaths and presence of

lipid laden macrophages (Fig. 160). Astrocytes become swollen and axons may also swell and disappear. In advanced cases, mineral (mineralization, calcification) is deposited in the vertebral canal. These mineral deposits contain calcium and phosphate and, although they may compress the spinal cord, they probably represent changes secondary to nerve degeneration. Aseptic necrosis of bone, intervertebral disc herniation, dural fibrosis and fibrosis of nerve root sleeves have also been described in severe cases (Burek, 1978).

PERIPHERAL NERVE, SPINAL NERVE ROOTS

Non-neoplastic lesions

Degeneration (radicular myelinopathy, degenerative myelopathy)

A spontaneous degenerative condition of peripheral nerves in association with the presence of degenerative lesions in the spinal cord and spinal nerve roots has been described in several strains of aged rat (Burek et al., 1976; Cotard-Bartley et al., 1981; Krinke et al., 1981).

The condition is characterized by focal swelling of the myelin sheaths or segmental demyelinization and the presence of myelin-laden or foamy macrophages (Fig. 160). Frank cholesterol granulomas may also be seen and mast cells can be found in considerable quantities. The sciatic and tibial nerves appear to be the peripheral nerves most commonly affected (Cotard-Bartley et al., 1981), but the lumbar and ventral spinal nerve roots are often even more severely damaged. Changes may also be seen in dorsal spinal roots, spinal tracts and cauda equina (see Spinal cord, above).

Severe cases become increasingly apparent in rats of two years of age and older (Burek, 1978), when there is often clinical evidence of posterior paresis or paralysis. In such advanced cases muscle atrophy may be present, mineral deposition (mineralization) may occur in the spinal canal and there may be intervertebral disc herniation and necrosis of vertebral bone (see under Spinal cord, above). Electron microscopic examination suggests that the primary defect is swelling of myelin and demyelinization. In a recent study, Krinke (1983) has suggested that this occurs secondary to shrinkage of axons, resulting in focal accumulation of lipid debris within spinal nerve roots.

The cause is unknown, but it must be remembered that swelling of myelin is a change that can also be induced by a number of specific toxic agents and metabolic disorders (Krinke et al., 1981).

Neoplasia

The commonest and most important neoplasm arising in the peripheral nerves in man is the neurilemmoma (neurolemmoma, Schwann cell tumour, schwannoma, neurinoma, perineurial fibroblastoma), the numerous synonyms of which indicate the various theories of histogenesis (Symmers, 1979). On the basis of electron microscopic evidence, it is generally believed to be principally a tumour of the Schwann cell. By contrast, the neurofibroma is seen much less commonly in man and this diagnosis is generally restricted to those cases of Von Recklinghausen's neurofibromatosis (Symmers, 1979).

Spontaneous tumours of the peripheral nervous system in the rat are only rarely reported and diagnoses include neurofibroma and neurofibrosarcoma (Schardein et al., 1968; Burek, 1978; Goodman et al., 1979, 1980). However, the precise histogenesis of these spindle cell tumours remains to be elucidated, particularly in view of the lack of ultrastructural study. It has been in fact stated that the precise histogenetic classification of schwannomas in man, totally on the basis of light microscopic appearance, is an almost impossible task in many instances (Hajdu, 1979). We prefer not to group spindle cell tumours as peripheral nerve tumours unless there is reasonable morphological evidence of nerve sheath origin.

Thus, the term neurilemmoma (schwannoma, neurinoma, neuroma) whether benign or malignant is reserved for tumours composed of interlacing bundles of elongated spindle cells resembling peripheral nerve, as well as the classical palisading of the nuclei (Antoni's B areas), that are seen in human tumours of this type and can be induced in peripheral nerves by the administration of powerful carcinogens (Mennel and Zülch, 1976). However, the distinction from leiomyoma and leiomyosarcoma may not be easy, particularly as both may exhibit nuclear palisading (Symmers, 1979). Reticulin fibres may be abundant in both types. Neurilemmomas are generally solid tumours but central liquefactive necrosis is quite common and cystic cavities may form. The malignant neurilemmoma (malignant schwannoma), although rare in man, is reported occasionally as a spontaneous tumour in the rat. A granular cell variant of a rat neurilemmoma has also been described (Berman et al., 1978).

However, with these malignant and, therefore, more pleomorphic variants, differential diagnosis may be particularly difficult. Recent electron microscopic study has even shown Schwann cell differentiation in human tumours with typical light microscopic features of malignant fibrous histiocytomas (Herrera et al., 1982).

Ganglioneuromas   By contrast, these tumours are well-defined spontaneous tumours in some strains of rats, usually arising in the adrenal gland and associated with pheochromocytomas (see Adrenal gland in Chapter X). They are believed to arise from primitive neural crest cells that give rise to both ganglion cells and cells of the adrenal medulla (Reznik et al., 1980). They are characterized histologically by the presence of well-differentiated ganglion cells and proliferating spindle cells of Schwann cell type. They may be locally invasive tumours (malignant ganglioneuroma).

EYE

Although ophthalmoscopy and slit-lamp biomicroscopy are the primary methods in assessment of ocular toxicity, histopathological examination of the eye is necessary for complete assessment of the eye, and it is an area of study that calls for particularly close cooperation between clinical toxicologists and pathologists to obtain the best results (Saunders, 1967). Spontaneous ophthalmic modifications are seen throughout the lifespan of laboratory animals. Drugs and chemical compounds administered either locally or systemically may also produce ophthalmic changes and they can mimic those of spontaneous origin. The fact that changes are related to administration of chemical compounds or drugs may only be evident by their increased incidence or earlier onset. Thus a major problem for the investigator is to distinguish the spontaneous from the drug-related lesions (Taradach and Greaves, 1983). The major spontaneously arising lesions seen on histopathological examination are described below.

Conjunctiva

Non-neoplastic lesions

Inflammation   Although mild non-specific conjunctival inflammation (minimal focal acute and chronic inflammation, conjunctivitis) may be seen fairly frequently in rats, marked inflammation of the conjunctiva is usually seen in association with corneal inflammation (keratitis) (see under Cornea, below). Such severe inflammation is associated most commonly in the rat with the sialodacryoadenitis virus, although inflammation of bacterial origin has been reported (Heywood, 1973; Roberts and Gregory, 1980).

As severe conjunctivitis usually occurs in association with inflammation in other structures of the anterior segment of the eye (cornea, iris, ciliary body), Saunders and Rubin (1975) group all these lesions under the general heading of inflammation of the anterior segment in rats (see below).

Neoplasia

Squamous cell carcinoma   Ocular squamous carcinoma, a tumour of older animals (Kircher, 1978), is only uncommonly reported in rats (Goodman et al., 1979). Well-differentiated keratinizing squamous carcinoma has been occasionally seen to arise spontaneously from the conjunctiva in the aged Sprague-Dawley rat at Amboise. It is a locally invasive neoplasm and may infiltrate the globe of the eye.

Harderian and lacrimal glands

The harderian gland is particularly well developed in rodents, occupying a considerable part of the orbit including parts posterior to the eyeball (Sakai, 1981). It is characterized histologically by the presence of tubulo-alveolar end-pieces with wide lumina and absence of a duct system within the gland itself. It is unusual to see the main excretory duct in histological sections. The harderian gland is the sole example of a gland that secretes lipid by a merocrine mechanism (exocytosis) and, in rats, the secretions also contain porphyrin. The rat eye is supplied with one intraorbital and one extraorbital lacrimal gland, both composed of serous cells rather similar to those of the parotid gland, although normally nuclei may be considerably more pleomorphic.

Non-neoplastic lesions
Chromodacryorrhea   Although not strictly speaking a histopathological term, it is important in pathology to recognize this condition characterized by an excessive outpouring of the red secretions of the harderian gland, for it may be mistaken for blood (Harkness and Ridgeway, 1980). Such excessive secretion may be provoked by non-specific stimuli such as stress, and specific agents such as cholinergic drugs (Harkness and Ridgeway, 1980). Some drugs may stimulate secretion from the harderian gland so intensely that the globe of the eye may sink into the orbit as a result of gland emptying (Brückner, 1951).

Inflammation   The rat harderian and lacrimal glands are particularly affected by the sialodacryoadenitis virus complex. Histopathologically, changes may be of variable severity but they comprise acute and chronic inflammation (diffuse), oedema, and even widespread necrosis with eventual squamous metaplasia of glandular tissue (Jonas et al., 1969).

A much more localized, but somewhat similar, necrotizing inflammation of the harderian gland has also been described as a sequela to obtaining blood samples by the orbital bleeding technique (McGee and Maronpot, 1979). Lesions resolve during the course of several weeks leaving residual focal glandular atrophy, fibrosis and chronic inflammatory cell infiltration (focal chronic inflammation). Chronic inflammation may be seen without any other associated changes or clear cause (Figs 161 and 162). Leakage of pigment and a granulomatous reaction (granulomatous inflammation) may be seen in some cases.

Neoplasia
Although tumours of the harderian and lacrimal glands are well described in mice, they are uncommon in rats. However, occasionally adenomas and adenocarcinomas are seen in these glands in the aged rat (Goodman et al., 1979).

Cornea

Non-neoplastic lesions
The anatomical site of the cornea renders it particularly susceptible to damage by a variety of external agents, including drugs and chemicals administered systemically, for they may be secreted into tears.

Changes in the cornea observed by ophthalmological examination are best grouped into opacity, dystrophy and keratitis (Taradach and Greaves, 1983). However, these alterations do not necessarily translate into well-defined histopathological entities. Mild focal opacification of the cornea may represent transient oedema not easily seen in the usual histological sections. It may be difficult to distinguish the various diffuse opacities occurring spontaneously in the rat from sequelae of keratoconjunctivitis, especially in the older animal (Taradach et al., 1981). For these reasons, lesions seen histopathologically fall generally into two groups, inflammation and dystrophy (degeneration, deposition).

Inflammation (keratitis)   Keratitis signifies inflammation of the cornea but the character and severity of the inflammation varies with the causative agent and the animal population. Minimal, focal inflammation of the cornea consists of focal infiltration of the cornea by inflammatory cells. Associated oedema may be seen, and this may be characterized by corneal cloudiness on ophthalmological examination. It has been suggested that such lesions may sometimes represent the results of mild abrasions or slight trauma (Taradach et al., 1981).

Drugs like clonidine, which reduce lacrimal secretions in the rat, may also produce focal inflammation of the cornea accompanied by focal oedema in the epithelial cells, representing a drug-induced form of keratoconjunctivitis sicca (Weisse et al., 1978).

The rat is more liable than either the mouse or hamster to develop severe inflammation of the cornea (keratitis) usually associated with inflammation of the conjunctiva (keratoconjunctivitis).

Several disease patterns have been described but the most important is that caused by the sialodacryoadenitis virus. Histopathological findings are of variable severity but include acute and chronic inflammation, vascularization, epithelial proliferation (hyperplasia, acanthosis) and even corneal ulceration. Associated inflammatory lesions may be found in salivary and ocular glands (see under Salivary glands in Chapter VI, Harderian and lacrimal glands, above). As experimental infections have established that the sialodacryoadenitis virus arrives relatively late in the course of the disease to the ophthalmic adnexae, it has been proposed that ophthalmic lesions are secondary to obstruction of normal lacrimal secretions (Jacoby et al., 1975; Lai et al., 1976).

Bacteriological examination of keratoconjunctivitis in the rat may reveal mixtures of organisms (Saunders, 1967), although coagulase positive staphlococci, streptococci, and *Pasteurella multocida* have been incriminated as causative agents (Saunders and Rubin, 1975; Heywood, 1973; Roberts and Gregory, 1980).

Dystrophy (degeneration, deposition)   The term dystrophy implies a degenerative condition which, in a number of species, embraces such lesions as fatty degeneration, lipidoses, pigmentation and mineralization. Such degenerative changes are poorly defined in the rat, but a not infrequent lesion observed is hyalinization or mineralization (calcification) in Bowman's membrane or anterior corneal stroma. These changes may be the result of previous keratitis (Saunders, 1967). The fact that similar hyalinization of the rat cornea is seen after narcotic analgesic administration suggests it may also result from epithelial dessication (Roerig et al., 1980). Subepithelial deposits of calcium or calcium-like material have been also reported to occur in diabetic rats (Friend et al., 1982).

One of the most common age-related histological changes reported in the cornea of old rats in some colonies is thickening of Descemet's membrane (Weisse et al., 1974), although this change is not of great pathological importance. The endothelial cells on the inner surface of the cornea and bordering on the membrane of Descemet also show age-related changes and these are similar to those occurring in man. Scanning electron microscopy reveals endothelial loss with age and a compensatory spreading and thinning of surviving cells in the rat cornea (Fitch et al., 1982).

Neoplasia
Primary tumours of the rat cornea are extremely rare. A dermoid tumour (really

a choristoma or developmental malformation) has been reported (Nichols and Yanoff, 1969).

Uveal tract

Non-neoplastic lesions

Inflammation   The ciliary body and iris may be involved in an inflammatory process extending from the cornea. An acute iridocyclitis (acute inflammation) has been observed in the rat as a result of infection with the sialodacryoadenitis virus (Weisbroth and Peress, 1977).

Fibrosis and sclerosis   Histological examination of the rat eye may reveal increased fibrosis or sclerosis of the ciliary body and iris root with advancing age (Weisse et al., 1974).

Haemorrhage   Clinically, haemorrhage may be observed in the anterior chamber of the eye (ephema) unassociated with any evidence of other pathology, presumably a result of minor trauma. Such haemorrhage usually resolves without sequelae. Histologically, evidence of congestion or frank haemorrhage may be seen, although it is most often a result of orbital blood sampling prior to autopsy.

   Although some congenital malformations such as clefts or holes in the iris (colobomas) or persistent papillary membranes (persistent embryonic structure) are seen in the rat eye when examined clinically (Taradach et al., 1981; Taradach and Greaves, 1983), these are uncommonly visualized in routine histological preparations.

Synechia   Although ophthalmological examination reveals a variety of papillary alterations such as persistent papillary membranes, papillary strands and ectopic pupil, the most important histological finding is often attachment of the iris margin to the anterior cortex of the lens or the corneal endothelium (synechia, adhesion). The attachment may occur as a congenital condition or follow inflammation in the anterior chamber (Taradach and Greaves, 1983). Widespread attachment of the iris to the lens may be accompanied by glaucoma and retinal atrophy presumably because of obstruction to the flow of the aqueous (see Glaucoma, below).

Glaucoma   Glaucoma is generally characterized in the rat by unilateral enlargement of the globe of the eye and protrusion from the orbit, and usually follows blockage of the filtration of the aqueous, as a result of intraocular inflammation (Saunders, 1967). The causation may not be clear in all cases. It should be noted in this context that an increase in eyeball size with age has been reported in the Fischer 344 rat (Shinowara et al., 1982).

Neoplasia

   Although melanomas, vascular smooth muscle, epithelial and neuroepithelial tumours of the iris and uvea are reported in man and animals (Kircher, 1978), such tumours are extremely rare in untreated rats.

Melanoma   Roe et al. (1963) reported benign tumours of melanin-containing cells, with the histological appearance of naevi in the connective tissue of the iris of pigmented August hooded rats treated with urethane in the neonatal period. No such tumours were induced in similarly treated Wistar rats.

Although malignant melanomas of spindle cell type arising in the region of the ciliary body in albino rats have been reported (Magnusson et al., 1978), we have observed no convincing evidence of the presence of melanin in orbital spindle cell tumours in the Sprague-Dawley rat.

Lesions of the lens

Opacity and cataract
   The lens is an avascular organ and it depends on diffusion of nutrients through the aqueous and, to a lesser extent, the vitreous humor for its integrity (Grimes, 1974). Any change in its metabolic activity may cause cloudiness which may be detected by ophthalmological examination. Slit-lamp biomicroscopy is particularly sensitive in this respect (Bellhorn, 1981) and this method may reveal insignificant lens opacities quite commonly. For this reason, the term cataract, in our laboratory, is reserved for irreversible opacities present at birth, advanced or unequivocably progressive or evolving opacities, and the term opacity is used to group other lesser changes seen on ophthalmological examination (Taradach and Greaves, 1983).

Histopathological examination using the usual routine techniques is a much less sensitive method for detecting minor changes in the lens. However, with careful technique, histological changes may be seen which correspond to lesions seen by biomicroscopy (Balazs et al., 1970). Cells of the lens (lens fibres) may show changes in staining intensity, swelling (cytoplasmic alteration), vacuolization (cytoplasmic vacuolization) or frank disintegration (degeneration) with residual cystic spaces (cystic degeneration, cystic change) (Fig. 163). Amorphous cytoplasmic debris may accumulate in the lens substance. These changes arise spontaneously in the aged rat (Balazs et al., 1970), although similar disintegration of lens fibres may be seen in chemically-induced cataracts (Bellows, 1963).

Displacement (luxation)
   Displacement of the lens may be observed in glaucomatous eyes, probably secondary to distortion of the ocular globe (Saunders, 1967).

Lesions of the retina

Retinal atrophy (retinal dystrophy, retinal degeneration, retinopathy)
   Although retinal atrophy may be induced by chemical compounds, it can arise spontaneously in untreated rat populations for a variety of reasons. In order to avoid misinterpretation of retinal changes in toxicological studies, it is necessary to have a clear idea of possible causes (Weisse et al., 1974), particularly as it may be impossible to distinguish between spontaneous atrophy and atrophy induced by chemicals on ophthalmological or histological grounds only (Bellhorn, 1981). Atrophy may be related to factors such as age, strain, ambient light intensity, temperature, nutritional factors, or may follow retinal inflammation (chorioretinitis) and glaucoma (Tara-

dach and Greaves, 1983). The albino rat is particularly sensitive to the noxious effects of high light intensity, and for this reason it is important to distribute cages randomly in relation to the light source. It has been shown that rats housed on shelves and racks nearer to light sources are more likely to develop severe retinal damage than those housed further away (Bellhorn, 1980).

In general, retinal atrophy in the rat is characterized by loss of photoreceptor cells, histologically most evident as a reduction in the number of nuclei in the outer nuclear layer, normally about 8-10 nuclei thick in younger rats (Stötzer et al., 1970; Weisse et al., 1974). Dependent on causation, these changes may vary from a slight reduction in cell nuclear number to a complete loss of all photoreceptor cells. In early or mild cases, inner layers remain intact, although there may also be a slight reduction in the inner nuclear layer in the senile animal (Weisse et al., 1974). Severe retinal atrophy is, however, accompanied by marked loss of inner retinal layers, as well as proliferation of retinal vessels which are observed transversing the retina and proliferating in the underlying pigment epithelium (Weisse et al., 1974; Lai et al., 1978). Cystoid cavities may also be seen (cystic change, cystic degeneration) and intra-retinal hyaline deposits have also been described (Weisse et al., 1974).

Careful studies of the aged albino rat retina housed under controlled ambient light have shown that age-related or true senile degeneration tends to produce fairly mild retinal atrophy which is most marked towards the retinal periphery, and that atrophy induced by artificial lighting tends to be more severe in the posterior pole (Noell et al., 1966; Weisse et al., 1974), although senile and light-induced atrophy may be inter-related (Lai et al., 1978). It has been recently shown that glucose utilization of the retina generally closely parallels the loss of photoreceptor cells (Shinowara et al., 1982). Differences in incidence and severity may also exist between the common strains used in toxicological work, although inherited retinal atrophy in the Royal College of Surgeon's strain (RCS) occurs earlier, and is characterized histologically by the persistence of focal areas of debris between the pigment epithelium and neural retina (Von Sallman and Grimes, 1972).

There are few reports of drug-induced retinal toxicity in the rat (Heywood, 1982); proprionic acid derivatives, however, do appear to have a primary toxic effect on photoreceptor cells, although histologically this is characterized by an apparent migration of photoreceptor nuclei (outer nuclear layer) and not frank early loss (Lee et al., 1979). By contrast, chloroquine seems to have a primary effect on the ganglion cells and inner nuclear layer in the rat retina, although all layers degenerate in advanced cases (Gregory et al., 1969).

Atrophy following inflammatory eye disease, particularly sialodacryoadenitis, is often unilateral whereas light-induced, inherited and chemical-induced atrophy is bilateral.

Retinal detachment

True retinal detachment has been described in the Sprague-Dawley rat, and attributed to exudate (oedema) between the sensory retinal layer and the pigment epithelium (Heywood, 1976). The cause of this change, whether it is reversible or whether it precedes the development of retinal atrophy or retinal folds or rosettes (see below), remains uncertain.

Retinal folds, rosettes

These are characterized by infolding of all retinal layers, and are seen occasionally in the rat, presumably congenital in origin (Rubin, 1974), although a relationship with acquired retinal detachment has been suggested (see above).

Inflammation (chorioretinitis, retinitis)

Frank inflammation of the retina (retinitis, chorioretinitis) is a relatively unimportant spontaneous condition in well-housed rat colonies (Taradach and Greaves, 1983). However, inflammation may involve the retina and this can lead to focal or diffuse retinal atrophy (see above). It is presumably caused by a similar range of organisms implicated in inflammation of the anterior segment of the eye (Saunders, 1967; Saunders and Rubin, 1975).

Other changes in the retina

A number of other changes of possible toxicological significance have been described in the rat retina. Drug-induced lipidosis characterized by accumulation of lipid-laden, foamy macrophages (foam cells) in the retina have been described (Drenckhahn and Hullmann-Rauch, 1978). Ultrastructural study of the retina after the administration of a number of chemical compounds has also revealed the accumulation of myelinoid bodies (myeloid bodies, myelinosomes) in the cytoplasms of inner retinal cells and pigment epithelial cells (Heywood, 1982). These drug-induced myelinoid bodies are thought to form because the drugs bind to lipidic membranes, thus making them difficult to break down, or from selective inhibition of lysosomal enzymes (Ghadially, 1982).

Lesions of retinal blood vessels

Vascular lesions are only infrequently seen in the retina in the rat, although from time to time evidence of spontaneous vascular disease may be seen (see under Cardiovascular System, Chapter V). Spontaneously hypertensive rats more commonly show alterations of retinal vessels. In spontaneously hypertensive rats, vascular irregularity as observed by ophthalmoscopic examination has been shown by microscopic study to be due to dilatation of arterioles with associated focal smooth muscle loss (Parr, 1978).

Retinal haemorrhage

Occasionally, spontaneous haemorrhages are seen in normotensive rats (Rubin, 1974) as well as hypertensive rats (Parr, 1978). Drug-induced changes in blood coagulation may similarly cause retinal haemorrhage (Heywood, 1982).

Neoplasia

Primary tumours of retinal elements are extremely rare in the rat and none have been observed at Amboise. Soft tissue sarcomas arising in the orbit may infiltrate the retina (see Lesions of the extraocular orbital tissues, below). However, a single primary retinal sarcoma has been reported in the literature (MacKenzie and Garner, 1973).

Lesions of the vitreous

The most common lesion in the rat vitreous, particularly among younger rats, is persistence of the foetal hyaloid system (hyaloid vessel remnants). These may give rise to haemorrhage into the vitreous of the albino rat but this usually resolves completely (Taradach and Greaves, 1983).

Fibrosis and calcification of the vitreous is occasionally observed in rodents (Taradach and Greaves, 1983).

Lesions of the optic nerve

Changes in the optic nerve are readily diagnosed by the standard clinical and histological techniques (Heywood, 1982). Histologically, they are similar to those described for other nerves (see Peripheral nerve, spinal nerve roots, above).

Atrophy

A variety of insults to the eye may give rise to optic atrophy and these include pressure from trauma, tumour or faulty bone growth as well as frank inflammation (optic neuritis) (Saunders and Rubin, 1975). Tract degeneration and gliosis has been described in association with spontaneous retinal atrophy (Mawdesley-Thomas, 1969). Demyelinization with atrophy has also been observed following drug treatment in the rat (Lessell, 1976).

Hypoplasia

A true hypoplasia of the optic nerve has been described in the rat, and it is presumably of congenital origin (Rubin, 1974).

Oedema, papilloedema

Accumulation of oedema fluid (papilloedema) in the optic disc may arise from a number of causes including the administration of drugs, the presence of raised intracranial pressure, or space-occupying lesions in the orbit. It has been described in the spontaneously hypertensive rat (Irinoda, 1972).

It is generally assessed that vascular stasis is a major element in the development of papilloedema, although this is unlikely to be the only factor (Cook, 1980).

Coloboma of the optic nerve

Coloboma represents a congenital defect, due to persistence of the choroid tissue, a coloboma of the optic nerve sheath often being associated with a coloboma of the iris. It is histologically characterized by protrusion of the retina between the edge of the lamina cribrosa and the sclera into the optic nerve sheath (Saunders, 1967).

Neoplasia

Tumours of cranial nerves (neurofibroma, neurilemmoma or schwannoma) can be induced by systemic and local application of powerful carcinogens (Mennel and Zülch, 1976). However, such tumours of the optic nerve have not been seen at Amboise. Optic gliomas, neuromas and ganglioneuromas have been very occasionally reported in the literature (Bullock and Curtis, 1930; Fitzgerald et al., 1974).

Lesions of the extraocular orbital tissues (orbit, orbital region)

A similar spectrum of change is found in these tissues (fat, connective tissue, muscle, bone, nerves and blood vessels) as at other sites. Inflammation of the periocular tissues, including muscle, is occasionally seen as is muscular atrophy. Vascular changes such as intimal proliferation have been described in association with retinal atrophy (Mawdesley-Thomas, 1969).

Although metastatic tumours, particularly those of lymphoreticular origin, are not uncommonly observed in the orbit, primary tumours arising from orbital soft tissues are extremely rare (Taradach and Greaves, 1983). The only such tumours seen in rats at Amboise have been malignant fibrous histiocytomas or undifferentiated spindle cell sarcomas arising in the orbit and infiltrating the globe of the eye (see under Integumentary System, Chapter I).

EAR

Introduction

The rat ear has not attracted much attention from pathologists, probably because the guinea pig has been judged as an animal highly suited to auditory research (see review by McCormick and Nuttall, 1976). The result is that accumulated data on the guinea pig ear is abundant whilst by contrast information on the rat ear is lacking. The ear is also protected by massive bony structures so that the usual histological techniques are less readily applied in the routine context.

Anatomically, the ear is usually divided into the:

1) *External ear* consisting of the auricle and the external auditory (acoustic) meatus. Three groups of modified sebaceous (Zymbal's) glands are present in the external ear. Two are situated in the anterior and the posterior wall of the auditory meatus, the larger third gland inferiorly (Pliss, 1973).

2) *Middle ear* or tympanic cavity separated from the external ear by the nasopharynx via the eustachian (auditory) tube.

3) *Inner ear* which contains the sensory apparatus of hearing and equilibrium.

External ear

Inflammation

The external ear, being composed of skin and subcutaneous tissue develops a similar range of inflammatory disorders to those found elsewhere in the skin (see Skin/ Subcutaneous tissue in Chapter I). The protruding auricle renders it particularly liable to traumatic damage. Inflammation may also accompany foreign bodies and tumours present within the external auditory meatus.

Foreign bodies

Foreign bodies such as fragments of food and other debris as well as masses of cerumen are reported commonly in the external auditory meatus of rats (Kelemen, 1978).

Neoplasia

Tumours are occasionally observed on, or in, the external ear of the aged untreated rat. The usual range of tumours found in the skin and subcutaneous tissues may be found (see Skin/Subcutaneous tissue in Chapter I). We have occasionally observed small spindle cell sarcomas (fibrous histiocytomas) on the auricle itself. More common are neoplasms arising in the auditory sebaceous gland but reported incidences for this tumour are still below 1% in untreated aged rats (Deerberg and Rehm, 1981). Such incidences imply that one or two of these tumours are usually seen in most carcinogenicity studies.

Carcinoma   Most tumours of the auditory sebaceous glands present as ulcerating and infiltrating masses within or just below the external auditory meatus, probably mostly arising in the largest (inferior) gland (Pliss, 1973). Histologically, these neoplasms are composed of carcinomatous cells showing squamous (squamous carcinoma) or sebaceous differentiation (sebaceous carcinoma). Most commonly, if enough tissue is examined, both squamous and sebaceous differentiation is found within the same tumour (sebaceous squamous carcinoma) (Fig. 164). Keratinization is often marked. Great masses of keratin may form or keratin may be present as small keratin pearls. Differentiation is variable even within the same tumour and neoplastic cells often infiltrate widely into the surrounding tissues including the inner ear and auricular cavity. Pulmonary metastases are also found. Such tumours usually necessitate the early sacrifice of the animal.

Adenoma   Sebaceous adenomas showing no evidence of tissue invasion are occasionally observed in untreated rats (Squire et al., 1978).

Middle ear

Inflammation

Acute and chronic inflammation (acute and chronic otitis media) are the most important lesions of the middle ear, principally by virtue of the communication between the middle ear cavity and the upper respiratory tract (Fig. 165). Inflammatory lesions of great severity are not particularly common, although the usual respiratory pathogens are implicated (see Respiratory Tract, Chapter IV). Otitis media may also accompany neoplastic disease of the external auditory meatus.

Neoplasia

We have observed no primary middle ear neoplasm in our rat populations. Carcinomas arising in the external ear can infiltrate middle ear structures.

Inner ear

There has been comparatively little morphological study of the inner ear in the rat. The anatomy of the guinea pig ear renders it much more accessible to morphological study. It is somewhat larger than the rat ear and the otic capsule is not embedded in the temporal bone as in the rat, which makes it far easier to expose inner ear structures using the surface preparation techniques of Hawkins (Engström et al., 1964;

Hawkins and Engström, 1964). Therefore, the guinea pig is the best model for studies on ototoxicity. However, simple histological sectioning of the rat petrous bone can yield at least some useful histological information.

We have observed little evidence of primary inner ear disease although inflammation and neoplasia may spread from adjacent structures.

REFERENCES

ANVER, M.R., COHEN, B.J., LATTUADA, C.P. and FOSTER, S.J. (1982): Age-associated lesions in barrier-reared male Sprague-Dawley rats: A comparison between Hap:(SD) and Crl:COBS-CD(SD) stocks. *Exp.Aging Res., 8,* 3-24.

BAILEY, P. and CUSHING, H. (1926): A classification of the gliomata. In: *A Classification of the Tumours of the Glioma Group on a Histiogenetic Basis with a Correlated Study of Prognosis,* pp. 53-95. Lippincott, Philadelphia.

BALAZS, T., OHTAKE, S. and NOBLE, J.F. (1970): Spontaneous lenticular changes in the rat. *Lab.Anim.Care, 20,* 215-219.

BELLHORN, R.W. (1980): Lighting in the animal environment. *Lab.Anim.Sci., 30,* 440-448.

BELLHORN, R.W. (1981): Laboratory animal ophthalmology. In: K.N. Gelatt (Ed.), *Veterinary Ophthalmology,* Chap. 19, pp. 649-671. Lea and Febiger, Philadelphia.

BELLOWS, J.G. (1963): Lens opacities produced by cataractogenic agents. *Am.J.Ophthalmol., 55,* 537-541.

BERMAN, J.J., RICE, J.M. and STRANDBERG, J. (1978): Granular cell variants in a rat Schwannoma. Evidence of neurogenic origin of granular cell tumor (myoblastoma). *Vet. Pathol., 15,* 725-731.

BRÜCKNER, R. (1951): Spaltlampenmikroskopie und Ophthalmoskopie am Auge von Ratte und Maus. *Doc.Ophthalmol., 5-6,* 452-554.

BULLOCK, F.D. and CURTIS, M.R. (1930): Spontaneous tumours of the rat. *J. Cancer Res., 14,* 1-115.

BUREK, J.D. (1978): Age-associated pathology. In: *Pathology of Aging Rats,* Chap. 4, pp. 29-167. CRC Press, West Palm Beach, FL.

BUREK, J.D., VAN DER KOGEL, A.J. and HOLLANDER, C.F. (1976): Degenerative myelopathy in three strains of aging rats. *Vet.Pathol., 13,* 321-331.

COLEMAN, G.L., JACOBY, R.O., BHATT, P.N., SMITH, A.L. and JONAS, A.M. (1983): Naturally occurring lethal parvovirus infection of juvenile and young-adult rats. *Vet.Pathol., 20,* 49-56.

COOK, C.A.G., revised by MORGAN, G. (1980): The eyes. In: W.St.C. Symmers (Ed.), *Systemic Pathology, 2nd Ed., Vol. 6,* Chap. 40, pp. 2824-2895. Churchill Livingstone, Edinburgh.

COTARD-BARTLEY, M.P., SECCHI, J., GLOMOT, R. and CAVANAGH, J.B. (1981): Spontaneous degenerative lesions of peripheral nerves in aging rats. *Vet.Pathol., 18,* 110-113.

DAGLE, G.E., SWICKER, G.M. and RENNE, R.A. (1979): Morphology of spontaneous brain tumors in the rat. *Vet.Pathol., 16,* 318-324.

DEERBERG, F. and REHM, S. (1981): Tumours of the external auditory canal and the auditory sebaceous glands in Han:WIST rats. *Z.Versuchstierk., 23,* 134-137.

DOUGLAS, R.J., CLARK, G.M., TRUNCER, P.C. and TRENEER, C.M. (1981): Effects of aging on formalin-fixed brain weight in mice and rats. *Gerontology, 27,* 127-132.

DRENCKHAHN, D. and HULLMAN-RAUCH, R. (1978): Drug induced retinal lipoidosis. *Exp.Mol.Pathol., 8,* 360-371.

ENGSTRÖM, H., ADES, H.W. and HAWKINS, J.E.Jr (1964): Cytoarchitecture of the organ of Corti. *Acta Oto-Laryngol., Suppl. 188*, 92-99.

FITCH, K.L., NADAKAVUKAREN, M.J. and RICHARDSON, A. (1982): Age-related changes in the corneal endothelium of the rat. *Exp.Gerontol., 17*, 179-183.

FITZGERALD, J.E., SCHARDEIN, J.L. and KURTZ, S.M. (1974): Spontaneous tumors of the central nervous system in albino rats. *J.Natl Cancer Inst., 52*, 265-273.

FRIEND, J., ISHII, Y. and THOFT, R.A. (1982): Corneal epithelial changes in diabetic rats. *Ophthalmic Res., 14*, 269-278.

GHADIALLY, F.N. (1980): Differential diagnosis of eosinophilic granular cell tumours. In: *Diagnostic Electron Microscopy of Tumours*, Chap. 9, pp. 103-115. Butterworths, London.

GHADIALLY, F.N. (1982): Lysosomes. In: *Ultrastructural Pathology of the Cell and Matrix, 2nd Ed.*, Chap. 7, pp. 435-579. Butterworths, London.

GOODMAN, D.G., WARD, J.M., SQUIRE, R.A., CHU, K.C. and LINHART, M.S. (1979): Neoplastic and non-neoplastic lesions in aging F344 rats. *Toxicol.Appl. Pharmacol., 48*, 237-248.

GOODMAN, D.G., WARD, J.M., SQUIRE, R.A., PAXTON, M.B., REICHARDT, W.D., CHU, K.C. and LINHART, M.S. (1980): Neoplastic and non-neoplastic lesions in aging Osborne-Mendel rats. *Toxicol.Appl.Pharmacol., 55*, 433-447.

GREAVES, P. and RABEMAMPIANINA, Y. (1982): Choice of rat strain: A comparison of the general pathology and the tumour incidence in 2-year old Sprague-Dawley and Long-Evans rats. In: New Toxicology for Old. *Arch.Toxicol., Suppl. 5*, 298-303.

GREGORY, M.H., RUTTY, D.A. and WOOD, R.D. (1969): Differences in the retinotoxic action of chloroquine and phenothiazine derivatives. *J.Pathol., 102*, 139-150.

GRIMES, T.D. (1974): Disorders of the canine lens. In: C.S.G. Grunsell and F.W.G. Hill (Eds), *The Veterinary Annual*, pp. 160-163. John Wright, Bristol.

HAJDU, S.I. (1979): Tumours of fibrous tissue. In: *Pathology of Soft Tissue Tumors*, pp. 94-454. Lea and Febiger, Philadelphia.

HARKNESS, J.E. and RIDGEWAY, M.D. (1980): Chromodacryorrhea in laboratory rats *(Rattus norvegicus)*: Aetiological considerations. *Lab.Anim.Sci., 30*, 841-844.

HAWKINS, J.E.Jr and ENGSTRÖM, H. (1964): Effect of kanamycin on cochlear cytoarchitecture. *Acta Oto-Laryngol., Suppl. 188*, 100-106.

HERRERA, G.A., REIMANN, E.F. and SALINAS, J.A. (1982): Malignant Schwannomas presenting as malignant fibrous histiocytomas. *Ultrastruct.Pathol., 3*, 253-261.

HEYWOOD, R. (1973): Some clinical observations on the eyes of Sprague-Dawley rats. *Lab.Anim., 7*, 19-27

HEYWOOD, R. (1976): Retinal detachment in the rat. *Lab.Anim., 10*, 389-392.

HEYWOOD, R. (1982): Histopathological and laboratory assessment of visual function. *Environm.Hlth Perspect., 44*, 35-45.

HOLLANDER, C.F., BUREK, J.D., BOORMAN, G.A., SNELL, K.C. and LAQUEUR, G.L. (1976): Granular cell tumors of the central nervous system of rats. *Arch.Pathol. Lab.Med., 100*, 445-447.

HSU, C.K. (1979): Parasitic diseases. In: H.J. Baker, J.R. Lindsey and S.H. Weisbroth (Eds), *The Laboratory Rat, Vol. I, Biology and Diseases*, Chap. 12, pp. 307-331. Academic Press, New York.

IRINODA, K. (1972): On the fundus changes of spontaneously hypertensive rats compared with essential hypertension in man. *Acta Fifth Afro-Asian Congress of Ophthalmology, Tokyo.*

JACOBY, R.O., BHATT, P.N. and JONAS, A.M. (1975): Pathogenesis of sialodacryoadenitis in gnotobiotic rats. *Vet.Pathol., 12*, 196-209.

JACOBY, R.O., BHATT, P.N. and JONAS, A.M. (1979): Viral diseases. In: H.J. Baker, J.R. Lindsey and S.H. Weisbroth (Eds), *The Laboratory Rat, Vol. 1, Biology and Diseases*, Chap. 11, pp. 271-306. Academic Press, New York.

JONAS, A.M., CRAFT, J., BLACK, C.L., BHATT, P.N. and HILDING, D. (1969): Sialo-dacryoadenitis in the rat. A light and electron microscopic study. *Arch.Pathol., 88*, 613-622.

JORTNER, B.S. and PERCY, D.H. (1978): The nervous system. In: K. Benirschke, F.M. Garner and T.C. Jones (Eds), *Pathology of Laboratory Animals, Vol. 1*, Chap. 5, pp. 319-421. Springer-Verlag, New York.

KELEMEN, G. (1978): Diseases of the ear. In: K. Benirschke, F.M. Garner and T.C. Jones (Eds), *Pathology of Laboratory Animals, Vol. 1*, Chap. 9, pp. 620-640. Springer-Verlag, New York.

KIRCHER, C.H. (1978): Pathology of the eye. In: K. Benirschke, F.M. Garner and T.C. Jones (Eds), *Pathology of Laboratory Animals, Vol. 1*, Chap. 9, pp. 640-662. Springer-Verlag, New York.

KRABBE, K.H. (1923): Pineal gland, especially in relation to problem on its supposed significance in sexual development. *Endocrinology, 7*, 379-414.

KRINKE, G. (1983): Spinal radiculoneuropathy in aging rats: Demyclination secondary to neuronal dwindling. *Acta Neuropathol., 59*, 63-69.

KRINKE, G., SUTER, J. and HESS, R. (1981): Radicular myelinopathy in aging rats. *Vet. Pathol., 18*, 335-341.

LAI, Y.L., JACOBY, R.O., BHATT, P.N. and JONAS, A.M. (1976): Keratoconjunctivitis associated with sialodacryoadenitis in rats. *Invest.Ophthalmol., 15*, 538-541.

LAI, Y.L., JACOBY, R.O. and JONAS, A.M. (1978): Age-related and light-associated retinal changes in Fischer rats. *Invest.Ophthalmol.Visual Sci., 17*, 634-638.

LEE, K.P., GIBSON, J.R. and SHERMAN, H. (1979): Retinopathic effects of 2-amino pro-prionic derivatives in the rat. *Toxicol.Appl.Pharmacol., 51*, 219-232.

LESSELL, S. (1976): Histopathology of experimental ethambutol intoxication. *Am.J.Med. Sci., 272*, 765-769.

MacKENZIE, W.F. and GARNER, F.M. (1973): Comparison of neoplasms in six sources of rats. *J.Natl Cancer Inst., 50*, 1243-1257.

MAGNUSSON, G., MAJEED, S. and OFFER, J.M. (1978): Intraocular melanoma in the rat. *Lab.Anim., 12*, 249-252.

MAWDESLEY-THOMAS, L.E. (1968): Ependymitis in a rat. *J.Pathol.Bacteriol., 95*, 317-319.

MAWDESLEY-THOMAS, L.E. (1969): Retinal atrophy in the Wistar rat. In: S.D. Baker and J. Tripod (Eds), *Proc.Europ.Soc. for the Study of Drug Toxicity, Vol. 10, Senzitisation to Drugs*, pp. 164-174. Excerpta Medica Foundation, Amsterdam.

MAWDESLEY-THOMAS, L.E. and NEWMAN, A.J. (1974): Some observations on spon-taneously occurring tumours of the central nervous system of Sprague-Dawley derived rats. *J.Pathol., 112*, 107-116.

McCORMICK, J.G. and NUTTALL, A.L. (1976): Auditory research. In: J.E. Wagner and P.J. Manning (Eds), *The Biology of the Guinea Pig*, Chap. 19, pp. 281-303. Academic Press, New York.

McGEE, M.A. and MARONPOT, R.R. (1979): Harderian gland dacryoadenitis in rats result-ing from orbital bleeding. *Lab.Anim.Sci., 29*, 639-641.

MEIER-RUGE, W. (1982): Experimental pathology and pharmacology in brain research and aging. *Life Sci., 17*, 1627-1636.

MENNEL, H.D. and ZÜLCH, K.J. (1976): Tumours of the central and peripheral nervous sys-tem. In: V.S. Turusov (Ed.), *Pathology of Tumours in Laboratory Animals, Vol. 1, Tumours of the Rat, Part 2*, pp. 295-311. IARC Scientific Publ. No. 6, Lyon.

NICHOLS, C.W. and YANOFF, M. (1969): Dermoid of a rat cornea. *Pathol.Vet., 6*, 214-216.

NOELL, W.K., WALKER, V.S., KANG, B.S. and BERMAN, S. (1966): Retinal damage by light in rats. *Invest.Ophthalmol., 5*, 450-473.

PARR, J.C. (1978): Retinal arterioles in the New Zealand strain of genetically hypertensive rats. *Aust.J.Ophthalmol., 4*, 58-65.

231

PLISS, G.B. (1973): Tumours of the auditory sebaceous glands. In: V.S. Turusov (Ed.), *Pathology of Tumours in Laboratory Animals, Vol. 1, Tumours of the Rat, Part 1*, pp. 23-30. IARC Scientific Publ. No. 5, Lyon.

REZNIK, G., WARD, J.M. and REZNIK-SCHÜLLER (1980): Ganglioneuromas in the adrenal medulla of F344 rat. *Vet.Pathol., 17*, 614-621.

RICHTER, C.B., ESTES, P.C. and TENNANT, R.W. (1972): Spontaneous stem-cell leukaemia in young Sprague-Dawley rats. *Lab.Invest., 26*, 419-428.

ROBERTS, S.A. and GREGORY, B.J. (1980): Facultative Pasteurella ophthalmitis in Hooded Lister rats. *Lab.Anim., 14*, 323-324.

ROE, F.J.C., MILLICAN, D. and MALLET, J.M. (1963): Induction of melanotic lesions of the iris in rats by urethane given during the neonatal period. *Nature (London), 199*, 1201-1202.

ROERIG, D.L., HASEGAWA, T., HARRIS, G.J., LYNCH, K.L. and WANG, R.I.H. (1980): Occurrence of corneal opacities in rats after acute administration of 1-alpha-acetylmethadol. *Toxicol.Appl.Pharmacol., 56*, 155-163.

RUBIN, L.F. (1974): Rat and rabbit fundus. In: *Atlas of Veterinary Ophthalmoscopy*, Chap. 7, pp. 367-397. Lea and Febiger, Philadelphia.

RUBINSTEIN, L.J. (1972): Classification and grading. In: *Tumours of the Central Nervous System. Atlas of Tumour Pathology, Second Series, Fascicle 6*, pp. 7-17. AFIP, Washington, DC.

SAKAI, T. (1981): The mammalian Harderian gland: Morphology, biochemistry and physiology. *Arch.Histol.Jpn, 44*, 299-333.

SASS, B., RABSTEIN, L.S., MADISON, R., NIMS, R.M., PETERS, R.L. and KELLOFF G.J. (1975): Incidence of spontaneous neoplasms in F344 rats throughout the natural lifespan. *J.Natl Cancer Inst., 54*, 1449-1456.

SAUNDERS, L.Z. (1967): Ophthalmic pathology in rats and mice. In: E. Cotchin and F.J.C. Roe (Eds), *Pathology of Laboratory Rats and Mice*, Chap. 12, pp. 349-370. Blackwell Scientific, Oxford.

SAUNDERS, L.Z. and RUBIN, L.F. (1975): Inflammation of the anterior segment in rats. In: *Ophthalmic Pathology of Animals*, pp. 26-29. Karger, Basel.

SCHARDEIN, J.L., FITZGERALD, J.E. and KAUMP, D.H. (1968): Spontaneous tumors in Holtzman-source rats of various ages. *Vet.Pathol., 5*, 238-252.

SHINOWARA, N.L., LONDON, E.D. and RAPOPORT, S.L. (1982): Changes in retinal morphology and glucose utilization in aging albino rats. *Exp.Eye Res., 34*, 517-530.

SQUIRE, R.A., GOODMAN, D.G., VALERIO, M.G., FREDRICKSON, T.N., STRANDBERG, J.D., LEVITT, M.H., LINGEMAN, C.H., HARSHBARGER, J.C. and DAWE, C.J. (1978): Tumours. In: K. Benirschke, F.M. Garner and T.C. Jones (Eds), *Pathology of Laboratory Animals, Vol. 2*, Chap. 12, pp. 1051-1283. Springer-Verlag, New York.

STÖTZER, H., WEISSE, I., KNAPPEN, F. and SEITZ, R. (1970): Die Retina-Degeneration der Ratte. *Arzneim.Forsch.* (Drug Res.), *20*, 811-817.

SUMI, N., STAVROU, D., FROHBERG, H. and JOCHMANN, G. (1976): The incidence of spontaneous tumors of the central nervous system of Wistar rats. *Arch. Toxicol., 35*, 1-13.

SYMMERS, W.St.C. (1979): Tumours of peripheral nerves. In: W.St.C. Symmers (Ed.), *Systemic Pathology, Vol. 5, 2nd Ed.*, Chap. 35, pp. 2334-2342. Churchill Livingstone, Edinburgh.

TARADACH, C. and GREAVES, P. (1983): Spontaneous eye lesions in laboratory animals: Incidence in relation to age. *CRC Crit.Rev.Toxicol.*, in press.

TARADACH, C., REGNIER, B. and PERRAUD, J. (1981): Eye lesions in Sprague-Dawley rats: Type and incidence in relation to age. *Lab.Anim., 15*, 285-287.

VON SALLMAN, L. and GRIMES, P. (1972): Spontaneous retinal degeneration in mature Osborne-Mendel rats. *Arch.Ophthalmol., 88*, 404-411.

VRIEND, J. (1981): The pineal and melatonin in the regulation of pituitary-thyroid axis. *Life Sci., 29,* 1929-1936.

WEIL, C.S. (1970): Significance of organ-weight changes in food safety evaluation. In: F.J.C. Roe (Ed.), *Metabolic Aspects of Food Safety,* Chap. 16, pp. 419-449. Blackwell Scientific, Oxford.

WEISBROTH, S.H. (1979): Bacterial and mycotic diseases. In: H.J. Baker, J.R. Lindsey and S.H. Weisbroth (Eds), *The Laboratory Rat, Vol. 1, Biology and Diseases,* Chap. 9, pp. 193-241. Academic Press, New York.

WEISBROTH, S.H. and PERESS, N. (1977): Ophthalmic lesions and dacryoadenitis: a naturally occurring aspect of sialodacryoadenitis virus infection of the laboratory rat. *Lab.Anim. Sci., 27,* 466-473.

WEISSE, I., STÖTZER, H. and SEITZ, R. (1974): Age and light-dependant changes in the rat eye. *Virchows Arch.A: Pathol.Anat.Histol., 362,* 145-156.

WEISSE, I., HOEFKE, W., GREENBERG, S., GAIDA, W., STÖTZER, H. and KREUZER, H. (1978): Ophthalmological and pharmacological studies after administration of clonidine in rats. *Arch.Toxicol., 41,* 89-98.

ZIMMERMAN, H.M. and INNES, J.R.M. (1979): Tumours of the central and peripheral nervous systems. In: V.S. Turusov (Ed.), *Pathology of Tumours in Laboratory Animals, Vol. 2, Tumours of the Mouse,* pp. 629-653. IARC Scientific Publ. No. 23, Lyon.

233

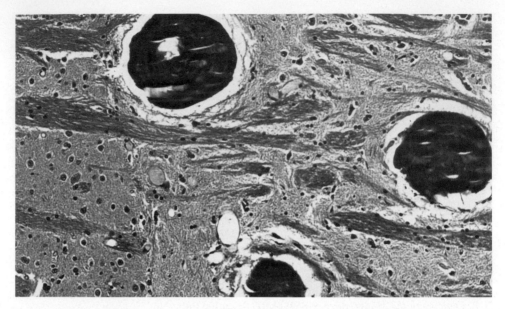

Fig. 154 Basophilic bodies, incidental findings in the cerebrum of a 26-month-old Long-Evans rat. (HE, ×105)

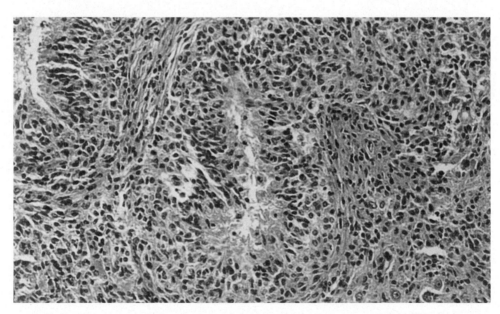

Fig. 155 Glioma. This poorly differentiated glioma (glioblastoma multiforme) was found in the cerebrum of a Long-Evans male rat, found moribund at 26 months of age. Focal zones of degeneration are present, surrounded by palisades of tumour cells. (HE, ×130)

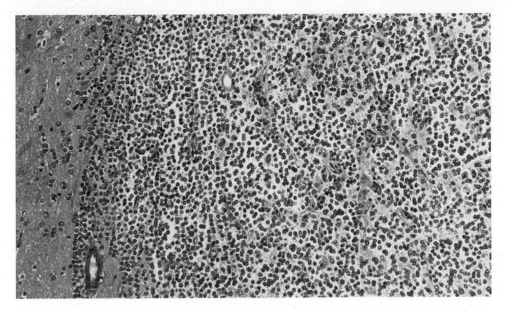

Fig. 156   Oligodendroglioma, found as a round nodule in the anterior part of the cerebrum in a 14-month-old Sprague-Dawley rat which was found dead. It is a well-differentiated, localized neoplasm showing the typical monotonous compact cellular pattern. Cells are regular with spheroidal nuclei. (HE, × 105)

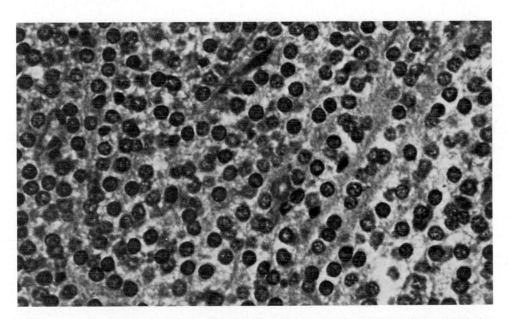

Fig. 157   Oligodendroglioma, same case as in Figure 156. Spheroidal nuclei and pale indistinct cytoplasm are visible at this magnification. (HE, × 450)

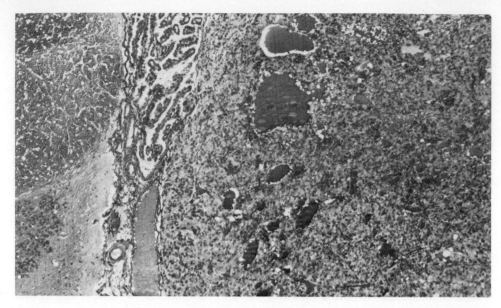

Fig. 158   Pineal tumour (pineocytoma) found in the pineal gland of a 24-month-old Sprague-Dawley rat. There is compression of brain substance by a cellular vascular neoplasm. (HE, × 33)

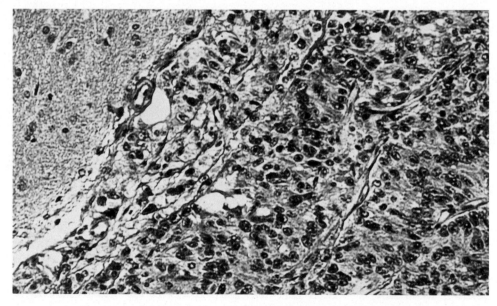

Fig. 159   Pineal tumour, same case as in Figure 158, showing the cords of tumour cells. (HE, × 105)

236

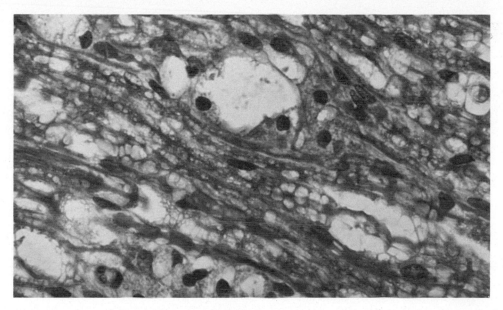

Fig. 160   Degeneration of the spinal cord in a 26-month-old Sprague-Dawley female rat which developed paralysis of both hindlegs prior to scheduled sacrifice. Swelling of axon sheaths and the presence of lipid-laden macrophages are characteristic. Similar changes may be found in spinal roots and peripheral nerves. (HE, × 450)

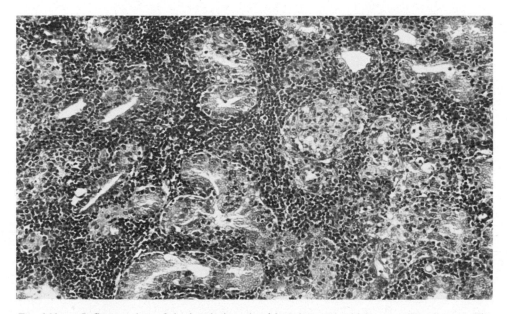

Fig. 161   Inflammation of the harderian gland in a 2-month-old Sprague-Dawley rat. The gland is diffusely infiltrated by chronic inflammatory cells. This inflammation was unilateral and was not associated with sialoadenitis or orbital blood sampling. (HE, × 105)

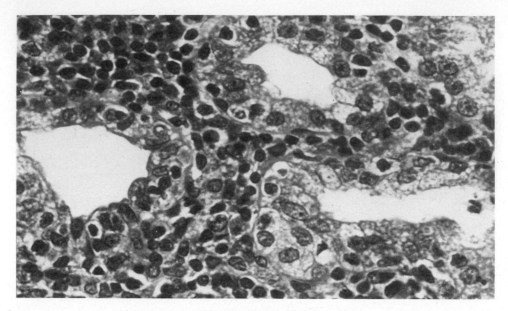

Fig. 162 Harderian gland inflammation, same case as in Figure 161, showing the lympho-cytic nature of the inflammatory infiltrate. (HE, × 450)

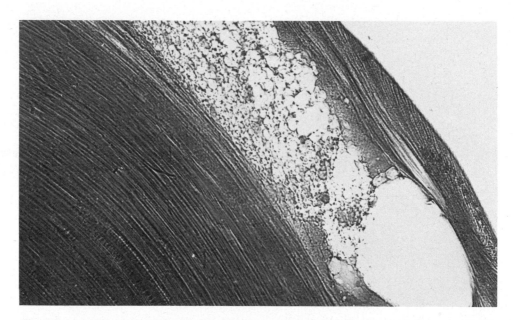

Fig. 163 Cataract: cytoplasmic vacuolization and cystic degeneration in the equatorial cor-tex of the lens in a male Sprague-Dawley rat, 2 months of age, fed a 50% galactose diet. (HE, × 105; colloidin-embedded tissue)

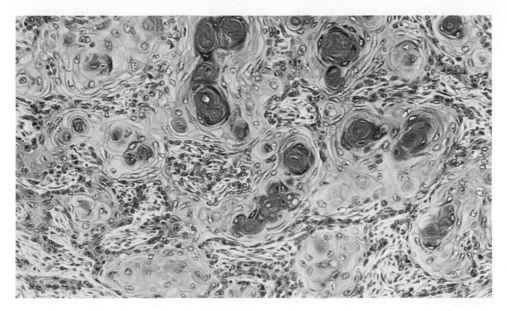

Fig. 164   A typical appearance of the sebaceous squamous carcinoma found arising from the auditory sebaceous glands in a moribund, 16-month-old Sprague-Dawley male. There is sebaceous differentiation and keratin pearl formation. This tumour widely infiltrated the right side of the neck and metastases were found in the lungs (see also Fig. 56). (HE, × 105)

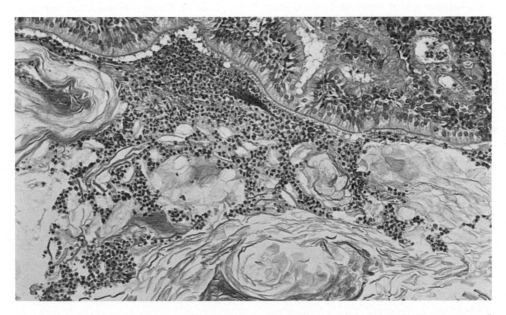

Fig. 165   Otitis media in a moribund, 17-month-old Sprague-Dawley male rat. Acute and chronic inflammatory cells are present in the middle ear cavity and there is accumulation of cellular debris and keratin. The lining columnar epithelium is intact in this section. (HE, × 105)

239

Appendix

THE PATHOLOGICAL EVALUATION OF TOXICOLOGICAL STUDIES

This appendix is intended as a guide to the general principles of pathological diagnosis as practiced within the discipline of Toxicology. The authors came to this discipline with the training and experience of human diagnostic pathology which naturally colours their approach to the subject. The principles, nevertheless, remain essentially the same and are based upon two important precepts: the first is concerned with how diagnoses are made and the second with how they are reported.

Histopathology, within the context of drug safety evaluation – as in its role in human medical practice – is a clinical discipline. Pathological diagnosis is a compendium of the available information on the individual under study – albeit laboratory animal or human being. It comprises, therefore, an assessment of the clinical findings, the clinical chemistry and haematology, and the macroscopic observations at autopsy, together with the information that is gained from examining the tissues under the microscope. The pathologist, therefore, is not engaged in 'slide reading' – as so often inaccurately stated – but in making a pathological diagnosis. There are occasions when it is advisable to evaluate slides without knowing which are from control and which are from treated animals (see below), but this should not be a routine practice in the first instance.

The second important issue is concerned with the mechanism of reporting the diagnostic findings. In human surgical pathology, the pathologist's report is frequently fundamental to the choice of treatment to be given and, therefore, to the eventual well-being of the patient. Great care needs to be taken, therefore, to ensure that the report is not misinterpreted by the clinician: every pathologist learns, with experience, to live with the serious consequences of his written opinion, upon which depends the fate and, not infrequently, the life of the patient. Furthermore, he has to be prepared to face the possibility of future litigation based upon his opinion. The toxicological pathologist is faced with similar circumstances, it behoves him too, therefore, not only to do everything within his capabilities to ensure the correct evaluation of a study but to show clearly in his report that it has been so evaluated. Society, through the agency of Regulatory Authorities,\expects nothing less; when consideration is given to the strict code of practice that has held true for human pathology for some time, it is surprising to think that Good Laboratory Practice as part of Drug Safety Evaluation is only a recent phenomenon[1,2,3].

[1]U.S. Department of Health, Education, and Welfare, Food and Drug Administration: *Nonclinical Laboratory Studies. Good Laboratory Practice Regulations*. Federal Register, Vol. 43, No. 247 (59986-60025) 1978.
[2]U.S. Environmental Protection Agency: *Pesticide Programs. Proposed Guidelines for Registering Pesticides in the U.S.. Hazard Evaluation: Humans and Domestic Animals*. Federal Register, Vol. 43, No. 163 (37366-37403) 1978.
[3]U.S. Environmental Protection Agency: *Proposed Health Effects Test Standards for Toxic Substances Control Act Test Rules. Good Laboratory Practice Standards for Health Effects*. Federal Register, Vol. 44, No. 91 (27334-27375) 1979.

Much of the pathologist's method of working is common sense; the points detailed below are emphasized because they are especially important and are sometimes over looked.

The protocol of a toxicological study

The pathologist must be involved in the design of the protocol. He should be familiar with the pharmacology, if known, and the chemical structure of the test compound. It is his responsibility to decide which tissues need to be examined microscopically, which organs need to be weighed and what special investigations – electron microscopy, histochemistry, etc. – are called for.

The autopsy (macroscopic observations)

Because the macroscopic observations form an integral part of the eventual pathological diagnosis, Regulatory Guidelines insist, justifiably, that a pathologist be present at the autopsy. It is not necessary that the macroscopic observations be any more than a guide to the eventual microscopic evaluation: a simple computerized system with approximately 80 sites and a similar number of morphological observations will suffice (Naylor, 1981).

It is important that all salient macroscopic observations made at autopsy appear in the report and that all tumours are counted with their dimensions and localisation noted. Any clinical observation made during the animal's life requires that the particular organ system affected should be minutely examined. If neurological signs – suggestive of a neurotoxic effect – have been elicited, it is just as important to ensure that an adequate sample of peripheral nerve and correct levels of the spinal cord with brain are taken as it is to use special stains. If, despite having been described as present clinically, no mass or any other type of lesion is found, then it should be diligently searched for and the autopsy report should detail that no abnormality was detected.

Most laboratories find that a system with the prosectors working in pairs is optimal – one dissecting, the other weighing organs and recording the observations. As there should be minimal delay in fixing the tissues if samples are needed for histochemistry or electron microscopy, these should be handled by a third technician.

All the tissues listed in the protocol need to be sampled. Even if autolysis is suspected, it should be the practice to still take all tissues: the diagnosis of autolysis is best made under the microscope. In any case, it must not be left to technicians undertaking an autopsy to decide that tissues do not merit sampling because they are apparently autolysed.

Microscopic observations

Correlation between macroscopy and microscopy

All gross observations must be accounted for histologically: some explanation must appear under the heading 'microscopic observations' in the report that corresponds to the changes noted at autopsy. For this reason, it is logical that for each animal the gross and histological observations appear juxtaposed in the report. The importance of this is obvious, especially in the case of tumours. The critical reasoning behind a carcinogenicity bioassay is to compare the action of the test compound with a hypothetical carcinogen. It is known that carcinogens increase the number of animals with tumours, the number of tumours per animal and shorten the time of appearance of usually spontaneous tumours (Carter, 1978; Faccini, 1981). Therefore, not only do all the masses noted clinically – with their time of appearance – need to be accounted for at autopsy, but they need to be diagnosed microscopically. Incidentally, to undertake this task without the aid of a computerized system of pathology is extremely difficult. The problem that autolysis poses to this correlation is discussed below.

If a macroscopic observation has been made at autopsy and yet no obvious abnormality can be seen in the tissue section, this problem needs to be addressed. For microscopic observations considered to be of a minor order, a microscopic description such as 'no abnormality detected in this section' is quite appropriate. A macroscopic observation of a major order such as nodule or mass, however, needs to be treated differently: further levels need to be cut into the tissue block and if still no abnormality is found the remaining wet tissue needs to be embedded and sectioned. If this manoeuvre still fails to discover the nodule or mass, this needs to be stated in the report, together with details of the efforts taken to account for the macroscopic finding. The report will eventually be reviewed by a Regulatory Authority, and a clear and precise presentation of such cases will help to avoid delays and a possible demand for a resubmission of the report. The same rigorous methods are called for in those cases where tissues are not available for histological evaluation, either because they were not taken at autopsy, lost in processing – an occasional hazard with small tissues – or too autolyzed to be diagnosed microscopically. Addenda to a report, listing tissues not available together with the reason why is imperative. Furthermore, the summary tables of tumour incidence for each tissue should list the number of those tissues examined rather than the total number of animals examined for correct statistical analysis.

Autolyzed tissues

From the point of view of Good Laboratory Practice, it is preferable to evaluate the degree of autolysis microscopically and not macroscopically at autopsy. Autolysis may present a potential problem to chronic rodent studies and is one of the arguments used against proposals to increase the length of 'life-time' studies. In our experience at Amboise, however, this does not usually present a major problem because the animals are carefully supervised and moribund animals sacrificed. The degree of autolysis, however, is variable and often information can still be gleaned from even severely autolyzed tissues. The pathologist should beware, nonetheless, of attempting a diagnosis that requires a careful evaluation of cytology in autolyzed tissue. This holds true, particularly, in the case of tumours. Tumours in a carcinogenicity study may occur in animals that die before the end of the study and their tissues are sometimes consequently autolyzed. On the one hand, it diminishes the value of the study if such tumours are not assessed histologically, whereas, on the other hand, they cannot be diagnosed with the same confidence as tumours fixed at or near the time of sacrifice. A compromise can be reached and the following definitions are suggested.

Autolyzed mass
This term is reserved for those cases in which a mass was noted macroscopically at autopsy but where autolysis is sufficiently extensive to prevent cytological distinction between an inflammatory, hyperplastic or neoplastic process.

Autolyzed tumour
This term is reserved for those cases in which a mass observed macroscopically at autopsy cannot be accurately designated owing to partial autolysis but, nevertheless, the histological picture is compatible with a neoplastic rather than an inflammatory lesion.

Partial autolysis
This term is reserved as a qualification in those cases in which all or some of the tissues were partially affected by autolysis but the general architecture and cytology were sufficiently well preserved to allow diagnoses to be made.

Grading
Because test substances may have an aggravating or sometimes beneficial effect on spontaneous, background disease in laboratory animals, or conversely the coexistence of such disease may affect the animals' response to a compound being tested, it is desirable to use a form of grading. This is not an arbitrary process, however, and the pathologist should have a clear idea of the criteria he is going to employ in this grading. He is not always aware when he begins the microscopic evaluation of a study that a particular background disease may be affected. Furthermore, if it is an unexpected toxic effect that he is observing this may well not be apparent as a major problem until several animals or even whole dose groups have been examined. However, he should be forewarned of possible effects of this nature from his knowledge of the pharmacological action of the test compound and the effects on the clinical chemistry and haematological parameters. If the pathologist only becomes aware of the need to grade a lesion during the course of his histological examination after having already examined a percentage of the animals, he should list the criteria that he is going to employ in assessing the lesion and then examine all of the tissues in question using those criteria. Obviously, he should re-examine those animals that he had already examined. This procedure is especially advisable if a lesion appears to be present to a greater extent in treated animals, and if the pathologist only examined the treated animals after having looked at the controls. Under such circumstances, the re-examination should be undertaken using a randomisation procedure with masking of the slide labels so that the pathologist is not aware which are treated and which are control animals. Under these circumstances 'blind' assessment of slides is justified. As stated above, pathological diagnosis is not simply a question of evaluating microscopic changes and, therefore, cannot be undertaken blind. Histological assessment by grading, however, is a subjective procedure, open to bias and, frequently, is better undertaken under 'blind' conditions.

The error that arises from the pathologist becoming aware of the existence of a lesion only after he has examined a considerable number of animals has been aptly described as 'diagnostic drift' by F.J.C. Roe (1977) and it is a serious problem in drug safety evaluation. A good example of this phenomenon is the not too infrequent finding of a lesion that shows a higher incidence in the low and mid dose groups than the control and top dose groups. This arises in many instances from the fact that the pathologist examined the top dose and control animals first and only became aware of the lesion or its severity half way through the study. There are precautions than can be taken to avoid this error as has been suggested by Roe (1977): 'make a preliminary examination at random of sections from each dose group, make a point of grading lesions and avoid examining the top dose and control animals only at first. The art of pathology, as of most other pursuits, lies in the exercise of selectivity based on knowledge, experience, common sense and a preliminary assessment of sections from the experiment in question'.

It is imperative to have an adequate understanding of the pathological process involved before undertaking any grading. In the case of a common background lesion such as glomerulonephrosis, for example, the minimum criterion for its diagnosis will be the initial, early lesion (see Urinary Tract, Chapter VII): glomerulonephrosis (minimal), therefore, could be defined as the presence of occasional, focal areas with tubular changes comprising basophilia of the epithelial cytoplasm with nuclear pyknosis, karyorrhexis, etc., associated with thickening of the tubular basement membrane with or without fibrosis and an adjacent interstitial round cell infiltrate plus, possibly, thickening of the glomerular basement membrane. If several such areas are found, or there is a large focal area involving the full thickness of the cortex with obvious fibrosis and/or a dense inflammatory infiltrate, the lesion would be classified as moderate. In order to clearly distinguish the minimal lesion from the moderate one the pathologist must decide the 'cut off point' beforehand for statistical purposes, e.g. if only small foci are seen, 1-3 foci are counted as the minimal lesion, while 4 or more the moderate one. Similarly, the marked lesion will comprise at least 30% or perhaps 50% of the renal parenchyma. As long as the same criteria are applied to every animal, the system is most useful. There are always cases where it is difficult to decide in which category of grading the choice should fall, as bias may complicate such a decision, a 'blind' analysis of randomised slides is recommended.

The grading of compound-induced lesions follows the same principles and by weighing the severity from 1 to 3 or 1 to 5, for example, a histogram can be easily constructed by multiplying the number of animals by the score for each dose group and thus demonstrating a possible dose-related effect (Faccini, 1982).

Another important source of bias is in sampling: often the autopsy procedure will allow the prosector to take an extra section of a kidney because a macroscopic lesion has been observed. If consequently two separate sections of this animal are counted and only one from other animals, approximately double the number of nephrons are being assessed in this case in comparison to the others. There is no simple solution to this important problem: the choice lies between cutting an extra section from the other animals or only assessing one section from the animal in which an extra section has been taken. If the latter solution is adopted, the selection must be made 'blindly'.

A further example of a common 'background' lesion commonly affected by drug treatment is testicular atrophy. A grading of the severity of this lesion is difficult: it is usually focal and consequently, as the area of tubular change is, therefore, quite localized, a statistical sampling problem obtains because it involves the chance of a section through a roughly spherical object passing through a much smaller localized area, existing randomly in that sphere. A simple solution is to grade testicular sections with the method commonly used in testicular biopsies in man (Lendon, 1978) – the Tubular Fertility Index. This index is given as the percentage of tubules containing identifiable spermatogonia; usually a minimum of two hundred tubules are sampled. Obviously, the same number of tubules needs to be assessed in each animal.

As stressed above, histological grading without careful criteria for selection and rigorous statistical analysis is a minefield. Developments in morphometry especially with computer-aided techniques are likely to lead eventually to more accurate methods with a reduction in bias. A lot can be achieved, however, without sophisticated computer aids (Hang, 1980; Baak et al., 1977); any further discussion on morphometry, however, is outside the scope of this book.

REFERENCES

BAAK, J.P.A., OORT, J., BOUW, G.M. and STOLTE, L.A.M. (1977): Quantitative morphology: methods and materials, I. Stereology and morphometry. *Eur. J.Obstet.Gynecol.Reprod.Biol., 7,* 43-52.

CARTER, R.L. (1978): Long-term tests for carcinogenicity: the pathologist's view. In: A.D. Dayan and R.W. Brimblecombe (Eds), *Carcinogenicity Testing: Principles and Problems,* Chap. 1, pp. 1-15. MTP Press, Lancaster.

FACCINI, J.M. (1981): L'interprétation anatomopathologique dans les études de carcinogénicité sur les animaux de laboratoire. *Sci.Tech.Anim.Lab., 6/3,* 189-200.

FACCINI, J.M. (1982): A perspective on the pathology and cytochemistry of renal lesions. In: P.H. Bach, F.W. Bonner, J.W. Bridges and E.A. Lock (Eds), *Nephrotoxicity Assessment and Pathogenesis,* pp. 82-97. John Wiley and Sons, Chichester.

HANG, H. (1980): The significance of quantitative stereologic experimental procedures in pathology. *Pathol.Res.Practice, 166,* 144-164.

LENDON, M., HANN, I.M., PALMER, M.K., SHALET, S.M. and JONES, P.H. (1978): Testicular histology after combination chemotherapy in childhood for acute lymphoblastic leukaemia. *Lancet, 2,* 439-441.

NAYLOR, D.C. (1981): Principles and practice of recording data in toxicological pathology. *Meth.Inform.Med., 20,* 142-146.

ROE, F.J.C. (1977): Quantification and Computerisation of Histopathological Data. *Ciba Symposium* (unpublished).

Subject index